Business BASICS

A study guide for degree students

QUANTITATIVE METHODS

BPP PUBLISHING

First edition May 1995
Second edition October 1997

ISBN 0 7517 2118 2

British Library Cataloguing-in Publication Data

A catalogue record for this book
is available from the British Library

Published by
BPP Publishing Limited
Aldine House, Aldine Place
London W12 8AW

BPP would like to thank the following:
Geoff Williamson for authorial input and
Genesys Editorial for editorial and
production input.

CONTENTS

PREFACE

BUSINESS BASICS are targeted specifically at the needs of:

- students taking business studies degrees;
- students taking business-related modules of other degrees;
- students on courses at a comparable level;
- others requiring business information at this level.

This *Quantitative Methods* text has been written with two key goals in mind.

- To present a substantial and useful body of knowledge on quantitative methods at degree level. This is not just a set of revision notes – it explains the subject in detail and does not assume prior knowledge.
- To make learning and revision as easy as possible. Each chapter:
  - starts with an introduction and clear objectives;
  - contains numerous activities;
  - includes a chapter roundup summarising the points made;
  - ends with a quick quiz

  and at the back of the book you will find:
  - multiple choice questions and solutions;
  - exam style questions and solutions.

The philosophy of the series is thus to combine techniques which actively promote learning with a no-nonsense, systematic approach to the necessary factual content of the course.

BPP Publishing have for many years been the leading providers of targeted texts for students of professional qualifications. We know that our customers need to study effectively in order to pass their exams, and that they cannot afford to waste time. They expect clear, concise and highly-focused study material. As university and college education becomes more market driven, students rightly demand the same high standards of efficiency in their learning material. The BUSINESS BASICS series meets those demands.

BPP Publishing
October 1997

Titles in this series

Accounting
Law
Quantitative Methods
Information Technology
Economics
Marketing
Human Resource Management
Organisational Behaviour

You may order other titles in the series using the form at the end of this book. If you would like to send in your comments on this book, please turn to the review form following the order form.

HOW TO USE THIS STUDY GUIDE

This book can simply be read straight through from beginning to end, but you will get far more out of it if you keep a pen and paper to hand. The most effective form of learning is *active learning*, and we have therefore filled the text with exercises for you to try as you go along. We have also provided objectives, a chapter roundup and a quick quiz for each chapter. Here is a suggested approach to enable you to get the most out of this book.

(a) Select a chapter to study, and read the Signpost and objectives in the box at the start of the chapter.

(b) Next read the chapter roundup at the end of the chapter (before the quick quiz and the solutions to exercises). Do not expect this brief summary to mean too much at this stage, but see whether you can relate some of the points made in it to some of the objectives.

(c) Next read the chapter itself. Do attempt each exercise as you come to it. You will derive the greatest benefit from the exercises if you write down your solutions before checking them against the solutions at the end of the chapter.

(d) As you read, make use of the 'notes' column to add your own comments, references to other material and so on. Do try to formulate your own views. The more you engage in a dialogue with the book, the more you will get out of your study.

(e) When you reach the end of the chapter, read the chapter roundup again. Then go back to the objectives at the start of the chapter, and ask yourself whether you have achieved them.

(f) Finally, consolidate your knowlege by writing down your answers to the quick quiz. You can check your answers by going back to the text. The very act of going back and searching the text for relevant details will further improve your grasp of the subject.

(g) You can then try the multiple choice questions at the end of the book and the exam style questions to which you are referred at the end of the chapter. Alternatively, you could wait to do these until you have started your revision – it's up to you.

Further reading

While we are confident that the BUSINESS BASICS books offer excellent range and depth of subject coverage, we are aware that you will be encouraged to follow up particular points in books other than your main textbook, in order to get alternative points of view and more detail on key topics. We recommend the following books as a starting point for your further reading on *Quantitative Methods.*

Anderson, *Quantitative Methods for Business*, 6th Edition, Minneapolis/St Paul: West Pub Co 1995

Curwin & Slater, *Quantitative Methods for Business Decisions*, 4th Edition, Chapman & Hall 1996

Francis, *Business Mathematics and Statistics*, 4th Edition, DP Publications 1995

Lucey, *Quantitative Techniques*, 5th Edition, DP Publications 1996

Morris, *Quantitative Approaches in Business Studies*, 3rd Edition, Pitman 1996

Waters, *Quantitative Methods for Business*, Addison Wesley 1994

Wisniewski, *Quantitative Methods for Decision Makers*, Pitman 1995

THE POISSON DISTRIBUTION

Entries in the table give the probabilities that an event will occur x times when the average number of occurences is *m*.

	m									
x	**0.1**	**0.2**	**0.3**	**0.4**	**0.5**	**0.6**	**0.7**	**0.8**	**0.9**	**1.0**
0	.9048	.8187	.7408	.6703	.6065	.5488	.4966	.4493	.4066	.3679
1	.0905	.1637	.2222	.2681	.3033	.3293	.3476	.3595	.3659	.3679
2	.0045	.0164	.0333	.0536	.0758	.0988	.1217	.1438	.1647	.1839
3	.0002	.0011	.0033	.0072	.0126	.0198	.0284	.0383	.0494	.0613
4	.0000	.0001	.0003	.0007	.0016	.0030	.0050	.0077	.0111	.0153
5	.0000	.0000	.0000	.0001	.0002	.0004	.0007	.0012	.0020	.0031
6	.0000	.0000	.0000	.0000	.0000	.0000	.0001	.0002	.0003	.0005
7	.0000	.0000	.0000	.0000	.0000	.0000	.0000	.0000	.0000	.0001

	m									
x	**1.1**	**1.2**	**1.3**	**1.4**	**1.5**	**1.6**	**1.7**	**1.8**	**1.9**	**2.0**
0	.3329	.3012	.2725	.2466	.2231	.2019	.1827	.1653	.1496	.1353
1	.3662	.3614	.3543	.3452	.3347	.3230	.3106	.2975	.2842	.2707
2	.2014	.2169	.2303	.2417	.2510	.2584	.2640	.2678	.2700	.2707
3	.0738	.0867	.0998	.1128	.1255	.1378	.1496	.1607	.1710	.1804
4	.0203	.0260	.0324	.0395	.0471	.0551	.0636	.0723	.0812	.0902
5	.0045	.0062	.0084	.0111	.0141	.0176	.0216	.0260	.0309	.0361
6	.0008	.0012	.0018	.0026	.0035	.0047	.0061	.0078	.0098	.0120
7	.0001	.0002	.0003	.0005	.0008	.0011	.0015	.0020	.0027	.0034
8	.0000	.0000	.0001	.0001	.0001	.0002	.0003	.0005	.0006	.0009
9	.0000	.0000	.0000	.0000	.0000	.0000	.0001	.0001	.0001	.0002

	m									
x	**2.1**	**2.2**	**2.3**	**2.4**	**2.5**	**2.6**	**2.7**	**2.8**	**2.9**	**3.0**
0	.1225	.1108	.1003	.0907	.0821	.0743	.0672	.0608	.0550	.0498
1	.2572	.2438	.2306	.2177	.2052	.1931	.1815	.1703	.1596	.1494
2	.2700	.2681	.2652	.2613	.2565	.2510	.2450	.2384	.2314	.2240
3	.1890	.1966	.2033	.2090	.2138	.2176	.2205	.2225	.2237	.2240
4	.0992	.1082	.1169	.1254	.1336	.1414	.1488	.1557	.1622	.1680
5	.0417	.0476	.0538	.0602	.0668	.0735	.0804	.0872	.0940	.1008
6	.0146	.0174	.0206	.0241	.0278	.0319	.0362	.0407	.0455	.0504
7	.0044	.0055	.0068	.0083	.0099	.0118	.0139	.0163	.0188	.0216
8	.0011	.0015	.0019	.0025	.0031	.0038	.0047	.0057	.0068	.0081
9	.0003	.0004	.0005	.0007	.0009	.0011	.0014	.0018	.0022	.0027
10	.0001	.0001	.0001	.0002	.0002	.0003	.0004	.0005	.0006	.0008
11	.0000	.0000	.0000	.0000	.0000	.0001	.0001	.0001	.0002	.0002
12	.0000	.0000	.0000	.0000	.0000	.0000	.0000	.0000	.0000	.0001

THE POISSON DISTRIBUTION (continued)

Entries in the table give the probabilities that an event will occur x times when the average number of occurences is *m*.

	m									
x	**3.1**	**3.2**	**3.3**	**3.4**	**3.5**	**3.6**	**3.7**	**3.8**	**3.9**	**4.0**
0	.0450	.0408	.0369	.0334	.0302	.0273	.0247	.0224	.0202	.0183
1	.1397	.1304	.1217	.1135	.1057	.0984	.0915	.0850	.0789	.0733
2	.2165	.2087	.2008	.1929	.1850	.1771	.1692	.1615	.1539	.1465
3	.2237	.2226	.2209	.2186	.2158	.2125	.2087	.2046	.2001	.1954
4	.1733	.1781	.1823	.1858	.1888	.1912	.1931	.1944	.1951	.1954
5	.1075	.1140	.1203	.1264	.1322	.1377	.1429	.1477	.1522	.1563
6	.0555	.0608	.0662	.0716	.0771	.0826	.0881	.0936	.0989	.1042
7	.0246	.0278	.0312	.0348	.0385	.0425	.0466	.0508	.0551	.0595
8	.0095	.0111	.0129	.0148	.0169	.0191	.0215	.0241	.0269	.0298
9	.0033	.0040	.0047	.0056	.0066	.0076	.0089	.0102	.0116	.0132
10	.0010	.0013	.0016	.0019	.0023	.0028	.0033	.0039	.0045	.0053
11	.0003	.0004	.0005	.0006	.0007	.0009	.0011	.0013	.0016	.0019
12	.0001	.0001	.0001	.0002	.0002	.0003	.0003	.0004	.0005	.0006
13	.0000	.0000	.0000	.0000	.0001	.0001	.0001	.0001	.0002	.0002
14	.0000	.0000	.0000	.0000	.0000	.0000	.0000	.0000	.0000	.0001

	m									
x	**4.1**	**4.2**	**4.3**	**4.4**	**4.5**	**4.6**	**4.7**	**4.8**	**4.9**	**5.0**
0	.0166	.0150	.0136	.0123	.0111	.0101	.0091	.0082	.0074	.0067
1	.0679	.0630	.0583	.0540	.0500	.0462	.0427	.0395	.0365	.0337
2	.1393	.1323	.1254	.1188	.1125	.1063	.1005	.0948	.0894	.0842
3	.1904	.1852	.1798	.1743	.1687	.1631	.1574	.1517	.1460	.1404
4	.1951	.1944	.1933	.1917	.1898	.1875	.1849	.1820	.1789	.1755
5	.1600	.1633	.1662	.1687	.1708	.1725	.1738	.1747	.1753	.1755
6	.1093	.1143	.1191	.1237	.1281	.1323	.1362	.1398	.1432	.1462
7	.0640	.0686	.0732	.0778	.0824	.0869	.0914	.0959	.1002	.1044
8	.0328	.0360	.0393	.0428	.0463	.0500	.0537	.0575	.0614	.0653
9	.0150	.0168	.0188	.0209	.0232	.0255	.0281	.0307	.0334	.0363
10	.0061	.0071	.0081	.0092	.0104	.0118	.0132	.0147	.0164	.0181
11	.0023	.0027	.0032	.0037	.0043	.0049	.0056	.0064	.0073	.0082
12	.0008	.0009	.0011	.0013	.0016	.0019	.0022	.0026	.0030	.0034
13	.0002	.0003	.0004	.0005	.0006	.0007	.0008	.0009	.0011	.0013
14	.0001	.0001	.0001	.0001	.0002	.0002	.0003	.0003	.0004	.0005
15	.0000	.0000	.0000	.0000	.0001	.0001	.0001	.0001	.0001	.0002

AREA UNDER THE NORMAL CURVE

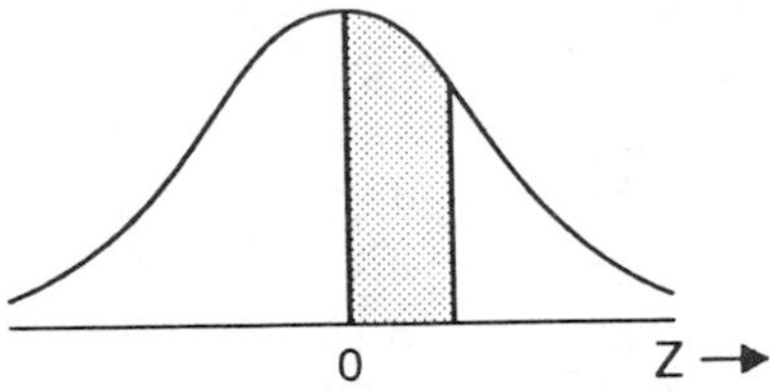

This table gives the area under the normal curve between the mean and the point Z standard deviations above the mean. The corresponding area for deviations below the mean can be found by symmetry.

$Z = \frac{(x-\mu)}{\sigma}$	**0.00**	**0.01**	**0.02**	**0.03**	**0.04**	**0.05**	**0.06**	**0.07**	**0.08**	**0.09**
0.0	.0000	.0040	.0080	.0120	.0160	.0199	.0239	.0279	.0319	.0359
0.1	.0398	.0438	.0478	.0517	.0557	.0596	.0636	.0675	.0714	.0753
0.2	.0793	.0832	.0871	.0910	.0948	.0987	.1026	.1064	.1103	.1141
0.3	.1179	.1217	.1255	.1293	.1331	.1368	.1406	.1443	.1480	.1517
0.4	.1554	.1591	.1628	.1664	.1700	.1736	.1772	.1808	.1844	.1879
0.5	.1915	.1950	.1985	.2019	.2054	.2088	.2123	.2157	.2190	.2224
0.6	.2257	.2291	.2324	.2357	.2389	.2422	.2454	.2486	.2517	.2549
0.7	.2580	.2611	.2642	.2673	.2704	.2734	.2764	.2794	.2823	.2852
0.8	.2881	.2910	.2939	.2967	.2995	.3023	.3051	.3078	.3106	.3133
0.9	.3159	.3186	.3212	.3238	.3264	.3289	.3315	.3340	.3365	.3389
1.0	.3413	.3438	.3461	.3485	.3508	.3531	.3554	.3577	.3599	.3621
1.1	.3643	.3665	.3686	.3708	.3729	.3749	.3770	.3790	.3810	.3830
1.2	.3849	.3869	.3888	.3907	.3925	.3944	.3962	.3980	.3997	.4015
1.3	.4032	.4049	.4066	.4082	.4099	.4115	.4131	.4147	.4162	.4177
1.4	.4192	.4207	.4222	.4236	.4251	.4265	.4279	.4292	.4306	.4319
1.5	.4332	.4345	.4357	.4370	.4382	.4394	.4406	.4418	.4429	.4441
1.6	.4452	.4463	.4474	.4484	.4495	.4505	.4515	.4525	.4535	.4545
1.7	.4554	.4564	.4573	.4582	.4591	.4599	.4608	.4616	.4625	.4633
1.8	.4641	.4649	.4656	.4664	.4671	.4678	.4686	.4693	.4699	.4706
1.9	.4713	.4719	.4726	.4732	.4738	.4744	.4750	.4756	.4761	.4767
2.0	.4772	.4778	.4783	.4788	.4793	.4798	.4803	.4808	.4812	.4817
2.1	.4821	.4826	.4830	.4834	.4838	.4842	.4846	.4850	.4854	.4857
2.2	.4861	.4864	.4868	.4871	.4875	.4878	.4881	.4884	.4887	.4890
2.3	.4893	.4896	.4898	.4901	.4904	.4906	.4909	.4911	.4913	.4916
2.4	.4918	.4920	.4922	.4925	.4927	.4929	.4931	.4932	.4934	.4936
2.5	.4938	.4940	.4941	.4943	.4945	.4946	.4948	.4949	.4951	.4952
2.6	.4953	.4955	.4956	.4957	.4959	.4960	.4961	.4962	.4963	.4964
2.7	.4965	.4966	.4967	.4968	.4969	.4970	.4971	.4972	.4973	.4974
2.8	.4974	.4975	.4976	.4977	.4977	.4978	.4979	.4979	.4980	.4981
2.9	.4981	.4982	.4982	.4983	.4984	.4984	.4985	.4985	.4986	.4986
3.0	.49865	.4987	.4987	.4988	.4988	.4989	.4989	.4989	.4990	.4990
3.1	.49903	.4991	.4991	.4991	.4992	.4992	.4992	.4992	.4993	.4993
3.2	.49931	.4993	.4994	.4994	.4994	.4994	.4994	.4995	.4995	.4995
3.3	.49952	.4995	.4995	.4996	.4996	.4996	.4996	.4996	.4996	.4997
3.4	.49966	.4997	.4997	.4997	.4997	.4997	.4997	.4997	.4997	.4998
3.5	.49977									

STUDENT'S T DISTRIBUTION

1 tail	5%	2.5%	1%	0.5%	0.05%
df 2 tail	**10%**	**5%**	**2%**	**1%**	**0.1%**
1	6.31	12.7	31.8	63.7	637
2	2.92	4.30	6.96	9.92	31.6
3	2.35	3.18	4.54	5.84	12.9
4	2.13	2.78	3.75	4.60	8.61
5	2.01	2.57	3.36	4.03	6.87
6	1.94	2.45	3.14	3.71	5.96
7	1.89	2.36	3.00	3.50	5.41
8	1.86	2.31	2.90	3.36	5.04
9	1.83	2.26	2.82	3.25	4.78
10	1.81	2.23	2.76	3.17	4.59
11	1.80	2.20	2.72	3.11	4.44
12	1.78	2.18	2.68	3.05	4.32
13	1.77	2.16	2.65	3.01	4.22
14	1.76	2.14	2.62	2.98	4.14
15	1.75	2.13	2.60	2.95	4.07
16	1.75	2.12	2.58	2.92	4.01
17	1.74	2.11	2.57	2.90	3.96
18	1.73	2.10	2.55	2.88	3.92
19	1.73	2.09	2.54	2.86	3.88
20	1.72	2.09	2.53	2.85	3.85
21	1.72	2.08	2.52	2.83	3.82
22	1.72	2.07	2.51	2.82	3.79
23	1.71	2.07	2.50	2.81	3.77
24	1.71	2.06	2.49	2.80	3.74
25	1.71	2.06	2.48	2.79	3.72
26	1.71	2.06	2.48	2.78	3.71
27	1.70	2.05	2.47	2.77	3.69
28	1.70	2.05	2.47	2.76	3.67
29	1.70	2.05	2.46	2.76	3.66
30	1.70	2.04	2.46	2.75	3.65
40	1.68	2.02	2.42	2.70	3.55
60	1.67	2.00	2.39	2.66	3.46
120	1.66	1.98	2.36	2.62	3.37
∞	1.65	1.96	2.33	2.58	3.29

THE CHI-SQUARED DISTRIBUTION (χ^2)

	Percentage p										
Degrees of freedom	**99.5**	**99**	**97.5**	**95**	**90**	**10**	**5**	**2.5**	**1**	**0.5**	**0.1**
1	0.0000	0.0002	0.0010	0.0039	0.016	2.71	3.84	5.02	6.63	7.88	10.8
2	0.010	0.020	0.051	0.103	0.211	4.61	5.99	7.38	9.21	10.6	13.8
3	0.072	0.115	0.216	0.352	0.584	6.25	7.81	9.35	11.3	12.8	16.3
4	0.207	0.297	0.484	0.711	1.06	7.78	9.49	11.1	13.3	14.9	18.5
5	0.412	0.554	0.831	1.15	1.61	9.24	11.1	12.8	15.1	16.7	20.5
6	0.676	0.872	1.24	1.64	2.20	10.6	12.6	14.4	16.8	18.5	22.5
7	0.989	1.24	1.69	2.17	2.83	12.0	14.1	16.0	18.5	20.3	24.3
8	1.34	1.65	2.18	2.73	3.49	13.4	15.5	17.5	20.1	22.0	26.1
9	1.73	2.09	2.70	3.33	4.17	14.7	16.9	19.0	21.7	23.6	27.9
10	2.16	2.56	3.25	3.94	4.87	16.0	18.3	20.5	23.2	25.2	29.6
11	2.60	3.05	3.82	4.57	5.58	17.3	19.7	21.9	24.7	26.8	31.3
12	3.07	3.57	4.40	5.23	6.30	18.5	21.0	23.3	26.2	28.3	32.9
13	3.57	4.11	5.01	5.89	7.04	19.8	22.4	24.7	27.7	29.8	34.5
14	4.07	4.66	5.63	6.57	7.79	21.1	23.7	26.1	29.1	31.3	36.1
15	4.60	5.23	6.26	7.26	8.55	22.3	25.0	27.5	30.6	32.8	37.7
16	5.14	5.81	6.91	7.96	9.31	23.5	26.3	28.8	32.0	34.3	39.3
17	5.70	6.41	7.56	8.67	10.1	24.8	27.6	30.2	33.4	35.7	40.8
18	6.26	7.01	8.23	9.39	10.9	26.0	28.9	31.5	34.8	37.2	42.3
19	6.84	7.63	8.91	10.1	11.7	27.2	30.1	32.9	36.2	38.6	43.8
20	7.43	8.26	9.59	10.9	12.4	28.4	31.4	34.2	37.6	40.0	45.3
21	8.03	8.90	10.3	11.6	13.2	29.6	32.7	35.5	38.9	41.4	46.8
22	8.64	9.54	11.0	12.3	14.0	30.8	33.9	36.8	40.3	42.8	48.3
23	9.26	10.2	11.7	13.1	14.8	32.0	35.2	38.1	41.6	44.2	49.7
24	9.89	10.9	12.4	13.8	15.7	33.2	36.4	39.4	43.0	45.6	51.2
25	10.5	11.5	13.1	14.6	16.5	34.4	37.7	40.6	44.3	46.9	52.6
26	11.2	12.2	13.8	15.4	17.3	35.6	38.9	41.9	45.6	48.3	54.1
27	11.8	12.9	14.6	16.2	18.1	36.7	40.1	43.2	47.0	49.6	55.5
28	12.5	13.6	15.3	16.9	18.9	37.9	41.3	44.5	48.3	51.0	56.9
29	13.1	14.3	16.0	17.7	19.8	39.1	42.6	45.7	49.6	52.3	58.3
30	13.8	15.0	16.8	18.5	20.6	40.3	43.8	47.0	50.9	53.7	59.7

PRESENT VALUE TABLE

This table shows the present value of £1 per annum, receivable or payable at the end of n years.

Discount rates (r)

Years (n)	1%	2%	3%	4%	5%	6%	7%	8%	9%	10%	11%	12%
1	0.99	0.98	0.97	0.96	0.95	0.94	0.93	0.93	0.92	0.91	0.90	0.89
2	0.98	0.96	0.94	0.92	0.91	0.89	0.87	0.86	0.84	0.83	0.81	0.80
3	0.97	0.94	0.92	0.89	0.86	0.84	0.82	0.79	0.77	0.75	0.73	0.71
4	0.96	0.92	0.89	0.85	0.82	0.79	0.76	0.74	0.71	0.68	0.66	0.64
5	0.95	0.91	0.86	0.82	0.78	0.75	0.71	0.68	0.65	0.62	0.59	0.57
6	0.94	0.89	0.84	0.79	0.75	0.70	0.67	0.63	0.60	0.56	0.53	0.51
7	0.93	0.87	0.81	0.76	0.71	0.67	0.62	0.58	0.55	0.51	0.48	0.45
8	0.92	0.85	0.79	0.73	0.68	0.63	0.58	0.54	0.50	0.47	0.43	0.40
9	0.91	0.84	0.77	0.70	0.64	0.59	0.54	0.50	0.46	0.42	0.39	0.36
10	0.91	0.82	0.74	0.68	0.61	0.56	0.51	0.46	0.42	0.39	0.35	0.32
11	0.90	0.80	0.72	0.65	0.58	0.53	0.48	0.43	0.39	0.35	0.32	0.29
12	0.89	0.79	0.70	0.62	0.56	0.50	0.44	0.40	0.36	0.32	0.29	0.26
13	0.88	0.77	0.68	0.60	0.53	0.47	0.41	0.37	0.33	0.29	0.26	0.23
14	0.87	0.76	0.66	0.58	0.51	0.44	0.39	0.34	0.30	0.26	0.23	0.20
15	0.86	0.74	0.64	0.56	0.48	0.42	0.36	0.32	0.27	0.24	0.21	0.18

Discount rates (r)

Years (n)	13%	14%	15%	16%	17%	18%	19%	20%	30%	40%	50%
1	0.88	0.88	0.87	0.86	0.85	0.85	0.84	0.83	0.77	0.71	0.67
2	0.78	0.77	0.76	0.74	0.73	0.72	0.71	0.69	0.59	0.51	0.44
3	0.69	0.67	0.66	0.64	0.62	0.61	0.59	0.58	0.46	0.36	0.30
4	0.61	0.59	0.57	0.55	0.53	0.52	0.50	0.48	0.35	0.26	0.20
5	0.54	0.52	0.50	0.48	0.46	0.44	0.42	0.40	0.27	0.19	0.13
6	0.48	0.46	0.43	0.41	0.39	0.37	0.35	0.33	0.21	0.13	0.09
7	0.43	0.40	0.38	0.35	0.33	0.31	0.30	0.28	0.16	0.09	0.06
8	0.38	0.35	0.33	0.31	0.28	0.27	0.25	0.23	0.12	0.07	0.04
9	0.33	0.31	0.28	0.26	0.24	0.23	0.21	0.19	0.09	0.05	0.03
10	0.29	0.27	0.25	0.23	0.21	0.19	0.18	0.16	0.07	0.03	0.02
11	0.26	0.24	0.21	0.20	0.18	0.16	0.15	0.13	0.06	0.02	0.01
12	0.23	0.21	0.19	0.17	0.15	0.14	0.12	0.11	0.04	0.02	0.008
13	0.20	0.18	0.16	0.15	0.13	0.12	0.10	0.09	0.03	0.013	0.005
14	0.18	0.16	0.14	0.13	0.11	0.10	0.09	0.08	0.03	0.009	0.003
15	0.16	0.14	0.12	0.11	0.09	0.08	0.07	0.06	0.02	0.006	0.002

CUMULATIVE PRESENT VALUE TABLE

This table shows the cumulative present value of £1 per annum, receivable or payable at the end of each year for n years.

Years (n)	Discount rates (r) 1%	2%	3%	4%	5%	6%	7%	8%	9%	10%	11%	12%
1	0.99	0.98	0.97	0.96	0.95	0.94	0.93	0.93	0.92	0.91	0.90	0.89
2	1.97	1.94	1.91	1.89	1.86	1.83	1.81	1.78	1.76	1.74	1.71	1.69
3	2.94	2.88	2.83	2.78	2.72	2.67	2.62	2.58	2.53	2.49	2.44	2.40
4	3.90	3.81	3.72	3.63	3.55	3.47	3.39	3.31	3.24	3.17	3.10	3.04
5	4.85	4.71	4.58	4.45	4.33	4.21	4.10	3.99	3.89	3.79	3.70	3.60
6	5.80	5.60	5.42	5.24	5.08	4.92	4.77	4.62	4.49	4.36	4.23	4.11
7	6.73	6.47	6.23	6.00	5.79	5.58	5.39	5.21	5.03	4.87	4.71	4.56
8	7.65	7.33	7.02	6.73	6.46	6.21	5.97	5.75	5.53	5.33	5.15	4.97
9	8.57	8.16	7.79	7.44	7.11	6.80	6.52	6.25	6.00	5.76	5.54	5.33
10	9.47	8.98	8.53	8.11	7.72	7.36	7.02	6.71	6.42	6.14	5.89	5.65
11	10.37	9.79	9.25	8.76	8.31	7.89	7.50	7.14	6.81	6.50	6.21	5.94
12	11.26	10.58	9.95	9.39	8.86	8.38	7.94	7.54	7.16	6.81	6.49	6.19
13	12.13	11.35	10.63	9.99	9.39	8.85	8.36	7.90	7.49	7.10	6.75	6.42
14	13.00	12.11	11.30	10.56	9.90	9.29	8.75	8.24	7.79	7.37	6.98	6.63
15	13.87	12.85	11.94	11.12	10.38	9.71	9.11	8.56	8.06	7.61	7.19	6.81

Years (n)	Discount rates (r) 13%	14%	15%	16%	17%	18%	19%	20%	30%	40%	50%
1	0.88	0.88	0.87	0.86	0.85	0.85	0.84	0.83	0.77	0.71	0.67
2	1.67	1.65	1.63	1.61	1.59	1.57	1.55	1.53	1.36	1.22	1.11
3	2.36	2.32	2.28	2.25	2.21	2.17	2.14	2.11	1.82	1.59	1.41
4	2.97	2.91	2.85	2.80	2.74	2.69	2.64	2.59	2.17	1.85	1.60
5	3.52	3.43	3.35	3.27	3.20	3.13	3.06	2.99	2.44	2.04	1.74
6	4.00	3.89	3.78	3.68	3.59	3.50	3.41	3.33	2.64	2.17	1.82
7	4.42	4.29	4.16	4.04	3.92	3.81	3.71	3.60	2.80	2.26	1.88
8	4.80	4.64	4.49	4.34	4.21	4.08	3.95	3.84	2.92	2.33	1.92
9	5.13	4.95	4.77	4.61	4.45	4.30	4.16	4.03	3.02	2.38	1.95
10	5.43	5.22	5.02	4.83	4.66	4.49	4.34	4.19	3.09	2.41	1.97
11	5.69	5.45	5.23	5.03	4.84	4.66	4.49	4.33	3.15	2.44	1.98
12	5.92	5.66	5.42	5.20	4.99	4.79	4.61	4.44	3.19	2.46	1.98
13	6.12	5.84	5.58	5.34	5.12	4.91	4.71	4.53	3.22	2.47	1.99
14	6.30	6.00	5.72	5.47	5.23	5.01	4.80	4.61	3.25	2.48	1.99
15	6.46	6.14	5.85	5.58	5.32	5.09	4.88	4.68	3.27	2.48	2.00

Chapter 1

BASIC MATHEMATICS

Introduction

The first part of this chapter introduces some mathematical tools which you will often have to use. For instance, percentages and ratios are found in business contexts, for example in quoting interest rates, and powers and roots are a convenient way of expressing problems where a number is to be multiplied by itself several times. Formulae and equations show how different amounts, such as the quantity of goods and the cost of making these goods, are related to each other. Computer spreadsheets are a quick and accurate way of performing calculations and preparing various types of table incorporating numerical data. The theory of geometric progressions underpins some of the techniques used to assess the viability of a capital investment.

The last three sections of the chapter examine approximation and rounding. Sometimes it is impossible to obtain an accurate value for a large number (such as the population of a town), and some figures may only be easily measurable to the nearest whole number (the speed of a car, for example). In some cases it may not be necessary or desirable to express data as accurately as it is possible to measure them. In such circumstances, numbers are rounded. When calculations are made using rounded data, errors may be introduced into the results of the calculations and any subsequent conclusions that may be drawn from them and so we will look at the types of error that can occur, and how we can take account of such errors in calculations using rounded data.

In Chapter 2 we will move on to specific quantitative methods, beginning with ways of presenting data.

Your objectives

After completing this chapter you should:

(a) be able to deal with fractions, decimals, reciprocals, brackets, negative numbers and other mathematical symbols and be able to use your calculator to perform addition, subtraction, multiplication and division;

(b) be able to perform calculations involving percentages and ratios;

(c) understand the meaning of roots and powers and be able to calculate them;

(d) know how to construct and solve various types of equation;

(e) be able to draw the graph of both linear and non-linear equations;

(f) know how to perform matrix calculations;

(g) be able to construct formulae for spreadsheets;

(h) understand the construction of a geometric progression;

(i) be able to find the logarithm of a number;

(j) be able to round numbers and determine maximum and relative errors.

NOTES

1 INTEGERS, FRACTIONS AND DECIMALS

Definition

An *integer* is a whole number and can be either positive or negative.

1.1 The integers are therefore as follows.

$$\ldots, -5, -4, -3, -2, -1, 0, 1, 2, 3, 4, 5, \ldots$$

Definitions

Fractions (such as $\frac{1}{2}$, $\frac{1}{4}$, $\frac{19}{35}$, $\frac{101}{377}$, ...) and *decimals* (0.1, 0.25, 0.3135 ...) are both ways of showing parts of a whole.

1.2 Fractions can be turned into decimals by dividing the numerator by the denominator (in other words, dividing the top line by the bottom line). To turn decimals into fractions, all you have to do is remember that places after the decimal point stand for tenths, hundredths, thousandths and so on.

1.3 Sometimes a decimal number has too many digits in it for practical use. This problem can be overcome by rounding the decimal number to a specific number of significant digits by discarding digits using the following rule.

If the first digit to be discarded is greater than or equal to 5 then add 1 to the previous digit. Otherwise the previous digit is unchanged.

EXAMPLE: SIGNIFICANT DIGITS

(a) 187.392 correct to five significant digits is 187.39
Discarding the 2 causes nothing to be added to the 9.

(b) 187.392 correct to four significant digits is 187.4
Discarding the 9 causes 1 to be added to the 3.

(c) 187.392 correct to three significant digits is 187
Discarding the 3 causes nothing to be added to the 7.

Activity 1

What is 17.385 correct to four significant digits?

2 MATHEMATICAL NOTATION

Brackets

2.1 Brackets are commonly used to indicate which parts of a mathematical expression should be grouped together, and calculated before other parts. In other words, brackets can indicate a priority, or an order in which calculations should be made. The rule is as follows.

(a) Do things in brackets before doing things outside them.

(b) Subject to rule (a), do things in this order.

(i) Powers and roots

(ii) Multiplications and divisions, working from left to right

(iii) Additions and subtractions, working from left to right

2.2 Thus brackets are used for the sake of clarity. Here are some examples.

(a) $3 + 6 \times 8 = 51$. This is the same as writing $3 + (6 \times 8) = 51$.

(b) $(3 + 6) \times 8 = 72$. The brackets indicate that we wish to multiply the sum of 3 and 6 by 8.

(c) $12 - 4 \div 2 = 10$. This is the same as writing $12 - (4 \div 2) = 10$ or $12 - (4/2) = 10$.

(d) $(12 - 4) \div 2 = 4$. The brackets tell us to do the subtraction first.

2.3 A figure outside a bracket may be multiplied by two or more figures inside a bracket, linked by addition or subtraction signs. Here is an example.

$5(6 + 8) = 5 \times (6 + 8) = 5 \times 6 + 5 \times 8 = 70$

This is the same as $5(14) = 5 \times 14 = 70$

The multiplication sign after the 5 can be omitted, as shown here ($5(6 + 8)$), but there is no harm in putting it in ($5 \times (6 + 8)$) if you want to.

Similarly:

$5(8 - 6) = 5(2) = 10$

or

$5 \times 8 - 5 \times 6 = 10$

2.4 When two sets of figures linked by addition or subtraction signs within brackets are multiplied together, each figure in one bracket is multiplied in turn by every figure in the second bracket. Thus:

$(8 + 4)(7 + 2) = (12)(9) = 108$

or

$8 \times 7 + 8 \times 2 + 4 \times 7 + 4 \times 2 = 56 + 16 + 28 + 8 = 108$

Negative numbers

2.5 When a negative number (–p) is added to another number (q), the net effect is to subtract p from q.

(a) $10 + (-6) = 10 - 6 = 4$ (b) $-10 + (-6) = -10 - 6 = -16$

2.6 When a negative number (–p) is subtracted from another number (q), the net effect is to add p to q.

(a) $12 - (-8) = 12 + 8 = 20$ (b) $-12 - (-8) = -12 + 8 = -4$

2.7 When a negative number is multiplied or divided by another negative number, the result is a positive number.

(a) $-8 \times (-4) = +32$ (b) $-18/(-3) = +6$

NOTES

2.8 If there is only one negative number in a multiplication or division, the result is negative.

(a) $-8 \times 4 = -32$ (b) $3 \times (-2) = -6$

(c) $12/(-4) = -3$ (d) $-20/5 = -4$

Activity 2

Work out the following.

(a) $(72 - 8) - (-2 + 1)$

(b) $\frac{88+8}{12} + \frac{(29-11)}{-2}$

(c) $8(2 - 5) - (4 - (-8))$

(d) $\frac{-36}{9-3} - \frac{84}{3-10} - \frac{-81}{3}$

Reciprocals

Definition

The *reciprocal* of a number is just 1 divided by that number.

2.9 For example, the reciprocal of 2 is 1 divided by 2, in other words $\frac{1}{2}$.

Extra symbols

2.10 We will come across several other mathematical signs in this book but there are five which you should learn right away.

(a) > means 'greater than'. So $46 > 29$ is true, but $40 > 86$ is false.

(b) ≥ means 'is greater than or equal to'. So $4 \geq 3$ and $4 \geq 4$.

(c) < means 'is less than'. So $29 < 46$ is true, but $86 < 40$ is false.

(d) ≤ means 'is less than or equal to'. So $7 \leq 8$ and $7 \leq 7$.

(e) ≠ means 'is not equal to'. So we could write $100.004 \neq 100$.

NOTES

3 ADDITION, SUBTRACTION, MULTIPLICATION AND DIVISION

3.1 To ensure that you have understood how to deal with brackets and negative numbers and to check that you are able to use your calculator to perform addition, subtraction, multiplication and division, try the following activity.

Activity 3

Work out all answers to four decimal places, using a calculator.

(a) $(43 + 26.705) \times 9.3$

(b) $(844.2 \div 26) - 2.45$

(c) $\dfrac{45.6 - 13.92 + 823.1}{14.3 \times 112.5}$

(d) $\dfrac{303.3 + 7.06 \times 42.11}{1.03 \times 111.03}$

(e) $\dfrac{7.6 \times 1{,}010}{10.1 \times 76{,}000}$

(f) $(43.756 + 26.321) \div 171.036$

(g) $(43.756 + 26.321) \times 171.036$

(h) $171.45 + (-221.36) + 143.22$

(i) $66 - (-43.57) + (-212.36)$

(j) $\dfrac{10.1 \times 76{,}000}{7.6 \times 1{,}010}$

(k) $\dfrac{21.032 + (-31.476)}{3.27 \times 41.201}$

(l) $\dfrac{-33.33 - (-41.37)}{11.21 + (-24.32)}$

(m) $\dfrac{-10.75 \times (-15.44)}{-14.25 \times 17.15} + \left(\dfrac{16.23}{8.4 + 3.002}\right)$

(n) $\dfrac{-7.366 \times 921.3}{10{,}493 - 2{,}422.8} - \left(\dfrac{8.4 + 3.002}{16.23}\right)$

4 PERCENTAGES AND RATIOS

Definition

A *percentage* indicates the relative size or proportion of an item.

4.1 Percentages are used to indicate the *relative* size or proportion of items, rather than their absolute size. For example, if one office employs ten accountants, six secretaries and four supervisors, the *absolute* values of staff numbers and the *percentage* of the total work force in each type would be as follows.

	Accountants	*Secretaries*	*Supervisors*	*Total*
Absolute numbers	10	6	4	20
Percentages	50%	30%	20%	100%

4.2 The idea of percentages is that the whole of something can be thought of as 100%. The whole of a cake, for example, is 100%. If you share it out equally with a friend, you will get half each, or 100%/2 = 50% each.

4.3 To turn a percentage into a fraction or decimal you divide by 100. To turn a fraction or decimal back into a percentage you multiply by 100. Consider the following.

(a) $0.16 = 0.16 \times 100 = 16\%$

(b) $\frac{4}{5} \times 100 = \left(\frac{400}{5}\right)\% = 80\%$

(c) $40\% = \frac{40}{100} = \frac{2}{5} = 0.4$

4.4 There are two main types of situation involving percentages.

(a) You may be required to calculate a percentage of a figures, having been given the percentage.

Question: What is 40% of £64?

Answer: 40% of £64 = 0.4 × £64 = £25.60.

(b) You may be required to state what percentage one figure is of another, so that you have to work out the percentage yourself.

Question: What is £16 as a percentage of £64?

Answer: £16 as a percentage of £64 = $\frac{16}{64} \times 100\% = \frac{1}{4} \times 100\% = 25\%$

In other words, put the £16 as a fraction of the £64, and then multiply by 100%.

Discounts

4.5 To calculate discounts you have to be able to to manipulate percentages. The following activities illustrate the technique.

Activity 4

A travel agent is offering a 17% discount on the brochure price of a particular holiday to America. The brochure price of the holiday is £795.

Required

Calculate the price being offered by the travel agent.

Activity 5

(a) A television has been reduced from £490.99 to £340.99. What is the percentage reduction in price to three decimal places?

(b) A stereo cost £757 in 19X3 and £892 one year later. What is the percentage increase in price to one decimal place?

Profits

4.6 In your examinations you may be required to calculate profit, selling price or cost of sale of an item or number of items from certain information. To do this you need to remember the following crucial formula.

	Example
	%
Cost of sales	100
Plus Profit	25
Equals Sales	125

Profit may be expressed either as a percentage of cost of sales (such as 25% ($^{25}/_{100}$) mark-up) or as a percentage of sales (such as 20% ($^{25}/_{125}$) margin).

EXAMPLE: PROFITS AND PERCENTAGES

Delilah's Dresses sells a dress at a 10% margin. The dress cost the shop £100.

Required

Calculate the profit made by Delilah's Dresses.

SOLUTION

The margin is 10% (ie ($^{10}/_{100}$))

Let selling price = 100%

Profit = 10%

∴ Cost = 90% = £100

∴ 1% = (£100/90)

∴ 10% = profit = £100/90 × 10 = £11.11

EXAMPLE: PERCENTAGES AND PROFITS

Trevor's Trousers sells a pair of trousers for £80 at a 15% mark-up.

Required

Calculate the profit made by Delilah's Dresses.

SOLUTION

The mark-up is 15%.

Let cost of sales = 100%

Profit = 15%

∴ Selling price = 115% = £80

∴ 1% = £ ($^{£80}/_{115}$)

∴ 15% = profit = £ ($^{£80}/_{115}$) × 15 = £10.43

Proportions

4.7 A proportion means writing a percentage as a proportion of 1 (that is, as a decimal).

100% can be thought of as the whole, or 1. 50% is half of that, or 0.5. Consider the following.

Question: There are 14 women in an audience of 70. What proportion of the audience are men?

Answer: Number of men = 70 – 14 = 56

Proportion of men = $\frac{56}{70} = \frac{8}{10} = 80\% = 0.8$

(a) $\frac{8}{10}$ or $\frac{4}{5}$ is the *fraction* of the audience made up of men.

(b) 80% is the *percentage* of the audience made up of men.

(c) 0.8 is the *proportion* of the audience made up of men.

Activity 6

There are 30 students in a classroom, 17 of whom have blonde hair. What proportion of the students do not have blonde hair?

Ratios

4.8 Suppose Tom has £12 and Dick has £8. The ratio of Tom's cash to Dick's cash is 12:8. This can be cancelled down, just like a fraction, to 3 : 2.

4.9 Often an examination question will pose the problem the other way around: Tom and Dick wish to share £20 out in the ratio 3 : 2. How much will each receive?

4.10 Because 3 + 2 = 5, we must divide the whole up into five equal parts, then give Tom three parts and Dick two parts.

(a) £20 ÷ 5 = £4 (so each part is £4)

(b) Tom's share = 3 × £4 = £12

(c) Dick's share = 2 × £4 = £8

(d) *Check*: £12 + £8 = £20 (adding up the two shares in the answer gets us back to the £20 in the question)

4.11 This method of calculating ratios as amounts works no matter how many ratios are involved. Here is another example.

Question: A, B, C and D wish to share £600 in the ratio 6 : 1 : 2 : 3. How much will each receive?

Answer:

(a) Number of parts = 6 + 1 + 2 + 3 = 12

(b) Value of each part = £600 ÷ 12 = £50

(c) A: 6 × £50 = £300

B: 1 × £50 = £50

C: 2 × £50 = £100

D 3 × £50 = £150

(d) *Check*: £300 + £50 + £100 + £150 = £600

Activity 7

(a) Tom, Dick and Harry wish to share out £800. Calculate how much each would receive if the ratio used was:

(i) 3 : 2 : 5;

(ii) 5 : 3 : 2;

(iii) 3 : 1 : 1.

(b) Lynn and Laura share out a certain sum of money in the ratio 4 : 5, and Laura ends up with £6.

(i) How much was shared out in the first place?

(ii) How much would have been shared out if Laura had got £6 and the ratio had been 5 : 4 instead of 4 : 5?

5 ROOTS AND POWERS

Definitions

The *square root* ($\sqrt{\ }$)of a number is a value which, when multiplied by itself, equals the original number.

The *cube root* ($\sqrt[3]{\ }$)of a number is the value which, when multiplied by itself twice, equals the original number.

5.1 For example,

$\sqrt{9} = 3$, since $3 \times 3 = 9$

Similarly,

$\sqrt[3]{64} = 4$, since $4 \times 4 \times 4 = 64$

5.2 The *nth root* of a number is a value which, when multiplied by itself (n – 1) times, equals the original number.

5.3 *Powers* work the other way round.

Thus the 6th power of $2 = 2^6 = 2 \times 2 \times 2 \times 2 \times 2 \times 2 = 64$.

Similarly, $3^4 = 3 \times 3 \times 3 \times 3 = 81$.

Since $\sqrt{9} = 3$, it also follows that $3^2 = 9$, and since $\sqrt[3]{64} = 4$, $4^3 = 64$.

5.4 When a number with an index (a 'to the power of' value) is multiplied by the same number with the same or a different index, the result is that number to the power of the sum of the indices.

(a) $5^2 \times 5 = 5^2 \times 5^1 = 5^{(2+1)} = 5^3 = 125$

(b) $4^3 \times 4^3 = 4^{(3+3)} = 4^6 = 4{,}096$

5.5 Similarly, when a number with an index is divided by the same number with the same or a different index, the result is that number to the power of the first index minus the second index.

(a) $6^4 \div 6^3 = 6^{(4-3)} = 6^1 = 6$

(b) $7^8 \div 7^6 = 7^{(8-6)} = 7^2 = 49$

5.6 Any figure to the power of zero equals 1. $1^0 = 1$, $2^0 = 1$, $3^0 = 1$, $4^0 = 1$ and so on.

NOTES

5.7 An index can be a fraction, as in $16^{\frac{1}{2}}$. What $16^{\frac{1}{2}}$ means is the square root of 16 ($\sqrt{16}$ or 4). If we multiply by $16^{\frac{1}{2}}$ we get $16^{(\frac{1}{2}+\frac{1}{2})}$ which equals 16^1 and thus 16.

Similarly, $216^{\frac{1}{3}}$ is the cube root of 216 (which is 6) because $216^{\frac{1}{3}} \times 216^{\frac{1}{3}} \times 216^{\frac{1}{3}} = 216^{(\frac{1}{3}+\frac{1}{3}+\frac{1}{3})} = 216^1 = 216$.

5.8 An index can be a negative value. The negative sign represents a reciprocal. Thus 2^{-1} is the reciprocal of, or 1 over, 2^1.

$$2^1 = \frac{1}{2^1} = \frac{1}{2}$$

Likewise

$$2^{-2} = \frac{1}{2^2} = \frac{1}{4};\ 2^3 = \frac{1}{2^3} = \frac{1}{8};\ 5^{-6} = \frac{1}{5^6} = \frac{1}{15,625}$$

5.9 When we multiply or divide by a number with a negative index, the rules previously stated still apply.

(a) $9^2 \times 9^{-2} = 9^{(2+(-2))} = 9^0 = 1$ (That is, $9^2 \times \frac{1}{9^2} = 1$)

(b) $4^5 \div 4^{-2} = 4^{(5-(-2))} = 4^7 = 16,384$

(c) $3^8 \times 3^{-5} = 3^{(8-5)} = 3^3 = 27$

(d) $3^{-5} \div 3^{-2} = 3^{-5-(-2)} = 3^{-3} = \frac{1}{3^3} = \frac{1}{27}$. (This could be re-expressed as $\frac{1}{3^5} \div \frac{1}{3^2} = \frac{1}{3^5} \times 3^2 = \frac{1}{3^3}$.)

5.10 To calculate a power using a scientific calculator, you can use the [y^x] key.

For example, if you want to compute 7^4, put 7 in the display, then press the [y^x] key; next, key in 4 and then press the [=] key. The answer is then shown as 2,401.

ie 7[y^x] 4 [=] Answer: 2,401

Note. The [y^x] key is sometimes shown as the [x^y] key.

Activity 8

Work out the following, using your calculator as necessary.

(a) $(18.6)^{2.6}$

(b) $(18.6)^{-2.6}$

(c) $\sqrt[2.6]{18.6}$

(d) $(14.2)^4 \times (14.2)^{\frac{1}{4}}$

(e) $(14.2)^4 + (14.2)^{\frac{1}{4}}$

NOTES

6 FORMULAE AND EQUATIONS

Variables

6.1 So far all our problems have been formulated entirely in terms of specific numbers. However, think back to when you were calculating powers with your calculator earlier in this chapter. You probably used the x^y key on your calculator. x and y stood for whichever numbers we happened to have in our problem, for example, 3 and 4 if we wanted to work out 3^4. When we use letters like this to stand for any numbers we call them variables. When we work out 3^4, x stands for 3. When we work out 7^2, x will stand for 7: its value can vary.

6.2 The use of variables enables us to state general mathematical truths.

For example:

x	=	x
x^2	=	$x \times x$
If y	=	$0.5 \times x$, then $x = 2 \times y$

These are true *whatever* values x and y have. For example, let $y = 0.5 \times x$

If $y = 3$, $x = 2 \times y = 6$

If $y = 7$, $x = 2 \times y = 14$

If $y = 1$, $x = 2 \times y = 2$, and so on for any other choice of a value for y.

Formulae

6.3 We can use variables to build up useful formulae and then put in values for the variables, and get out a value for something we are interested in.

6.4 Let us consider an example. For a business, profit = revenue – costs. Since revenue = selling price × units sold, we can say that

profit = selling price × units sold – costs.

'Selling price × units sold – costs' is a formula for profit.

6.5 We can use single letters to make the formula quicker to write.

Let	x	=	profit
	p	=	selling price
	u	=	units sold
	c	=	cost

Then $x = p \times u - c$.

If we are then told that in a particular month, p = £5, u = 30 and c = £118, we can find out the month's profit.

Profit	=	$x = p \times u - c$ = £5 × 30 – £118
	=	£150 – £118 = £32

It is usual when writing formulae to leave out multiplication signs between letters. Thus $p \times u - c$ can be written as $pu - c$. We will also write (for example) 2x instead of $2 \times x$.

Equations

Definition

An *equation* is an expression of the relationship between variables.

6.6 In the above example, $pu - c$ was a formula for profit. If we write $x = pu - c$, we have written an equation. It says that one thing (profit, x) is equal to another ($pu - c$).

6.7 Sometimes, we are given an equation with numbers filled in for all but one of the variables. The problem is then to find the number which should be filled in for the last variable. This is called solving the equation.

6. 8 (a) Returning to $x = pu - c$, we could be told that for a particular month p = £4, u = 60 and c = £208. We would then have the *equation* x = £4 × 60 – £208. We can solve this easily by working out £4 × 60 – £208 = £240 – £208 = £32. Thus x = £32.

(b) On the other hand, we might have been told that in a month when profits were £172, 50 units were sold and the selling price was £7. The thing we have not been told is the month's costs, c. We can work out c by writing out the equation.

£172 = £7 × 50 – c

£172 = £350 – c

We need c to be such that when it is taken away from £350 we have £172 left. By simple arithmetic, we can find that c = £178.

6.9 This method would take far too long in more complicated cases, however, and we will now go on to look at a rule for solving equations, which will take us directly to the answers we want.

The rule for solving equations

6.10 To solve an equation, we need to get it into the form:

Unknown variable = something with just numbers in it, which we can work out.

We therefore want to get the unknown variable on one side of the = sign, and everything else on the other side.

6.11 The rule is that you can do what you like to one side of an equation, so long as you do the same thing to the other side straightaway. The two sides are equal, and they will stay equal so long as you treat them in the same way.

6.12 For example, you can do any of the following.

Add 37 to both sides.

Subtract 3x from both sides.

Multiply both sides by –4.329.

Divide both sides by (x + 2).

Take the reciprocal of both sides.

Square both sides.

Take the cube root of both sides.

6.13 We can do any of these things to an equation either before or after filling in numbers for the variables for which we have values.

6.14 (a) In Paragraph 6.8 above, we had

£172 = £350 – c.

We can then get

NOTES

$£172 + c = £350$ (add c to each side)

$c = £350 - £172$ (subtract £172 from each side)

$c = £178$ (work out the right hand side)

(b) $450 = 3x + 72$ (initial equation: x unknown)

$450 - 72 = 3x$ (subtract 72 from each side)

$\frac{450 - 72}{3} = x$ (divide each side by 3)

$126 = x$ (work out the left hand side)

(c) $3y + 2 = 5y - 7$ (initial equation: y unknown)

$3y + 9 = 5y$ (add 7 to each side)

$9 = 2y$ (subtract 3y from each side)

$4.5 = y$ (divide each side by 2)

(d) $\frac{\sqrt{3x^2 + x}}{2\sqrt{x}} = 7$ (initial equation: x unknown)

$\frac{3x^2 + x}{4x} = 49$ (square each side)

$(3x + 1)/4 = 49$ (cancel x in the numerator and the denominator of the left hand side: this does not affect the value of the left hand side, so we do not need to change the right hand side)

$3x + 1 = 196$ (multiply each side by 4)

$3x = 195$ (subtract 1 from each side)

$x = 65$ (divide each side by 3)

(e) Our example in Paragraph 6.6 was $x = pu - c$. We could change this, so as to give a formula for p.

$x = pu - c$

$x + c = pu$ (add c to each side)

$\frac{x + c}{u} = p$ (divide each side by u)

$p = \frac{x + c}{u}$ (swap the sides for ease of reading)

Given values for x, c and u we can now find p. We have rearranged the equation to give p in terms of x, c and u.

(f) Given that $y = \sqrt{3x + 7}$, we can get an equation giving x in terms of y.

$y = \sqrt{3x + 7}$

$y^2 = 3x + 7$ (square each side)

$y^2 - 7 = 3x$ (subtract 7 from each side)

$x = \frac{y^2 - 7}{3}$ (divide each side by 3, and swap the sides for ease of reading)

6.15 In equations, you may come across expressions such as $3(x + 4y - 2)$ (that is, $3 \times (x + 4y - 2)$). These can be rewritten in separate bits without the brackets, simply by multiplying the number outside the brackets by each item inside them. Thus $3(x + 4y - 2) = 3x + 12y - 6$.

NOTES

Activity 9

Question 1

Find the value of x in each of the following equations.

(a) $47x + 256 = 52x$

(b) $4\sqrt{x} + 32 = 40.6718$

(c) $\frac{1}{3x+4} = \frac{5}{2.7x-2}$

(d) $x^3 = 4.913$

(e) $34x - 7.6 = (17x - 3.8) \times (x + 12.5)$

Question 2

(a) Rearrange $x = (3y - 20)^2$ to get an expression for y in terms of x.

(b) Rearrange $2(y - 4) - 4(x^2 + 3) = 0$ to get an expression for x in terms of y.

7 LINEAR EQUATIONS

Definition

A *linear equation* has the general form $y = a + bx$

where
- y is the dependent variable, depending for its value on the value of x;
- x is the independent variable whose value helps to determine the corresponding value of y;
- a is a constant, that is, a fixed amount;
- b is also a constant, being the coefficient of x (that is, the number by which the value of x should be multiplied to derive the value of y).

7.1 Let us establish some basic linear equations. Suppose that it takes Joe Bloggs 15 minutes to walk 1 mile. How long does it take Joe to walk 2 miles? Obviously it takes him 30 minutes. How did you calculate the time? You probably thought that if the distance is doubled then the time must be doubled. How do you explain (in words) the relationships between the distance walked and the time taken? One explanation would be that every mile walked takes 15 minutes.

7.2 That is an explanation in words. Can you explain the relationship with an equation?

7.3 First you must decide which is the dependent variable and which is the independent variable. In other words, does the time taken depend on the number of miles walked or does the number of miles walked depend on the time it takes to walk a mile? Obviously the time depends on the distance. We can therefore let y be the dependent variable (time taken in minutes) and x be the independent variable (distance walked in miles).

7.4 We now need to determine the constants a and b. There is no fixed amount, so $a = 0$. To ascertain b, we need to establish the number of times by which the value of x should be multiplied to derive the value of y. Obviously $y = 15x$ where y is in minutes. If y were in hours then $y = \frac{1}{4}x$.

EXAMPLE: DERIVING A LINEAR EQUATION

A salesman's weekly wage is made up of a basic weekly wage of £100 and commission of £5 for every item he sells.

Required

Derive an equation which describes this scenario.

Solution

x = number of items sold and y = weekly wage

a = £100 and b = £5

$\therefore \quad y = 5x + 100$

7.5 Note that the letters used in an equation do not have to be x and y. It may be sensible to use other letters, for example we could use p and q if we are describing the relationship between the price of an item and the quantity demanded.

8 LINEAR EQUATIONS AND GRAPHS

8.1 One of the clearest ways of presenting the relationship between two variables is by plotting a linear equation as a straight line on a graph.

The rules for drawing graphs

8.2 A graph has a horizontal axis, the x axis and a vertical axis, the y axis. The x axis is used to represent the independent variable and the y axis is used to represent the dependent variable.

8.3 If calendar time is one variable, it is always treated as the independent variable. When time is represented on the x axis of a graph, we have the graph of a time series.

8.4 (a) If the data to be plotted are derived from calculations, rather than given in the question, make sure that there is a neat table in your working papers.

(b) The scales on each axis should be selected so as to use as much of the graph paper as possible. Do not cramp a graph into one corner.

(c) In some cases it is best not to start a scale at zero so as to avoid having a large area of wasted paper. This is perfectly acceptable as long as the scale adopted is clearly shown on the axis. One way of avoiding confusion is to break the axis concerned, as follows.

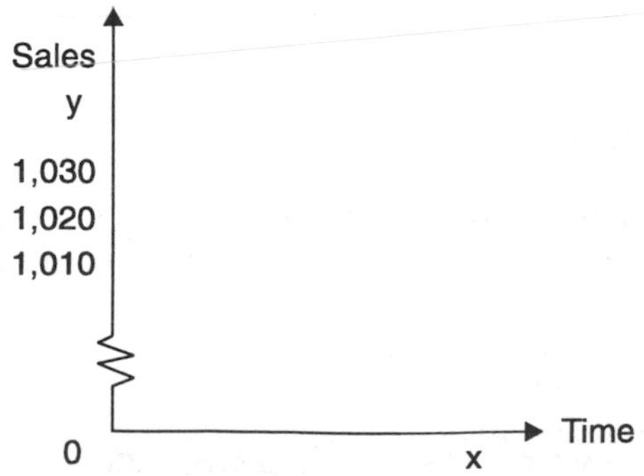

Figure 1.1 Graph with broken y axis

(d) The scales on the x axis and the y axis should be marked. For example, if the y axis relates to amounts of money, the axis should be marked at every £1, or £100 or £1,000 interval or at whatever other interval is appropriate. The axes must be marked with values to give the reader an idea of how big the values on the graph are.

(e) A graph should not be overcrowded with too many lines. Graphs should always give a clear, neat impression.

(f) A graph must always be given a title, and where appropriate, a reference should be made to the source of data.

EXAMPLE: DRAWING GRAPHS

Plot the graph for $y = 4x + 5$.

Consider the range of values from $x = 0$ to $x = 10$.

Solution

The first step is to draw up a table for the equation. Although the problem mentions $x = 0$ to $x = 10$, it is not necessary to calculate values of y for $x = 1$, 2, 3 etc. A graph of a linear equation can actually be drawn from just two (x, y) values but it is always best to calculate a number of values in case you make an arithmetical error. We have calculated five values. You could settle for three or four.

x	*y*
0	5
2	13
4	21
6	29
8	37
10	45

Graph of y = 4x +5

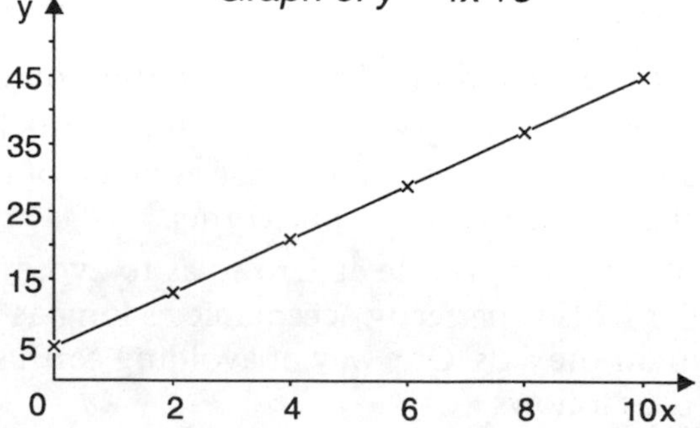

The intercept and the slope

8.5 The graph of a linear equation is determined by two things, the gradient (or slope) of the straight line and the point at which the straight line crosses the y axis.

Definition

The point at which the straight line crosses the y axis is known as the *intercept*.

8.6 Look back at the previous example. The intercept of $y = 4x + 5$ is $(0, 5)$. It is no coincidence that the intercept is the same as the constant represented by a in the general form of the equation $y = a + bx$. a is the value y takes when $x = 0$, in other words a constant, and so is represented on a graph by the point $(0, a)$.

Definition

The *gradient* of the graph of a linear equation is $(y_2 - y_1)/(x_2 - x_1)$ where (x_1, y_1) and (x_2, y_2) are two points on the straight line.

8.7 The slope of $y = 4x + 5 = (21 - 13)/(4 - 2) = 8/2 = 4$ where $(x_1, y_1) = (2, 13)$ and $(x_2, y_2) = (4, 21)$

Activity 10

Find the gradient of $y = 10 - x$.

8.8 Note that the gradient of $y = 4x + 5$ is positive whereas the gradient of $y = 10 - x$ is negative. A positive gradient slopes upwards from left to right whereas a negative gradient slopes downwards from left to right. The greater the value of the gradient, the steeper the slope.

8.9 Just as the intercept can be found by inspection of the linear equation, so can the gradient. It is represented by the coefficient of x (b in the general form of the equation). The slope of the graph $y = 7x - 3$ is therefore 7 and the slope of the graph $y = 3{,}597 - 263x$ is -263.

Activity 11

Find the intercept and slope of the graph of $4y = 16x - 12$.

9 SIMULTANEOUS AND NON-LINEAR EQUATIONS

Simultaneous equations

Definition

Simultaneous equations are two or more equations which are satisfied by the same variable values.

9.1 For example, we might have the following two linear equations.

$$y = 3x + 16$$
$$2y = x + 72$$

9.2 There are two unknown values, x and y, and there are two different equations which both involve x and y. There are as many equations as there are unknowns and so we can find the values of x and y.

NOTES

Graphical solution

9.3 One way of finding a solution is by a graph. If both equations are satisfied together, the values of x and y must be those where the straight line graphs of the two equations intersect.

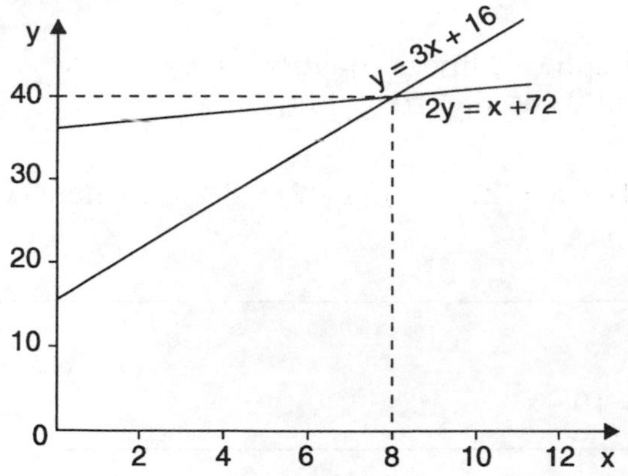

Figure 1.2 Finding a graphical solution

Since both equations are satisfied, the values of x and y must lie on both the lines. Since this happens only once, at the intersection of the lines, the value of x must be 8, and of y 40.

Algebraic solution

9.4 A more common method of solving simultaneous equations is by algebra.

(a) Returning to the original equations, we have:

$y = 3x + 16$ (1)

$2y = x + 72$ (2)

(b) Rearranging these, we have:

$y - 3x = 16$ (3)

$2y - x = 72$ (4)

(c) If we now multiply equation (4) by 3, so that the coefficient for x becomes the same as in equation (3), we get:

$6y - 3x = 216$ (5)

$y - 3x = 16$ (3)

(d) Subtracting (3) from (5) we get:

$5y = 200$

$y = 40$

(e) Substituting 40 for y in any equation, we can derive a value for x. Thus substituting in equation (4) we get:

$2(40) - x = 72$

$80 - 72 = x$

$8 = x$

(f) The solution is y = 40, x = 8.

Activity 12

Solve the following simultaneous equations using algebra.

$5x + 2y = 34$

$x + 3y = 25$

NOTES

Non-linear equations

9.5 In the previous sections we have been looking at equations in which the highest power of the unknown variable(s) is 1 (that is, the equation contains x, y but not x^2, y^3 and so on).

Definition

Non-linear equations are equations in which one variable varies with the nth power of another, where n > 1

9.6 We are now going to turn our attention to non-linear equations. The following are examples of non-linear equations.

$$y = x^2;\ \ y = 3x^3 + 2;\ \ 2y = 5x^4 - 6;\ \ y = -x^{12} + 3$$

9.7 It is common for a non-linear equation to include a number of terms, all to different powers. Here are some examples.

$$y = x^2 + 6x + 10 \qquad y = -12x^9 + 3x^6 + 6x^3 + 3x^2 - 1$$

$$2y = 3x^3 - 4x^2 - 8x + 10 \qquad 3y = 22x^8 + 7x^7 + 3x^4 - 12$$

9.8 Non-linear equations can be expressed in the form

$$y = ax^n + bx^{n-1} + cx^{n-2} + dx^{n-3} + \ldots + \text{constant.}$$

Consider the following equation.

$$y = -12x^9 + 3x^6 + 6x^3 + 2x^2 - 1$$

In this equation a = –12, b = 0, c = 0, d = 3, e = 0, f = 0, g = 6, h = 2, i =0, constant = –1 and n = 9.

Graphing non-linear equations

9.9 The graph of a linear equation, as we saw earlier, is a straight line. The graph of a non-linear equation, on the other hand, is *not* a straight line. Let us consider an example.

EXAMPLE: GRAPHING NON-LINEAR EQUATIONS

Graph the equation $y = -2x^3 + x^2 - 2x + 10$.

Solution

The graph of this equation can be plotted in the same way as the graph of a linear equation is plotted. Take a selection of values of x, calculate the corresponding values of y, plot the pairs of values and join the points together. The joining must be done using as smooth a curve as possible.

x	-3	-2	-1	0	1	2	3
$-2x$	6	4	2	0	–2	–4	–6
x^2	9	4	1	0	1	4	9
$-2x^3$	54	16	2	0	–2	–16	–54
10	10	10	10	10	10	10	10
y	79	34	15	10	7	–6	–41

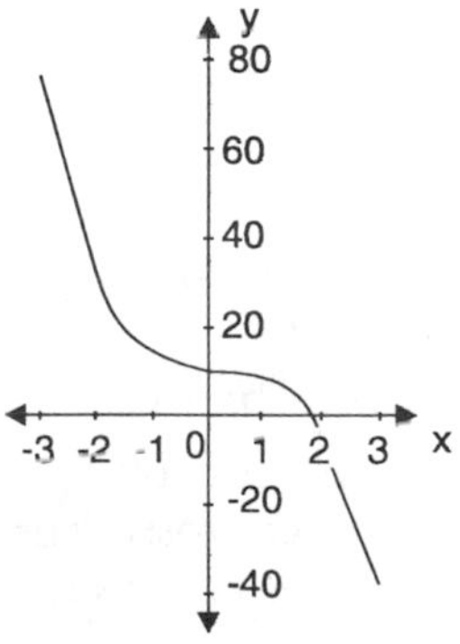

NOTES

Quadratic equations

Definition

Quadratic equations are a type of non-linear equation in which one variable varies with the square (or second power) of the other variable.

9.10 The following equations are all quadratic equations.

$y = x^2$ $\quad y = 5x^2 + 7$ $\quad 2y = -2x^2 - 3$ $\quad y = -x^2 + 3$

9.11 A quadratic equation may include a term involving the square and also a term involving the first power of a variable. Here are some examples.

$y = x^2 + 6x + 10$ $\quad 2y = 3x^2 - 4x - 8$ $\quad y = 2x^2 + 3x + 6$

9.12 All quadratic equations can be expressed in the form $y = ax^2 + bx + c$. For instance, in the equation $y = 3x^2 + 2x - 6$, $a = 3$, $b = 2$, $c = -6$.

Graphing a quadratic equation

9.13 The graph of a quadratic equation can be plotted using the method illustrated in the previous example.

EXAMPLE: GRAPHING A QUADRATIC EQUATION

Graph the equation $y = -2x^2 + x - 3$.

Solution

x	-3	-2	-1	0	1	2	3
$-2x^2$	-18	-8	-2	0	-2	-8	-18
-3	-3	-3	-3	-3	-3	-3	-3
y	-24	-13	-6	-3	-4	-9	-18

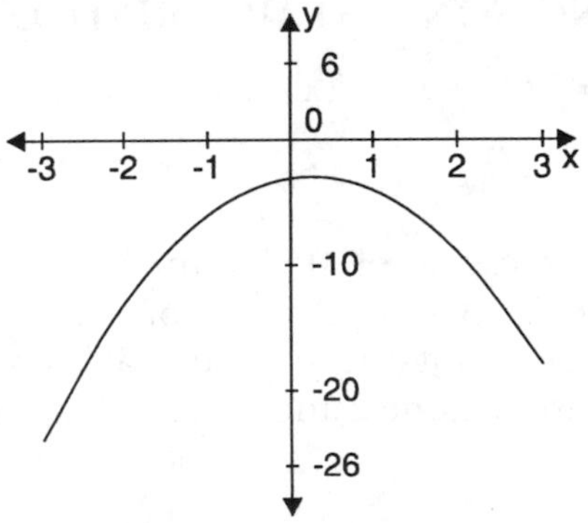

9.14 Graphs shaped like the one in the example are sometimes referred to as parabolas and they illustrate a number of points about the graph of the equation

$y = ax^2 + bx + c$.

(a) The constant term c determines the value of y at the point where the curve crosses the y axis (the intercept). In the graph above, $c = -3$ and the curve crosses the y axis at $y = -3$.

(b) The sign of a determines the way up the curve appears. If a is positive, the curve is shaped like a ditch, but if a is negative, as in the example, the curve is shaped like a bell.

A ditch-shaped curve is said to have a *minimum* point, whereas a bell-shaped curve is said to have a *maximum* point.

(c) The graph enables us to find the values of x when y = 0 (if there are any). In other words the graph allows us to solve the quadratic equation $0 = ax^2 + bx + c$.

For the curve in the example above we see that there are no such values (that is, $0 = -2x^2 + x - 3$ cannot be solved).

Solving quadratic equations

9.15 The graphical method is not, in practice, the most efficient way to determine the solution of a quadratic equation. Many quadratic equations have two values of x (called solutions for x or roots of the equation) which satisfy the equation for any particular value of y. These values can be found using the following formula.

$$\text{If } ax^2 + bx + c = 0 \text{ then } x = \frac{-b \pm \sqrt{(b^2 - 4ac)}}{2a}$$

EXAMPLE: QUADRATIC EQUATIONS

Solve $x^2 + x - 2 = 0$.

Solution

$$x = \frac{-1 \pm \sqrt{\left(1^2 - \left(4 \times 1 \times (-2)\right)\right)}}{2 \times 1} = \frac{-1 \pm \sqrt{(1+8)}}{2} = \frac{-1 \pm 3}{2}$$

$$\therefore \quad x = \frac{-4}{2} \text{ or } \frac{2}{2} \text{ ie } x = -2 \text{ or } x = 1$$

Quadratic equations with a single value for x

9.16 Sometimes, $b^2 - 4ac = 0$, and so there is only one solution to the quadratic equation. Let us solve $x^2 + 2x + 1 = 0$.

$$x = \frac{-2 \pm \sqrt{(2^2 - (4 \times 1 \times 1))}}{2} = \frac{-2 \pm 0}{2} = -1$$

This quadratic equation can only be solved by one value of x.

Cost behaviour, equations and graphs

9.17 Problems often deal with cost behaviour based on both linear and non-linear functions. Attempt the following activities which represent common business problems.

Activity 13

A company manufactures a product. The total fixed costs are £75 and the variable cost per unit is £5.

Required

(a) Find an expression for total costs in terms of q, the quantity produced.

(b) Use your answer to (a) to determine the total costs if 100 units are produced.

(c) Prepare a graph of the expression for total costs.

(d) Use your graph to determine the total cost if 75 units are produced.

Activity 14

A company manufactures a product, the total cost function for the product being given by C = (25 – q)q, where q is the quantity produced and C is in £.

Required

Calculate the total costs if 15 units are produced.

10 MATRICES

Definition

A *matrix* (plural *matrices*) is an array or table of numbers or variables.

10.1 For example, the table below is a matrix.

		Labour	
	Skilled	**Semi-skilled**	**Unskilled**
Factory P	100	75	250
Factory Q	40	40	200
Factory R	25	10	100

This table, showing the numbers of skilled, semi-skilled and unskilled workers in each of three factories, is a matrix with three rows and three columns; that is, its size is 3 × 3. A matrix with m rows and n columns is called an m × n matrix.

Definition

A table of numbers or variables which has just one row or column is called a *vector*.

10.2 A row vector is one row of numbers, and a column vector is a single column of numbers.

NOTES

10.3 A matrix is usually shown in large brackets. The example above would be written as follows.

$$\begin{pmatrix} 100 & 75 & 250 \\ 40 & 40 & 200 \\ 25 & 10 & 100 \end{pmatrix}$$

This takes some time to write out in full, so we may refer to a matrix by a single letter. For example, we could call the matrix above **X**.

10.4 Each figure in a matrix is called an element. An element is identified by the row and column in which it falls. For example, in the above matrix **X**, the element X32 is that in the third row and the second column, namely the number of semi-skilled workers at factory R, which is 10.

Matrix addition

10.5 Two matrices may be added together (or subtracted) provided they are of the same size. The addition is performed by adding the corresponding elements together. Continuing our first example of workers in factories, we might have a matrix A showing the effects on staffing levels of changing to new working practices, and a matrix B showing the effects of changing from gas power to electric power. A + B would show the effects of changing working practices and changing to electric power, while A – B would show the effects of changing working practices and changing back from electric to gas power.

Thus if

$$\mathbf{A} = \begin{pmatrix} 2 & 9 & -1 \\ 3 & -6 & -4 \\ -1 & 7 & 2 \end{pmatrix}$$

and

$$\mathbf{B} = \begin{pmatrix} 3 & 6 & 2 \\ -1 & -5 & 9 \\ 7 & -2 & -1 \end{pmatrix}$$

then

$$\mathbf{A + B} = \begin{pmatrix} 2+3 & 9+6 & -1+2 \\ 3-1 & -6-5 & -4+9 \\ -1+7 & 7-2 & 2-1 \end{pmatrix}$$

$$= \begin{pmatrix} 5 & 15 & 1 \\ 2 & -11 & 5 \\ 6 & 5 & 1 \end{pmatrix}$$

The revised matrix **X** for the total workforce, after both changes, would be

$$\mathbf{X + (A + B)} = \begin{pmatrix} 105 & 90 & 251 \\ 42 & 29 & 205 \\ 31 & 15 & 101 \end{pmatrix}$$

NOTES

$$\mathbf{A} - \mathbf{B} = \begin{pmatrix} 2-3 & 9-6 & -1-2 \\ 3+1 & -6+5 & -4-9 \\ -1-7 & 7+2 & 2+1 \end{pmatrix}$$

$$= \begin{pmatrix} -1 & 3 & -3 \\ 4 & -1 & -13 \\ -8 & 9 & 3 \end{pmatrix}$$

Matrix multiplication

10.6 Matrix multiplication is known as *scalar* multiplication. A scalar is an ordinary single number. If an entire matrix is multiplied by a scalar the effect is to multiply each element in the matrix by the scalar. Thus if:

$$\mathbf{A} = \begin{pmatrix} 2 & 9 & -1 \\ 3 & -6 & -4 \\ -1 & 7 & 2 \end{pmatrix}$$

then

$$3\mathbf{A} = \begin{pmatrix} 6 & 27 & -3 \\ 9 & -18 & -12 \\ -3 & 21 & 6 \end{pmatrix}$$

10.7 Two matrices can be multiplied together provided that the first matrix has the same number of columns as the second matrix has rows.

Thus if matrix **A** has four rows and two columns, and matrix **B** has two rows and three columns, the two can be multiplied together to get a product **AB**.

Since **A** is a 4×2 matrix and **B** is a 2×3 matrix, a product **AB** can be found, but a product matrix **BA** does not exist. **B** has three columns and **A** has four rows, therefore multiplication is impossible.

The elements in a product matrix are calculated as follows.

(a) Take the elements in the first row of the first matrix (say, matrix **A**) and multiply them by the corresponding elements in the first column of the second matrix (say, matrix **B**). The sum of the products then becomes the element in the first row and the first column of the product matrix.

(b) Similarly, the elements in row 2 of matrix **A** should be multiplied by the corresponding elements in column 1 of matrix **B**, and the sum of the products then becomes the element in row 2 and column 1 of the product matrix.

(c) This process must be repeated $m \times p$ times. The general rule is that the elements in row m of the first matrix should be multiplied by the corresponding elements in column p of the second matrix, and the sum of the products then becomes the element in row m and column p of the product matrix.

EXAMPLE: MATRIX MULTIPLICATION

Matrix **A** is a 2 × 3 matrix

$$\begin{pmatrix} 5 & 6 & 4 \\ 4 & 9 & 7 \end{pmatrix}$$

Matrix **B** is a 3 × 4 matrix

$$\begin{pmatrix} 3 & 5 & 5 & 5 \\ 6 & 4 & 4 & 0 \\ 0 & 3 & 5 & 5 \end{pmatrix}$$

Calculate matrix **C** where **C** = **AB**.

Solution

Matrix **C** will be a 2 × 4 matrix. We use C_{12} to denote the number in row 1, column 2, and so on.

Element in matrix C	Elements in xth row of A	Elements in xth column of B	
C_{11}	1st	1st	$= (5 \times 3) + (6 \times 6) + (4 \times 0) = 51$
C_{12}	1st	2nd	$= (5 \times 5) + (6 \times 4) + (4 \times 3) = 61$
C_{13}	1st	3rd	$= (5 \times 5) + (6 \times 4) + (4 \times 5) = 69$
C_{14}	1st	4th	$= (5 \times 5) + (6 \times 0) + (4 \times 5) = 45$
C_{21}	2nd	1st	$= (4 \times 3) + (9 \times 6) + (7 \times 0) = 66$
C_{22}	2nd	2nd	$= (4 \times 5) + (9 \times 4) + (7 \times 3) = 77$
C_{23}	2nd	3rd	$= (4 \times 5) + (9 \times 4) + (7 \times 5) = 91$
C_{24}	2nd	4th	$= (4 \times 5) + (9 \times 0) + (7 \times 5) = 55$

$$\text{Matrix } \mathbf{C} = \begin{pmatrix} 51 & 61 & 69 & 45 \\ 66 & 77 & 91 & 55 \end{pmatrix}$$

Activity 15

Let $\mathbf{A} = \begin{pmatrix} 2 & 1 \\ 0 & 3 \end{pmatrix}$

$\mathbf{B} = \begin{pmatrix} 5 & 1 & 0 \\ 2 & 3 & 1 \end{pmatrix}$

$\mathbf{C} = \begin{pmatrix} 3 & 1 \\ 0 & 2 \\ 1 & 4 \end{pmatrix}$

Find **AB**, **CA**, **BC** and **CB**.

NOTES

Null matrices

Definition

A *null matrix* is one in which every element is 0.

10.8 The null matrix behaves like the number 0 in calculations. Thus, if any matrix is multiplied by a null matrix the solution will also be a null matrix.

$$\begin{pmatrix} 0 & 0 \\ 0 & 0 \end{pmatrix} \times \begin{pmatrix} 6 & -1 \\ 2 & 3 \end{pmatrix} = \begin{pmatrix} 0 & 0 \\ 0 & 0 \end{pmatrix}$$

Identity matrices

Definition

An *identity* or *unit matrix* (often designated by **I**) is a square matrix which behaves like the number 1 in multiplication.

10.9 Each element on the main diagonal (top left to bottom right) of a unit matrix is 1 and all other elements are 0.

10.10 A unit matrix must be square, and the effect of multiplying a matrix by a unit matrix is to leave it unchanged.

$$\begin{pmatrix} 1 & 0 & 0 \\ 0 & 1 & 0 \\ 0 & 0 & 1 \end{pmatrix} \times \begin{pmatrix} 1 & 2 & 3 \\ 4 & 5 & 6 \\ 7 & 8 & 9 \end{pmatrix} = \begin{pmatrix} 1 & 2 & 3 \\ 4 & 5 & 6 \\ 7 & 8 & 9 \end{pmatrix}$$

$$\mathbf{I} \times \mathbf{A} = \mathbf{A}$$

Inverse of a matrix

10.11 The inverse of a square matrix **A** is represented by $\mathbf{A}^{-1}$ and can be defined by the equation:

$$\mathbf{A}\mathbf{A}^{-1} = \mathbf{A}^{-1}\mathbf{A} = \mathbf{I}$$

This means that if **A** is multiplied by its inverse or vice versa the product is an identity matrix.

The inverse of a 2 × 2 matrix can be found as follows.

$$\text{If } \mathbf{A} = \begin{pmatrix} a & b \\ c & d \end{pmatrix} \text{ then } \mathbf{A}^{-1} = \frac{1}{ad - bc}\begin{pmatrix} d & -b \\ -c & a \end{pmatrix}$$

Activity 16

Find the inverse of matrix A = $\begin{pmatrix} \mathbf{7} & \mathbf{9} \\ \mathbf{3} & \mathbf{2} \end{pmatrix}$

Solving simultaneous equations using matrices

10.12 Matrices are widely used for solving simultaneous equations. The following example illustrates how this is done.

NOTES

EXAMPLE: SOLVING SIMULTANEOUS EQUATIONS

Solve the equations

$5x + 9y = -30$

$6x - 2y = 28$

using matrix algebra.

Solution

In a matrix format the equations can be stated as:

$$\begin{pmatrix} 5 & 9 \\ 6 & -2 \end{pmatrix}\begin{pmatrix} x \\ y \end{pmatrix} = \begin{pmatrix} -30 \\ 28 \end{pmatrix}$$

Invert the square matrix, to get:

$$\frac{1}{5\times(-2)-9\times 6}\begin{pmatrix} -2 & -9 \\ -6 & 5 \end{pmatrix}$$

$$= \frac{-1}{64}\begin{pmatrix} -2 & -9 \\ -6 & 5 \end{pmatrix}$$

$$= \begin{pmatrix} 2/64 & 9/64 \\ 6/64 & -5/64 \end{pmatrix}$$

Multiply both sides of the equation by this inverse.

$$\begin{pmatrix} 2/64 & 9/64 \\ 6/64 & -5/64 \end{pmatrix}\begin{pmatrix} 5 & 9 \\ 6 & -2 \end{pmatrix}\begin{pmatrix} x \\ y \end{pmatrix} = \begin{pmatrix} 2/64 & 9/64 \\ 6/64 & -5/64 \end{pmatrix}\begin{pmatrix} -30 \\ 28 \end{pmatrix}$$

$$\begin{pmatrix} 1 & 0 \\ 0 & 1 \end{pmatrix}\begin{pmatrix} x \\ y \end{pmatrix} = \begin{pmatrix} 3 \\ -5 \end{pmatrix}$$

So $x = 3$ and $y = -5$.

11 FORMULAE FOR SPREADSHEETS

11.1 Spreadsheets are commonly used in a wide variety of courses and modules. If you haven't already met them, you undoubtedly will in the very near future. Building formulae in the cells of a spreadsheet is an important skill and should be acquired early on in your course.

11.2 A formula refers to other cells in the spreadsheet, and performs some sort of computation with them. For example, if cell C1 contains the formula +A1 –B1 this means that the contents of cell B1 should be subtracted from the contents of cell A1 and the result displayed in cell C1. Note that a formula starts with a '+' in most packages to distinguish it from text. In Lotus 1-2-3, a formula must start with one of the following characters: +, –, $ or @. In Excel, a formula must start with =.

NOTES

11.3 By working through the following examples you will assimilate the knowledge required.

EXAMPLE: EASY SREADSHEET FORMULA

Below is a spreadsheet processing budgeted sales figures for three geographic areas for the first quarter of the year.

	A	B	C	D	E
1		JAN	FEB	MARCH	TOTAL
2	NORTH	2,431	3,001	2,189	7,621
3	SOUTH	6,532	5,826	6,124	18,482
4	WEST	895	432	596	1,923
5	TOTAL	9,858	9,259	8,909	28,026
6					
7					
8					

Required

What formula would you put in the following cells?

(a) Cell B5

(b) Cell E4

(c) Cell E5

Solution

(a) + B2 + B3 + B4

(b) + B4 + C4 + D4

(c) Either + E2 + E3 + E4 or + B5 + C5 + D5

NOTES

EXAMPLE: FORMULA IN A BALANCE SHEET MODEL

Consider the balance sheet model shown below.

	A	B	C	D	E
1			£'000	£'000	
2					
3	Fixed assets: cost				
4	Accumulated depreciation				
5	Net book value				
6	*Current assets:*				
7	Stocks				
8	Debtors				
9	Cash				
10					
11	*Current liabilities:*				
12	Overdraft				
13	Creditors				
14	Taxation				
15					
16	Net current assets				
17					
18	Net assets				

Required

Define the formulae required for the following operations.

(a) In cell C10: calculate the sum of the current assets

(b) In cell C15: calculate the sum of the current liabilities

(c) In cell D5: calculate cost of fixed assets less accumulated depreciation

(d) In cell D16: calculate current assets less current liabilities

(e) In cell D18: calculate the sum of fixed assets and net current assets

Solution

(a) In cell C10: + C7 + C8 + C9

(b) In cell C15: + C12 + C13 + C14

(c) In cell D5: + D3 – D4

(d) In cell D16: + C10 – C15

(e) In cell D18: +D5 + D16 (alternatively + D5 + C10 – C15)

More complicated formulae

11.4 So far we have used a formula to add and subtract. Formulae can be used to perform a variety of calculations. Here are some examples.

(a) +C4*5. This formula multiplies the value in C4 by 5. The result will appear in the cell holding the formula.

(b) +C4*B10. This multiplies the value in C4 by the value in B10.

(c) +C4/E5. This divides the value in C4 by the value in E5. (Note that * means multiply and / means divide by.)

(d) +C4*B10 – D1. This multiplies the value in C4 by that in B10 and then deducts the value in D1 from the result. Note that generally the computer will perform multiplication before addition or subtraction.

NOTES

(e) +C4+17.5%. This adds 17.5% to the value in C4. It could be used to calculate a price including 17.5% VAT.

(f) + (C4+C5+C6)/3. This, in effect, calculates the average of the values in C4, C5 and C6. Note that the brackets tell the computer to perform the addition first. Without the brackets the computer would first divide the value in C6 by 3 and then add the result to the total of the values in C4 and C5.

(g) If may be quicker, when totalling a long row or column of figures, to use the formula @ SUM (B2..B12).

EXAMPLE: MORE COMPLICATED FORMULAE

The following four insurance salesmen earn a basic salary of £14,000 pa. They also earn a commission of 2% of sales. The following spreadsheet has been created to process their commission and total earnings.

	A	B	C	D	E
1	*Salesmen:*	*Salary and commission*			
2	*Name*	*Sales*	*Salary*	*Commission*	*Total earnings*
3					
4	*Ken*	284,000	14,000	5,680	19,680
5	*Mike*	193,000	14,000	3,860	17,860
6	*Alf*	12,000	14,000	240	14,240
7	*Jack*	152,000	14,000	3,040	17,040
8					
9	*Total*	641,000	56,000	12,820	68,820

Required

Give an appropriate formula for the following cells.

(a) Cell D4

(b) Cell E6

(c) Cell D9

(d) Cell E9

Solution

(a) +B4*0.02

(b) +C6+D6

(c) +D4+D5+D6+D7; or @SUM(D4..D7)

(d) One of the following would be suitable.

(i) +E4+E5+E6+E7

(ii) @SUM(E4..E7)

(iii) +C9+D9

11.5 Note that a formula which calculates a percentage of a value, such as commission as a percentage of sales, could be used in preparing a payroll. For example, National Insurance or pension contributions may be a set percentage of salary.

NOTES

11.6 A business will often need to compare its results with budgets or targets to see how far it has exceeded, or fallen short of, its expectations. It is useful to express variations as a percentage of the original target, for example sales may be 10% higher than predicted.

EXAMPLE: SPREADSHEET FORMULAE INVOLVING PERCENTAGE DIFFERENCES

Continuing the example of the insurance salesmen, a spreadsheet could be set up as follows showing differences between actual sales and target sales, and expressing the difference as a percentage of target sales.

	A	B	C	D	E	F
1	*Salesmen:*	*Actual sales v target sales*				
2	*Name*	*Target sales*	*Actual sales*	*Difference*	*Difference as a % of target*	
3						
4	*Ken*	275,000	284,000	9,000	3.27	
5	*Mike*	200,000	193,000	–7,000	–3.50	
6	*Alf*	10,000	12,000	2,000	20.00	
7	*Jack*	153,000	152,000	–1,000	–0.65	
8						
9	*Total*	638,000	641,000	3,000	0.47	
10						
11						

Required

Give a suitable formula for the following cells.

(a) Cell D4

(b) Cell E6

(c) Cell E9

Solution

(a) +C4 – B4

(b) (D6/B6)*100. With some spreadsheets, for example Lotus 1-2-3, you do not need to use brackets because the formula automatically operates from left to right where you have both multiplication and division. The formula would thus be +D6/B6*100.

(c) (D9/B9)*100 or +D9/B9*100. Note that in (c) you cannot simply add up the individual percentage differences. This is because the percentages are based on very different quantities. For example, Alf has exceeded his target by 20%, but this is only £2,000, while Ken's 3.27% difference is actually £9,000. You should always use your common sense in thinking about any formula you choose to put in.

Spreadsheets and budgets

11.7 It is useful to have an awareness of budgeting. Read through the following example to give you an idea of how to set up a spreadsheet which will assist in the budgeting process.

11.8 The cost accountant of a small company wishes to computerise the cash flow

NOTES

projections using a spreadsheet package. The cash flow projection is to provide a monthly cash flow analysis over a five-year period. The following data is relevant.

(a) Initial cash held by the company on 1 January 19X1 is expected to be £15,000.

(b) Sales in January are expected to be £25,000, and a growth rate of 2% per month in sales is predicted throughout the forecast period.

(c) The company buys stock one month in advance and pays in cash.

(d) On average, payment is received from customers as follows.
  (i) 60% one month in arrears
  (ii) 40% two months in arrears

  All sales are on credit. There are no bad debts.

(e) The cost of sales is 65% of sales value. Overhead costs (cash expenses) are expected to be £6,500 per month, rising by 5% at the start of each new calendar year.

(f) Purchases of capital equipment and payments of tax, interest charges and dividends must also be provided for within the model. The interest rate on bank overdrafts is expected to be 1% per month.

Inserting text

11.9 The first job is to put in the various headings that you want on the model. There is a facility within the program that enables you to specify the text for any column, combined columns or rows of data. (It is usually convenient to start the tabulation at row 1 and column A, although this is not essential.)

11.10 The cost accountant might decide to label the spreadsheet rows and columns as follows.

	: A :	B :	C :	D :	E :	F :
1:		19X1				
2:		Jan	Feb	March	April	May
3:		£	£	£	£	£
4:	Sales					
5:	Cash receipts					
6:	One months in arrears					
7:	Two months in arrears					
8:	Three months in arrears					
9:	Total receipts					
10:						
11:	Cash payments					
12:	Stock					
13:	Overheads					
14:	Interest					
15:	Tax					
16:	Dividends					
17:	Capital purchases					
18:	Total payments					
19:						
20:	Cash receipts less payments					
21:	Balance b/f					
22:	Balance c/f					

NOTES

Inserting formulae

11.11 The next stage in constructing a model is to put in the calculations you want the computer to carry out, expressed as formulae. The formulae required can be constructed in a variety of ways. One way would be to insert some 'constant' values into cells of the spreadsheet.

	Column
A	*B*
Row	
23: Sales growth factor per month	1.02
24: Interest rate per month	0.01
25: Debts paid within 1 month	0.6
26: Debts paid within 2 months	0.4
27: Debts paid within 3 months	0
28: Bad debts	0
29: Cost of sales as proportion of sales	0.65

Alternatively, these values could be specified in the formulae in the spreadsheet.

11.12 Unlike the text, these formulae will not be shown on the spreadsheet itself, but at the bottom of the screen. So at this stage, the spreadsheet looks just the same as it did after setting up the headings – but when the cursor is on a cell where a formula has been input, then that formula is shown at the bottom of the screen.

11.13 Examples of constructing formulae for the spreadsheet are as follows.

(a) The formulae for sales in February 19X1, in this example, would be (+B4*B23), in March 19X1 (+ C4*B23), in April 19X1 (+ D4*B23) and so on. Replication of the formula could be used to save input time.

(b) The formula for cash receipts in April 19X1 would be:

E6 = +D4*B25

E7 = +C4*B26

E8 = +B4*B27

E9 = +E6 + E7 + E8

(c) Cash payments for stock would be expressed as the cost of sales in the previous month; for February 19X1, this would be:

C12 = +B4*B29

(d) Total cash payments in May 19X1 would be the sum of cells F12 to F17.

F18 = @ SUM (F12..F17)

Inserting numerical data

11.14 The last stage in setting up a spreadsheet is to input data. Input data would include the opening cash balance on 1 January 19X1, dividend and tax payments, capital purchases, sales in January 19X1, the constant values (in our example in column B, rows 23 to 29) and the other data needed to establish cash receipts and payments in the first month or so of the forecast period (for example, receipts in January 19X1 will depend on sales in November and December 19X0, which the simplified model shown here has not provided for). With this input data, and the spreadsheet formulae, a full cash flow projection for the five-year period can be produced and, if required, printed out.

12 GEOMETRIC PROGRESSIONS

Definition

A *geometric progression* is a sequence of numbers in which there is a common or constant ratio between adjacent terms.

12.1 Some examples of geomtric progressions are as follows.

(a) 2, 4, 8, 16, 32, where there is a common ratio of 2.

(b) 121, 110, 100, 90.91, 82.64, where (allowing for rounding differences in the fourth and fifth terms) there is a common ratio of 1/1.1 = 0.9091.

12.2 An algebraic representation of a geometric progression is as follows.

$A, AR, AR^2, AR^3, AR^4, \ldots, AR^{n-1}$

where A is the first term
R is the common ratio
n is the number of terms

EXAMPLE: A GEOMETRIC PROGRESSION

A sales manager has reported that sales in the next year will amount to 5,000 units of product. He also estimates that sales will then increase in volume by 40% a year until year 6. What sales volume would be expected in year 6?

Solution

We require the sixth term in the geometric progression.

A = year 1 sales = 5,000

R = rate of growth = 140% (Note that R = 140% or 1.4, not 40% or 0.4.)

n = 6

$$T_6 = 5{,}000 \times 1.4^{(6-1)}$$

$$= 5{,}000 \times 5.37824$$

= 26,891.2 units (say 26,891 units)

The sum of a geometric progression

12.3 It is sometimes necessary to calculate the sum of the terms in a geometric progression. For example, suppose that a factory expects to produce 4,000 units in week 1 and to increase output by 20% each week for three more weeks.

Total output in the four weeks = 4,000 + 4,800 + 5,760 + 6,912 = 21,472 units

12.4 The calculation is relatively straightforward when the progression consists of a small number of terms. However, when we wish to calculate the sum of longer geometric progressions, it is easier to use a formula.

12.5 The formula for the sum (S) of a geometric progression is derived as follows.

$S = A + AR + AR^2 + AR^3 + ... + AR^{n-1}$ (1)

Multiply both sides of the equation by R to give:

$RS = AR + AR^2 + AR^3 + ... + AR^n$ (2)

Subtract (1) from (2).

$RS - S = AR^n - A$

$\therefore S(R - 1) = A(R^n - 1)$

$$\therefore S = \frac{A\left(R^n - 1\right)}{R - 1}$$

12.6 In the example above, we have the following.

$S = 4{,}000 + 4{,}000 \times 1.2 + 4{,}000 \times 1.2^2 + 4{,}000 \times 1.2^3$

$1.2S = 4{,}000 \times 1.2 + 4{,}000 \times 1.2^2 + 4{,}000 \times 1.2^3 + 4{,}000 \times 1.2^4$

$1.2S - S = (4{,}000 \times 1.2^4) - 4{,}000$

$$S = \frac{4{,}000\left(1.2^4 - 1\right)}{\left(1.2 - 1\right)}$$

$= +21{,}472$ units

Geometric progressions are particularly important in financial mathematics.

13 LOGARITHMS

Definition

The *logarithm* of a number is the power to which 10 must be raised to equal that number.

13.1 Your calculator might well enable you to work out complex values with little difficulty. For example, if you want the value of 1.12^{15} it could be a simple matter of entering two values into your calculator to obtain an answer.

13.2 However, when sophisticated calculators are unavailable, logarithms are one way of doing compounding arithmetic relatively easily. Furthermore, knowledge of logarithms enables us to ascertain the rate of change of a variable over time. Let us start by seeing what logarithms actually are.

13.3 The figure 10 can be expressed as 10^1. Similarly,

1	can be expressed as 10^0
100	can be expressed as 10^2
1,000	can be expressed as 10^3
10,000	can be expressed as 10^4

and so on.

To multiply 100 by 1,000, one way of expressing the calculation is

$100 \times 1{,}000 = 10^2 \times 10^3 \quad = 10^{(2+3)}$

$= 10^5$

$= 10{,}000$

NOTES

13.4 Logarithms work on the same principle.

Every number can be converted into 10 to a certain power. For example:

2	$= 10^{0.3010}$
20	$= 10^{1.3010}$
200	$= 10^{2.3010}$

How do we know this?

(a) Any value between 1 (10^0) and 10 (10^1) must have a 'to a certain power' value between 0 and 1.

(b) Similarly, any value between 10 (10^1) and 100 (10^2) must have a 'to a certain power' value between 1 and 2.

(c) Again, any value between 100 (10^2) and 1,000 (10^3) must have a 'to a certain power' value between 2 and 3.

This explains the figures to the left of the decimal points.

The value to the right of the decimal points, for 2, 20, 200 and indeed for 2,000, 20,000, 0.2, 0.02 and so on, is the same, and it is found by looking it up in logarithm tables. Tables are given at the front of this Study Guide. For 2, we look at row 20, column 0 and find .3010.

13.5 Here are some more examples to illustrate the use of logarithm tables.

(a) (i) The logarithm of 2.4 is 0.3802.

The value to the left of the decimal point is 0 because we want the logarithm of a figure between 1 and 10.

The value to the right of the decimal point is found from the tables, row 24, column 0.

(ii) The logarithm of 24 is 1.3802.

(iii) The logarithm of 240 is 2.3802.

(b) The logarithm of 2.45 is 0.3892. The value to the right of the decimal point is found from the tables, row 24, column 5.

(c) The logarithm of 24.8 is 1.3945. The value to the right of the decimal point is found from the tables, row 24, column 8.

(d) What about the logarithm of 2.026? The value to the right of the decimal point is found from the tables by starting at row 20 column 2 (0.3054) and then looking at the columns 1–9 on the far right of the table for the value in column 6, which is 13. This is added to the 3054 to get 3067, and the logarithm of 2.026 is 0.3067.

13.6 To convert a logarithm answer back to a 'normal' number, we can again use tables.

(a) There are antilogarithm tables, similar to logarithm tables, but which are used to convert logarithms back to normal numbers.

(b) Alternatively, you can find the solution by looking for the logarithm within the logarithm tables.

Logarithms of values between 0 and 1

13.7 We know that $10^0 = 1$ and $10^{-1} = 0.1$.

It follows that numbers between 0.1 and 1 ought to have logarithms between 0 and –1.

Similarly, since $10^{-2} = 0.01$, it follows that numbers between 0.01 and 0.1 ought to have logarithms between –1 and –2.

13.8 This is so. The logarithm of 0.2 is written $\bar{1}.3010$, pronounced 'bar one point 3010'.

The bar means minus and so $\bar{1} = -1$, $\bar{2} = -2$ and so on. So the logarithm of 0.2, which is $\bar{1}.3010$, is minus 1 *plus* 0.3010.

(a) Any figure from 0.1 up to just less than 1 has a logarithm with $\bar{1}$ to the left of the decimal point.

(b) Any figure from 0.01 up to just less than 0.1 has a logarithm with $\bar{2}$ to the left of the decimal point.

(c) Similarly, any figure from 0.001 up to just less than 0.01 has a logarithm with $\bar{3}$ to the left of the decimal point.

Logarithms and the examination

13.9 Logarithm tables are usually provided in examinations and we have worked through this section using tables since this provides a greater understanding of how logarithms are devised.

In the examination you can, of course, use your calculator. Most calculators do not use the $\bar{1}$, $\bar{2}$ system but give you negative numbers where appropriate (–0.3979 for log 0.4).

14 ROUNDING

14.1 There are three methods of rounding and these will be illustrated using the figure 18,600.

(a) *Rounding up*: 18,600 would be expressed as 19,000 to the nearest thousand above.

(b) *Rounding down*: 18,600 would be expressed as 18,000 to the nearest thousand below.

(c) *Rounding to the nearest round amount*: 18,600 would be expressed as 19,000 to the nearest thousand.

Method (c) is the most commonly used.

In rounding to the nearest unit, a value ending in 0.5 is usually rounded up. Thus 3.5 rounded to the nearest unit would be 4.

14.2 Rounding can be specified to the nearest whole unit (as above), by the number of decimal places (3.94712 to two decimal places is 3.95), or by the number of significant digits.

NOTES

Activity 17

(a) What is £482,365.15 to the nearest:

(i) £1

(ii) £100

(iii) £1,000

(iv) £10,000?

(b) What is 843.668 correct to:

(i) one decimal place

(ii) two decimal places?

(c) What is 628.0273 to:

(i) five significant figures

(ii) four significant figures?

Spurious accuracy

14.3 Spurious accuracy arises when a statistic gives the impression that it is more accurate than it really is. For example we might see stated '24.68% of women over the age of 30 are smokers'. This result is probably based on a sample and so we know that it cannot be as accurate as it seems: the two decimal places have arisen simply because of the arithmetic of the calculations. It would be less misleading to state 'approximately 25% of women over the age of 30 are smokers'. This removes the spurious accuracy implied by the decimal places.

15 MAXIMUM ERRORS

Absolute errors

15.1 Suppose that the population of a country is stated as 40 million. It is quite likely that this figure has been rounded to the nearest million. We could therefore say that the country's population is

40 million ± 500,000

where 40 million is the *estimate* of the population and 500,000 is the *maximum absolute error.*

15.2 In general terms an estimate with a maximum absolute error can be expressed as a ± b.

Relative errors

15.3 The error in the population of the country could also be expressed as

40 million ± 1.25%

where 500,000 is 1.25% of 40 million. In this instance the maximum error is a *maximum relative error* and is calculated as

$$\frac{\text{maximum absolute error}}{\text{estimate}} \times 100\%.$$

NOTES

16 ERRORS AND CALCULATIONS

16.1 If calculations are made using values that have been rounded then the results of such calculations will only be approximate. However, provided that we are aware of the maximum errors that can occur, we can still draw conclusions from the results of the calculations.

16.2 There are two rules to remember when performing calculations involving rounded or approximate numbers.

(a) *Addition/subtraction*

When two or more rounded or approximate numbers are added or subtracted the maximum absolute error in the result equals the sum of the individual maximum absolute errors.

(b) *Multiplication/division*

When two or more rounded or approximate numbers are multiplied or divided, the approximate maximum relative error in the result is obtained by adding the individual maximum relative errors.

We will use an example to illustrate these rules.

EXAMPLE: ERRORS

A chemical producer plans to sell 50,000 litres (to the nearest 1,000 litres) of a particular chemical at a price of £10 (to the nearest pound) per litre.

The cost of materials used to produce the chemicals is expected to be £100,000 but depending on wastage levels this is subject to an error of ± 5%. Labour costs are estimated to be £300,000 ± 10%, depending on overtime working and pay negotiations.

Required

Calculate the maximum absolute error and the maximum relative error in revenue and costs of production.

Solution

	Estimate	*Maximum absolute error*	*Maximum relative error* %
Quantity sold	50,000 litres	500 litres	1
Price	£10	£0.50	5
Materials	£100,000	£5,000	5
Labour	£300,000	£30,000	10

(a) Revenue = quantity sold × price
= (50,000 ± 1%) × (£10 ± 5%)
= (50,000 × £10) ± (1% + 5%)
= £500,000 ± 6%
= £500,000 ± £30,000

∴ Approximate maximum absolute error = £30,000
Approximate maximum relative error = 6%

Note that we need to use relative errors when doing multiplication/division calculations.

NOTES

EXAMPLE *continued*

(b) Costs of production = material + labour

= (£100,000 ± £5,000) + (£300,000 ± £30,000)
= (£100,000 + £300,000) ± (£5,000 + £30,000)
= £400,000 ± £35,000
= £400,000 ± 8.75 %

∴ Maximum absolute error = £35,000

Maximum relative error = 8.75%

Note that we need to use absolute errors when doing addition/subtraction calculations.

16.3 The rule in Paragraph 16.2(b) only gives an approximate maximum relative error. Let's see what the actual error would have been in the example above.

Maximum revenue = maximum quantity × maximum price

= (50,000 + 1%) × (£10 + 5%)
= 50,500 × £10.50
= £530,250

∴ Our approximation of the maximum absolute error was correct to within £(530,250 – 530,000) = £250.

Activity 18

Suppose that $A = \frac{J \times B}{M}$

where J and B are subject to a maximum relative error of 10% and M to a maximum relative error of 20%.

Required

(a) Calculate the approximate maximum relative error in A (using the rule in Paragraph 16.2).

(b) Calculate the actual maximum relative error.

Chapter roundup

- This chapter has covered the basic mathematics which you will need to understand before attempting the remainder of this Study Guide.
- Brackets indicate a priority or an order in which calculations should be made.
- The negative number rules are as follows.

  $-p + q = q - p$

  $q - (-p) = q + p$

  $-p \times -q = pq$ and $\frac{-p}{-q} = \frac{p}{q}$

  $-p \times q = -pq$ and $\frac{-p}{q} = \frac{-p}{q}$

- The reciprocal of a number is 1 divided by that number.
- Percentages are used to indicate the relative size or proportion of items, rather than their absolute size. To turn a percentage into a fraction or decimal you divide by 100%. To turn a fraction or decimal back into a percentage you multiply by 100%
- A percentage increase or reduction is calculated as (difference ÷ initial value) × 100%.
- A proportion means writing a percentage as a proportion of 1 (that is, as a decimal).
- Ratios show relative shares of a whole.
- The nth root of a number is a value which, when multiplied by itself (n – 1) times, equals the original number. Powers work the other way round.
- When we use letters to stand for any numbers we call them variables. The use of variables enables us to state general truths about mathematics.
- The general rule for solving equations is that you can do what you like to one side of an equation, so long as you do the same thing to the other side straightaway.
- A linear equation has the general form $y = a + bx$, where x is the independent variable and y the dependent variable, and a and b are fixed amounts.
- Make sure that you are aware of the rules for drawing graphs.
- The graph of a linear equation is a straight line. The intercept of the line on the y axis is a in $y = a + bx$ and the slope of the line is b.
- Simultaneous equations are two or more equations which are satisfied by the same variable values. They can be solved graphically or algebraically.
- In non-linear equations, one variable varies with the nth power of another, where $n > 1$. The graph of a non-linear equation is not a straight line.
- Quadratic equations are non-linear equations in which one variable varies with the square of the other variable.
- Formulae for spreadsheets follow a particular format. Ensure that you are able to construct formulae which incorporate addition, subtraction, multiplication, division and percentage differences.
- A geometric progression is a sequence of numbers in which there is a common ratio between adjacent terms.

NOTES

Chapter roundup *continued*

- The logarithm of a number is the power to which 10 has to be raised to get that number.
- Approximation arises if it is not possible to obtain an accurate figure or if a number has been rounded. Rounding can be specified to the nearest whole unit, by the number of decimal places or by the number of significant figures.
- Spurious accuracy arises when a statistic gives the impression that it is more accurate than it really is.
- Maximum errors can be absolute or relative.
- When two or more rounded or approximate numbers are multiplied or divided, the approximate maximum relative error in the result is obtained by adding the individual relative errors.
- You can determine the actual error in calculations involving only a few values/variables without using the two rules.
- Make sure that you have worked through all of the examples in this chapter since it provides the foundation for the remainder of the Study Guide.

Quick quiz

1 Is $3^3/_4$ an integer?

2 What is 1004.002955 to nine significant digits?

3 What is the product of a negative number and a negative number?

4 $217 \leq 217$. True or false?

5 How do you turn a fraction into a percentage?

6 Define the nth root of a number.

7 What is the difference between a formula and an equation?

8 What is a linear equation?

9 What are the rules for drawing graphs?

10 What is the intercept?

11 What are quadratic equations?

12 What quick formula could you use to total the values in cells F15 to F27 in a spreadsheet?

13 What is geometric progression?

14 What is the formula for the sum of a geometric progression?

15 What is the logarithm of 550.77? (Use your calculator)

16 What is spurious accuracy?

17 How is a maximum relative error calculated?

18 What are the two rules to remember when performing calculations using rounded or approximate numbers?

NOTES

Answers to activities

1 17.39

2 (a) $64 - (-1) = 64 + 1 = 65$
(b) $8 + (-9) = -1$
(c) $-24 - (12) = -36$
(d) $-6 - (-12) - (-27) = -6 + 12 + 27 = 33$

3 (a) 648.2565
(b) 30.0192
(c) 0.5313
(d) 5.2518
(e) 0.01
(f) 0.4097
(g) 11,985.69
(h) 93.31
(i) –102.79
(j) 100 (Note that this question is the reciprocal of part (e), and so the answer is the reciprocal of the answer to part (e).)
(k) –0.0775
(l) –0.6133
(m) 0.7443
(n) –1.5434

4 Let 100% = £795

$$\therefore 1\% = \frac{100\%}{100} = \frac{£795}{100} = £7.95$$

$\therefore$ 17% $= 17 \times 1\% = 17 \times £7.95 = £135.15$

$\therefore$ Price offered = £(795 – 135.15) = £659.85

Alternatively

Price offered = £795 × (100 – 17)% = £795 × 83% = £795 × 0.83 = £659.85

5 (a) Difference in price = £(490.99 – 340.99) = £150.00

$$\text{Percentage reduction} = \frac{150}{490.99} \times 100\% = 30.551\%$$

(b) Difference in price = £(892 – 757) = £135

$$\text{Percentage increase} = \frac{135}{757} \times 100\% = 17.8\%$$

6 (30 – 17)/30 × 100% = 43.33% = 0.4333

7 (a) (i) Total parts = 10
Each part is worth £800 ÷ 10 = £80
Tom gets 3 × £80 = £240
Dick gets 2 × £80 = £160
Harry gets 5 × £80 = £400

(ii) Same parts as (i) but in a different order.
Tom gets £400
Dick gets £240
Harry gets £160

(iii) Total parts = 5
Each part is worth £800 ÷ 5 = £160
Therefore Tom gets £480
Dick and Harry each get £160

(b) (i) Laura's share = £6 = 5 parts
Therefore one part is worth £6 ÷ 5 = £1.20
Total of 9 parts shared out originally
Therefore total was 9 × £1.20 = £10.80

NOTES

(ii) Laura's share = £6 = 4 parts

Therefore one part is worth £6 ÷ 4 = £1.50

Therefore original total was 9 × £1.50 = £13.50

8 (a) $(18.6)^{2.6} = 1,998.64$

(b) $(18.6)^{-2.6} = (\frac{1}{18.6})^{2.6} = 0.0005$

(c) $\sqrt[2.6]{18.6} = 3.078$

(d) $(14.2)^4 \times (14.2)^{1/4} = (14.2)^{4.25} = 78,926.98$

(e) $(14.2)^4 + (14.2)^{1/4} = 40,658.69 + 1.9412 = 40,660.6312$

9 **Solution 1**

(a)

$47x + 256$	=	$52x$	
256	=	$5x$	(subtract 47x from each side)
51.2	=	x	(divide each side by 5)

(b)

$4\sqrt{x} + 32$	=	40.6718	
$4\sqrt{x}$	=	8.6718	(subtract 32 from each side)
$\sqrt{x}$	=	2.16795	(divide each side by 4)
x	=	4.7	(square each side).

(c)

$\frac{1}{3x+4}$	=	$\frac{5}{2.7x-2}$	
$3x + 4$	=	$\frac{2.7x-2}{5}$	(take the reciprocal of each side)
$15x + 20$	=	$2.7x - 2$	(multiply each side by 5)
$12.3x$	=	-22	(subtract 20 and subtract 2.7x from each side)
x	=	-1.789	(divide each side by 12.3).

(d)

x^3	=	4.913	
x	=	1.7	(take the cube root of each side).

(e) $34x - 7.6 = (17x - 3.8) \times (x + 12.5)$

This one is easy if you realise that $17 \times 2 = 34$ and $3.8 \times 2 = 7.6$, so $2(17x - 3.8) = 34x - 7.6$

We can then divide each side by $17x - 3.8$ to get

2	=	$x + 12.5$	
-10.5	=	x	(subtract 12.5 from each side).

Solution 2

(a)

$x = (3y - 20)^2$	
$\sqrt{x} = 3y - 20$	(take the square root of each side)
$20 + \sqrt{x} = 3y$	(add 20 to each side)
$y = \frac{20 + \sqrt{x}}{3}$	(divide each side by 3, and swap the sides for ease of reading)

(b)

$2(y - 4) - 4(x^2 + 3) = 0$	
$2(y - 4) = 4(x^2 + 3)$	(add $4(x^2 + 3)$ to each side)
$0.5(y - 4) = x^2 + 3$	(divide each side by 4)
$0.5(y - 4) - 3 = x^2$	(subtract 3 from each side)
$x = \sqrt{0.5(y-4) - 3}$	(take the square root of each side, and swap the sides for ease of reading)
$x = \sqrt{0.5y - 5}$	

NOTES

10 Gradient = –1

11 4y = 16x – 12

The equation must be of the form y = a + bx

$y = -\frac{12}{4} + \frac{16}{4}x = -3 + 4x$

Intercept = a = –3, ie (0, -3)

Slope = 4

12

5x + 2y	=	34	(1)	
x + 3y	=	25	(2)	
5x + 15y	=	125	(3)	5 × (2)
13y	=	91	(4)	(3) – (1)
y	=	7		
x + 21	=	25		Substitute into (2)
x	=	25 – 21		
x	=	4		

The solution is x = 4, y = 7.

13 (a) Let C = total costs

C = total variable costs + total fixed costs

C = 5q + 75

(b) If q = 100, C = (5 × 100) + 75 = £575

(c) If q = 0, C = £75

If q = 100, C = £575

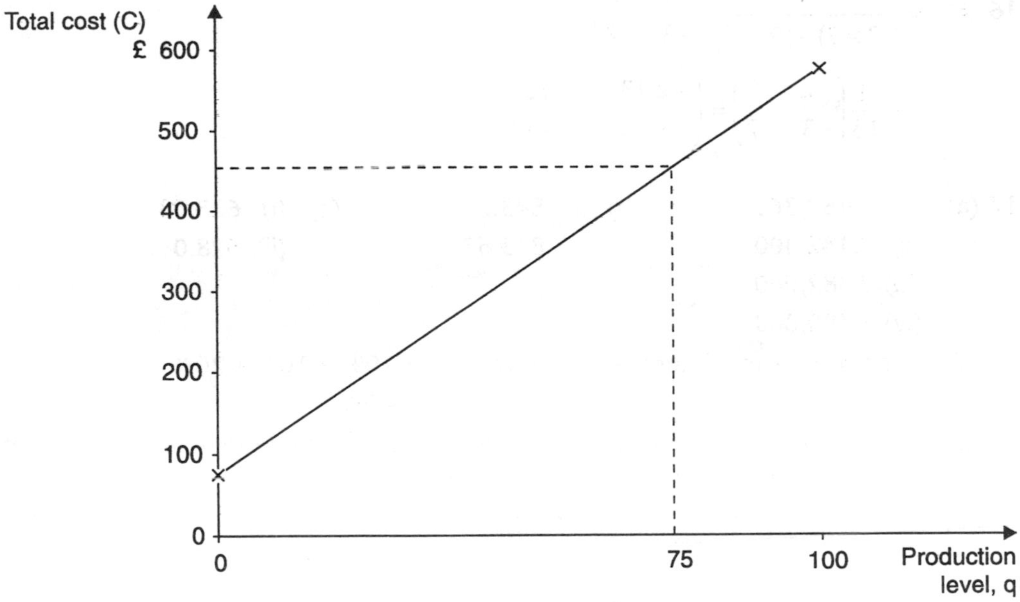

(d) From the graph above, if q = 75, C = £450

14 C = (25 – q)q

If q = 15, C = (25 – 15) × 15 = 10 × 15 = £150

15 $AB = \begin{pmatrix} ((2\times5)+(1\times2)) & ((2\times1)+(1\times3)) & ((2\times0)+(1\times1)) \\ ((0\times5)+(3\times2)) & ((0\times1)+(3\times3)) & ((0\times0)+(3\times1)) \end{pmatrix}$

$= \begin{pmatrix} 12 & 5 & 1 \\ 6 & 9 & 3 \end{pmatrix}$

NOTES

$$CA = \begin{pmatrix} ((3\times2)+(1\times0)) & ((3\times1)+(1\times3)) \\ ((0\times2)+(2\times0)) & ((0\times1)+(2\times3)) \\ ((1\times2)+(4\times0)) & ((1\times1)+(4\times3)) \end{pmatrix}$$

$$= \begin{pmatrix} 6 & 6 \\ 0 & 6 \\ 2 & 13 \end{pmatrix}$$

$$BC = \begin{pmatrix} ((5\times3)+(1\times0)+(0\times1)) & ((5\times1)+(1\times2)+(0\times4)) \\ ((2\times3)+(3\times0)+(1\times1)) & ((2\times1)+(3\times2)+(1\times4)) \end{pmatrix}$$

$$= \begin{pmatrix} 15 & 7 \\ 7 & 12 \end{pmatrix}$$

$$CB = \begin{pmatrix} ((3\times5)+(1\times2)) & ((3\times1)+(1\times3)) & ((3\times0)+(1\times1)) \\ ((0\times5)+(2\times2)) & ((0\times1)+(2\times3)) & ((0\times0)+(2\times1)) \\ ((1\times5)+(4\times2)) & ((1\times1)+(4\times3)) & ((1\times0)+(4\times1)) \end{pmatrix}$$

$$= \begin{pmatrix} 17 & 6 & 1 \\ 4 & 6 & 2 \\ 13 & 13 & 4 \end{pmatrix}$$

16 $A^{-1} = \dfrac{1}{((7\times2)-(9\times3))}\begin{pmatrix} 2 & -9 \\ -3 & 7 \end{pmatrix}$

$$= -\frac{1}{13}\begin{pmatrix} 2 & -9 \\ -3 & 7 \end{pmatrix} = \begin{pmatrix} -2/13 & 9/13 \\ 3/13 & -7/13 \end{pmatrix}$$

17 (a) (i) £482,365
(ii) £482,400
(iii) £482,000
(iv) £480,000

(b) (i) 843.7
(ii) 843.67

(c) (i) 628.03
(ii) 628.0

18 (a) Approximate maximum relative error = 10% + 10% + 20%
= 40%

(b) A is at a maximum when the numerator is big and the denominator small, that is when J and B are at a maximum and M at a minimum.

$$\text{Maximum } A = \frac{1.1J \times 1.1B}{0.8M} = \frac{1.5125JB}{M}$$

$\therefore$ Actual maximum positive relative error = 51.25%.

A is at a minimum when the numerator is small and the denominator big, that is when J and B are at a minimum and M at a maximum.

$$\text{Minimum } A = \frac{0.9J \times 0.9B}{1.2M} = \frac{0.675JB}{M}$$

$\therefore$ Actual maximum negative relative error = 32.5%

Further question practice

Now try the following practice questions at the end of this text.

Multiple choice questions **1–10**

Exam style question **1**

Chapter 2

THE COLLECTION OF DATA

Introduction

The words 'quantitative methods' often strike terror into the hearts of students. They conjure up images of complicated mathematical formulae, scientific analysis of reams of computer output and the drawing of strange graphs and diagrams. Such images are wrong. Quantitative methods simply involve collecting data, presenting them in a useful form and interpreting them.

You will soon discover that quantitative methods are nothing to be afraid of and that a knowledge of them will be extremely advantageous in your studies. The main advantage of quantitative techniques is that they offer a way to make sense of numbers. In a business environment, for example, a manager may collect all sorts of data on production levels, costs and sales, but the numbers on their own are unlikely to mean very much. By using quantitative techniques, a manager can try to make sense out of the numbers, which in turn should help in making sensible business decisions.

In this chapter we will be looking at data collection. In Chapter 3 we will consider how data should be presented once they have been collected.

Your objectives

After completing this chapter you should:

(a) be aware of the various types of data;

(b) know about the sources of secondary data;

(c) be able to design questionnaires;

(d) be aware of the advantages and disadvantages of interviews and postal questionnaires;

(e) know the appropriate sampling method to use in particular circumstances.

1 DATA

What are data?

1.1. 'Data' is a term that you will come across time and time again in your study of quantitative methods, but what does it mean?

Definition

Data is simply a 'scientific' term for facts, figures, information and measurements.

Data therefore include the number of people with red hair who pass their driving test each year, the number of goals scored by each football team in the second division in the current season to date, and the profit after tax for the past ten years of the four biggest supermarket chains.

Types of data

1.2 Data may be of several types. The first distinction to make is between attributes and variables.

Attributes and variables

Definition

An *attribute* is something an object has either got or not got.

1.3 An attribute cannot be measured. For example, an individual is either male or female. There is no measure of *how* male or *how* female somebody is: the sex of a person is an attribute.

Definition

A *variable* is something which can be measured.

1.4 For example, the height of a person is a variable which can be measured according to some scale (such as centimetres).

Discrete and continuous variables

1.5 Variables can be further classified as discrete or continuous.

(a) Discrete variables can only take a finite or countable number of values within a given range. Examples of such variables include 'goals scored by Chachont United against Willford City', 'shoe size' and 'number of people entering SupaSave SupaMarket in Rutminster between 9.05am and 9.10am on a particular day'. If we arbitrarily chose a range of 0 – 10, 2 goals could be scored but not 2½, a (British) shoe size could be 5½ but not 5.193 and 9 people could enter the supermarket but not 9.999.

(b) Continuous variables may take on any value. They are measured rather than counted. For example, it may be considered sufficient to measure the heights of a number of people to the nearest centimetre but there is no reason why the measurements should not be made to the nearest 1/100 cm. Two people who are found to have the same height to the nearest centimetre could almost certainly be distinguished if more precise measurements were taken.

NOTES

Activity 1

Look through the following list of surveys and decide whether each is collecting data on attributes, discrete variables or continuous variables.

(a) A survey of statistics textbooks, to determine how many diagrams they contain.

(b) A survey of cans in a shop, to determine whether or not each has a price sticker.

(c) A survey of athletes to find out how long they take to run a mile.

(d) A survey of the heights of telegraph poles in England.

Primary data and secondary data

1.6 The data used in a statistical survey, whether variables or attributes, can be either primary data or secondary data.

Definitions

Primary data are data collected especially for the purpose of whatever survey is being conducted.

Raw data are primary data which have not been processed at all, but are still just (for example) a list of numbers.

Secondary data are data which have already been collected elsewhere, for some other purpose, but which can be used or adapted for the survey being conducted.

1.7 An advantage of using primary data is that the investigator knows where the data came from, the circumstances under which they were collected, and any limitations or inadequacies in the data.

1.8 In contrast, note the following inadequacies of secondary data.

(a) Any limitations in the data might not be known to the investigator, because he or she did not collect them.

(b) The data might not be entirely suitable for the purpose they are being used for.

Secondary data are sometimes used despite their inadequacies, simply because they are available cheaply whereas the extra cost of collecting primary data would far outweigh their extra value.

Now that we have some idea of the different types of data, we can address ourselves to the problem of getting hold of them.

2 SOURCES OF SECONDARY DATA

2.1 Secondary data are data that were originally collected as primary data for a particular purpose or for general use, but are now being used for another purpose. The Government, for example, collects data to help with making decisions about running the country, and makes these data available to the public.

2.2 Examples of secondary data include the following.

(a) *Published statistics.* For example, the Government publishes statistics through the Office for National Statistics (ONS) (formed by the merger of the Central Statistical Office and the Office of Population Censuses and Surveys in April 1996). The European Union and the United Nations also publish statistics. So do various newspapers.

NOTES

(b) *Historical records*. The type of historical record used for a survey obviously depends on what survey is being carried out. An accountant producing an estimate of future company sales might use historical records of past sales.

Sources of published statistics

2.3 You may be expected to identify the sources of certain published statistics. As you will probably be aware, the range of published economic, business and accounting data is very wide, and a comprehensive knowledge of sources is impracticable. In this chapter the better known sources will be described.

2.4 All published statistics are a source of secondary data. Great care must be taken in using them, since the data may not be obtained or classified in precisely the same way as primary data collected *specifically* for the purpose of the current statistical analysis would be.

2.5 Despite the general shortcomings of secondary data there are many circumstances in which published statistics can be of great value. Many Government statistics are compiled at least partly for the purpose of being used in further analysis and explanatory notes are given so that people using the data know to what extent they are relevant to their needs and what level of confidence they can have in the results of their analysis.

The Office for National Statistics (ONS) and other bodies

2.6 The ONS publishes the following.

(a) The *Monthly Digest of Statistics* (which gives data for the recent past)

(b) The *Annual Abstract of Statistics* (which gives data over a much longer period)

(c) *Economic Trends* (published monthly)

(d) *Financial Statistics* (published monthly)

2.7 The European Union has a Statistical Office of the European Community (SOEC) which gathers statistics from each of the member countries. The SOEC has several statistical publications, including *Basic Statistics of the Community*.

2.8 The United Nations also publishes some statistics on the world economy (for example the statistical yearbook), and a yearbook of labour statistics is published by the International Labour Organisation.

2.9 In the remainder of this section, we shall concentrate on statistical publications in the UK.

The Department of Employment Gazette

2.10 The Department of Employment publishes statistics monthly about employment and unemployment, and about retail prices. The statistics which are published monthly in the *Department of Employment Gazette* include, for example, statistics on the following.

(a) Retail prices

(b) Employment

(c) Unemployment

(d) Unfilled job vacancies

(e) Wage rates

(f) Overtime

(g) Stoppages at work

2.11 Retail prices are very important to a wide variety of users.

(a) For the Government, the Retail Prices Index (RPI) indicates the degree of success there has been in fighting inflation.

(b) For employees, the RPI may give an indication of how much wages need to rise to keep pace with inflation.

(c) For consumers, the RPI indicates the increases to be expected in the prices of goods in shops.

(d) For businesses, the RPI may give a broad indication of how much costs should have been expected to rise over recent years and months.

(e) For pensioners and social security recipients, the movement in the RPI is used to update benefit levels.

The Bank of England Quarterly Bulletin

2.12 The Bank of England issues a quarterly publication which includes data on banks in the UK, the money supply and Government borrowing and financial transactions.

Population data

2.13 Data on the UK population, such as population numbers in total and by region, births, deaths and marriages, are produced monthly by ONS in a publication entitled *Population Trends*.

The ONS also produces an annual statistical review.

Every ten years, there is a full census of the whole population, and results of the census are published. The most recent census was in April 1991.

The Blue Book and the Pink Book

2.14 *The Blue Book on National Income and Expenditure* is published annually by the ONS, giving details of:

(a) gross national product (analysed into sections of the economy such as transport and communication, insurance, banking and finance, public administration and defence);

(b) gross national income (analysed into income from self-employment, income from employment, profits of companies, income from abroad and so on);

(c) gross national expenditure (analysed into expenditure on capital goods, expenditure by consumers and by public authorities, imports and so on).

2.15 This information is augmented by more detailed statistics, also provided in the Blue Book. There is also an annual *Pink Book, The UK Balance of Payments* which analyses the UK's external trade, external capital transactions (inflows and outflows of private capital) and official financing.

The Annual Abstract of Statistics

2.16 Most government statistics of economic and business data are brought together into a main reference book, the *Annual Abstract of Statistics*, which is published by the ONS. Notes about the data and definitions of the data provided are contained in the book.

NOTES

The Monthly Digest of Statistics

2.17 The ONS's *Monthly Digest of Statistics* is an abbreviated version of the *Annual Abstract*, updated and published monthly. A January supplement provides definitions. The information included in the *Monthly Digest* covers a wide range of topics, such as industrial output, production costs, prices and wages, social services, law enforcement, national income, external trade, retailing, transport, construction, agriculture and food.

Financial Statistics

2.18 The ONS publishes a monthly compilation of financial data in *Financial Statistics*. This gives statistics on a variety of financial topics.

(a) Government income, expenditure and borrowing

(b) Assets and liabilities of banks and statistics on other financial institutions, such as building societies, unit trusts, investment trusts, insurance companies and pension funds

(c) Companies (profits, sources and uses of capital funds, acquisitions and mergers, share trading and so on)

(d) Personal sector finance (loans for home buying, consumer credit, personal income expenditure and saving and so on)

(e) The overseas sector

(f) The money supply

(g) Issues of capital and Stock Exchange transactions

(h) Exchange rates, interest rates and share prices

Economic Trends

2.19 Like the *Monthly Digest of Statistics* and *Financial Statistics, Economic Trends* is a monthly publication of the ONS. As its name implies, its main purpose is to indicate trends, and the publication includes graphs as well as numerical statistics.

The Financial Times

2.20 The *Financial Times* and other newspapers and investment journals provide statistics about the Stock Market. These include the following.

(a) The FT-Actuaries All-Share Index (compiled jointly by the *Financial Times,* the Institute of Actuaries in London and the Faculty of Actuaries in Edinburgh). This is an index of share prices quoted on the Stock Exchange.

(b) The FTSE 100 index. This is a stock market index of 100 leading shares, compiled by the *Financial Times* and the Stock Exchange.

The *Financial Times* also includes various other items of daily information on financial matters.

(a) Foreign exchange rates

(b) Interest rates

(c) Gilts and other stock prices

3 SURVEY METHODS OF COLLECTING DATA

3.1 There are two basic methods of collecting primary data from individuals: you can ask people questions or observe their behaviour. The latter method of collection is called observation and is outside the scope of this Study Guide; the former involves the collection of data using surveys.

3.2 There are two main types of survey.

(a) Interviews

(b) Postal questionnaires

3.3 We will be looking at each type, and their respective advantages and disadvantages, in later sections.

3.4 Although surveys offer a quick, efficient and cost-effective way of obtaining the required data, they are not straightforward. Without skill, tact and expertise the results may easily become contaminated with bias and error and the conclusions subsequently drawn will be useless.

3.5 A famous example of this occurred years ago in the United States, when somebody was asked to conduct an opinion poll (which is a form of survey) on whether the next president was likely to be Democrat or Republican. The survey was carried out, but in an inappropriate way. The survey officer *telephoned* people, and in those days far more Republican than Democrat voters had telephones. The survey was useless, because it had not been planned properly.

3.6 The reason why the opinion poll turned out so badly was that the population for the survey had not been defined properly. In data collection, the word 'population' refers to the entire collection of items being considered. The opinion poll should have used the population 'all Americans of voting age', whereas it actually used the population 'all Americans with a telephone'.

Errors in survey methods of collecting data

3.7 There are three main types of error that can appear in survey methods of collecting data.

(a) *Sampling error* arises when the sample of the population surveyed (if the entire population is not being investigated) is not representative of the population from which it is drawn. For example, if a sample of the population of a city was composed entirely of babies less than three months old, the sample would obviously not be representative of the population of the city.

(b) *Response error* can occur even when all members of the population are surveyed and arises because respondents are either unable (through ignorance, forgetfulness or inarticulateness) or unwilling (due to time pressure, desire for privacy, guessing and so on) to respond.

(c) *Non-response error* can occur either if respondents refuse to take part in the survey or are 'not at home'.

3.8 Non-response in survey methods of data collection is a particular problem if those who refuse to take part in the survey are likely to be in some way different from those who do take part. The easiest way to reduce the effect of this situation is to try and increase the percentage of those taking part (responding).

(a) *Reducing non-response for interviews*

(i) The success of interviews relies on the quality of interaction between respondent and interviewer. Interviewers who give the impression of being pleasant, interesting and interested in respondents and who convincingly persuade them that their views are important will produce lower rates of refusal.

NOTES

(ii) If someone is 'not at home' the interviewer should call back.

(iii) Respondents can be promised gifts or monetary reward.

(b) *Reducing non-response for postal questionnaires*

(i) Contact respondents prior to despatching the questionnaire to ask whether they would be prepared to aid the study by completing a questionnaire.

(ii) Include a covering letter to explain why the data are being collected and to put the respondent in the appropriate frame of mind.

(iii) Include a freepost or stamped addressed envelope for ease of reply.

(iv) Provide a gift or monetary incentive upon questionnaire completion.

(v) Address the respondent by name. This not only increases the response rate but will encourage the named person to complete the questionnaire personally.

(vi) Use postal or telephone follow up reminders.

(vii) Carefully select a target audience who have particular interest in the topic.

4 QUESTIONNAIRE DESIGN

Deciding on the questions

Question content

4.1 When deciding on question content it is vital to think about the following.

(a) Is the question necessary?

(b) Will the respondent understand the question?

The language used should be that of the respondent group. Think about the different language used by managing directors and teenagers.

(c) Will the question elicit the required data?

A survey often fails to generate the required data because of badly phrased questions or questions that are too ambiguous to elicit specific information. Double-barrelled questions ('Do you often go to pubs and restaurants?') should be split, and words describing frequency ('often', 'slightly', 'somewhat') should be avoided as they have a wide range of interpretation.

Activity 2

What might be a better way of asking 'Do you often go to the cinema?'

(d) Does the respondent have the necessary data to be able to answer the question?

The ability of the respondent to answer will depend on three factors.

(i) If respondents do not know the answer to a question they may try to bluff their way out of what they see as an embarrassing situation by guessing. Such answers lead to errors in the conclusions drawn from the data collected. Questions should therefore be phrased so that it does not appear that the interviewer is suggesting that the respondent should know the answer.

(ii) Questions relating to unimportant/ infrequent events or to events some time in the past are likely to tempt respondents to guess. This may introduce error and so it is better to 'jog' respondents' memories in some way.

(iii) Even the most articulate of respondents may find it difficult to be verbally adept about their feelings, beliefs, opinions and motivations.

(e) Is the respondent willing and able to answer the questions?

A respondent may refuse to answer one or more questions on a questionnaire (non-response) or many 'refuse' by providing a wrong or distorted answer. Certain techniques can be employed to eliminate distorted, wrong or inaccurate answers.

(i) Assess whether the question is really necessary (especially if it will cause embarrassment or a loss of prestige).

(ii) Reassure respondents of the importance of the question and of the value of their response.

(iii) Begin a 'difficult' question with a statement which implies the topic of the question is common or quite usual.

(iv) Imply that the behaviour in which you are interested is an attribute of a third party (someone other than the respondent).

(v) Provide respondents with a card listing possible responses, identified by a letter or a number, to potentially embarrassing questions. Respondents need only provide the appropriate letter or number as their answer.

(vi) When analysing the data, replies to questions related to image or prestige should be upgraded or downgraded as necessary.

Activity 3

How might the following question be rephrased?

'Do you visit the pub to get drunk?'

Question phrasing

4.2 Given below is a checklist of factors to consider when translating data requirements into words.

(a) Use a style of language appropriate to the target population.

(b) Avoid long questions.

(c) Avoid vague and ambiguous words.

(d) Avoid biased words and leading questions.

(e) Do not use double-barrelled questions.

(f) Avoid negative questions.

(g) Do not encourage respondents to guess.

(h) Avoid questions which assume respondents possess all the relevant information pertaining to the question.

Types of response format

4.3 Questions can be open or closed. Open questions are difficult to analyse. An open question might be worded like this.

'How did you travel to work today?'

The responses may be so numerous that analysis becomes onerous and time consuming. The designer of the questionnaire should instead try to offer a full range of possible responses to the question, perhaps like this.

NOTES

'Please indicate how you travelled to work today.

By bus	☐
By train	☐
By private car	☐
On foot	☐
By bicycle/motorcycle	☐
I did not go to work today (illness, holidays etc)	☐
I work at home	☐
I do not work	☐

Other (please give details) ....'

The responses from this closed question will be much easier to analyse. It is important, however, to avoid putting such lists of responses in order of supposed popularity.

Activity 4

What types of problem can you envisage arising from the use of multiple choice questions? How can such problems be overcome?

Question sequence

4.4 (a) Start with quota control questions to determine right away whether the interviewee is the right type of person. Quota control questions might identify whether thc interviewee is employed or unemployed, under 40 over 40 and so on. Such questions enable you to terminate worthless interviews as early as possible.

(b) Move on to questions which will engage interest, reassure and give a foretaste of what is to follow.

(c) Questions should be in logical order as far as possible, but if difficult questions are necessary it may be more appropriate to put them at the end.

(d) Avoid questions which suggest the answers to later questions. This will cause bias.

Questionnaire layout

4.5 (a) Use good quality paper.

(b) The questionnaire should be as short as possible. Questionnaires that are too long may discourage the respondent from even starting.

(c) If respondents have to complete the questionnaire themselves, it must be as approachable as possible. Consider the use of lines, boxes, different typefaces or print sizes and small pictures. Use plenty of space.

(d) Make sure that the instructions which guide the respondent through the questionnaire are as user friendly as possible and are kept to a minimum.

(e) Explain the purpose of the survey at the beginning of the questionnaire and, where possible, guarantee confidentiality. Emphasise the date by which it must be returned.

(f) At the end of the questionnaire, thank the respondent and make it clear what they should do with the completed questionnaire.

Pretest, revision and final version of the questionnaire

4.6 Pretesting the questionnaire will uncover faults in its design before it is too late and should therefore ensure that the final version of the questionnaire gathers the required data.

5 INTERVIEWS

5.1 There are basically two types of interview that can be used to collect data, the personal (face to face) interview and the telephone interview.

Personal interviews

Advantages of personal interviews

5.2 (a) The interviewer is able to reduce respondent anxiety and allay potential embarrassment, thereby increasing the response rate and decreasing the potential for error.

(b) The interviewer's experience makes the routing of questions easier (for example, 'if yes go to question 7, if no go to question 10').

(c) Interviewers can ask, within narrow limits, for a respondent's answer to be clarified.

(d) The questions can be given in a fixed order with a fixed wording and the answers can be recorded in a standard manner. This will reduce variability if there is more than one interviewer involved in the survey.

(e) Standardised questions and ways of recording the responses mean that less skilled interviewers may be used, thereby reducing the cost of the survey.

(f) Pictures, signs and objects can be used.

Disadvantages of personal interviews

5.3 (a) They can be time consuming.

(b) The cost per completed interview can be higher than with other survey methods.

(c) Questionnaires can be difficult to design.

(d) Fully-structured interviews have particular disadvantages.

(i) Questions must be kept relatively simple, thus restricting the depth of data collected.

(ii) Questions must normally be closed because of the difficulties of recording answers to open questions.

(iii) Interviewers cannot probe vague or ambiguous replies.

Telephone interviews

5.4 Telephone interviews are a relatively fast and low-cost means of gathering data compared to personal interviews. They are most useful when only a small amount of information is required. They also benefit the respondent in terms of the short amount of time taken up by the interview.

5.5 CATI (computer-assisted telephone interviewing) has been used successfully by insurance services and banks as well as consumer research organisations. The telephone interviewer calls up a questionnaire on screen and reads questions to the respondent. Answers are then recorded instantly on computer. Complex questions with questionnaire routing may be handled in this way.

Advantages of telephone interviews

5.6 (a) The response is rapid.

(b) A wide geographical area can be covered fairly cheaply from a central location. There is no need for the interviewer to travel between respondents.

(c) It may be easier to ask sensitive or embarrassing questions.

NOTES

Disadvantages of telephone interviews

5.7 (a) A biased sample may result from the fact that a proportion of people do not have telephones and many of those who do are ex-directory.

(b) It is not possible to use 'showcards' or pictures.

(c) The refusal rate is much higher than with face-to-face interviews.

(d) It is not possible to see the interviewee's expression or to develop the rapport that is possible with personal interviews.

(e) The interview must be short.

(f) Respondents may be unwilling to participate for fear of being sold something.

6 POSTAL QUESTIONNAIRES

6.1 If the size of interviewer-induced error is likely to be large, or its magnitude cannot be predicted with any degree of accuracy, and if cost is an important factor when deciding on the data collection method, postal questionnaires should be seriously considered.

6.2 Because there is no one to clear up ambiguity in questions, the wording and sequence of the questionnaire must be carefully thought out before it is used.

Advantages of postal questionnaires

6.3 Postal questionnaires have the following advantages over personal interviews.

(a) The cost per person is likely to be less, so more people can be sampled.

(b) It is usually possible to ask more questions because the people completing the forms (the respondents) can do so in their own time.

(c) All respondents are presented with questions in the same way. There is no opportunity for an interviewer to influence responses (interviewer bias) or to misrecord them.

(d) It may be easier to ask personal or embarrassing questions in a postal questionnaire than in a personal interview.

(e) Respondents may need to look up information for the questionnaire. This will be easier if the questionnaire is sent to their home or place of work.

Disadvantages of postal questionnaires

6.4 On the other hand, the use of personal interviews does have certain advantages over the use of postal questionnaires.

(a) Large numbers of postal questionnaires may not be returned or may be returned only partly completed. This may lead to biased results if those replying are not representative of all people in the survey. Response rates are likely to be higher with personal interviews, and the interviewer can encourage people to answer all questions. Low response rates are a major problem with postal questionnaires.

(b) Misunderstanding is less likely with personal interviews because the interviewer can explain questions which the interviewee does not understand.

(c) Personal interviews are more suitable when deep or detailed questions are to be asked, since the interviewer can take the time required with each interviewee to explain the implications of the question. Also, the interviewer can probe for further information and encourage the respondent to think deeper.

7 SAMPLING

Definition

Sampling involves selecting a sample of items from a population.

7.1 Sampling is one of the most important subjects in quantitative methods. In most practical situations the population will be too large to carry out a complete survey and only a sample will be examined. A good example of this is a poll taken to try to predict the results of an election. It is not possible to ask everyone of voting age how they are going to vote: it would take too long and cost too much. So a sample of voters is taken, and the results from the sample are used to estimate the voting intentions of the whole population.

7.2 Occasionally a population is small enough that all of it can be examined: for example, the examination results of one class of students. This type of survey is quite rare, however, and usually the investigator has to choose some sort of sample.

Definition

When all of the population is examined, the survey is called a *census*.

7.3 You may think that using a sample is very much a compromise, but you should consider the following points.

(a) In practice, a 100% survey (a census) never achieves the completeness required.

(b) A census may require the use of semi-skilled investigators, resulting in a loss of accuracy in the data collected.

(c) It can be shown mathematically that once a certain sample size has been reached, very little extra accuracy is gained by examining more items.

(d) It is possible to ask more questions with a sample.

(e) The higher cost of a census may exceed the value of results.

(f) Things are always changing. Even if you took a census it could well be out of date by the time you completed it.

The choice of a sample

7.4 One of the most important requirements of sample data is that they should be complete. That is, the data should cover all areas of the population to be examined. If this requirement is not met, then the sample will be biased.

7.5 For example, suppose you wanted to survey the productivity of workers in a factory, and you went along every Monday and Tuesday for a few months to measure their output. Would these data be complete? The answer is no. You might have gathered very thorough data on what happens on Mondays and Tuesdays, but you would have missed out the rest of the week. It could be that the workers, keen and fresh after the weekend, work better at the start of the week than at the end. If this is the case, then your data will give you a misleadingly high productivity figure. Careful attention must therefore be given to the sampling method employed to produce a sample.

7.6 Sampling methods fall into three main groups.

(a) Random sampling

(b) Quasi-random sampling

(c) Non-random sampling

NOTES

8 RANDOM SAMPLING

8.1 To ensure that the sample selected is free from bias, random sampling must be used. Inferences about the population being sampled can then be made validly.

Definition

A simple *random sample* is a sample selected in such a way that every item in the population has an equal chance of being included.

8.2 For example, if you wanted to take a random sample of library books, it would not be good enough to pick them off the shelves, even if you picked them at random. This is because the books which were out on loan would stand no chance of being chosen. You would either have to make sure that all the books were on the shelves before taking your sample, or find some other way of sampling (for example, using the library index cards).

8.3 A random sample is not necessarily a perfect sample. For example, you might pick what you believe to be a completely random selection of library books, and find that every one of them is a detective thriller. It is a remote possibility, but it could happen. The only way to eliminate the possibility altogether is to take 100% survey (a census) of the books, which, unless it is a tiny library, is impractical.

Sampling frames

Definition

A *sampling frame* is a numbered list of all the items in the population.

8.4 If random sampling is used then it is necessary to construct a sampling frame. Once this has been made, it is easy to select a random sample, simply by generating a list of random numbers.

8.5 For instance, if you wanted to select a random sample of children from a school, it would be useful to have a list of names:

0 J Absolam

1 R Brown

2 S Brown

...

Now the numbers 0, 1, 2 and so on can be used to select the random sample. It is normal to start the numbering at 0, so that when 0 appears in a list of random numbers it can be used.

8.6 Sometimes it is not possible to draw up a sampling frame. For example, if you wanted to take a random sample of Americans, it would take too long to list all Americans.

8.7 A sampling frame should have the following characteristics.

(a) *Completeness.* Are all members of the population included on the list?

(b) *Accuracy.* Is the information correct?

(c) *Adequacy.* Does it cover the entire population?

(d) *Up to dateness.* Is the list up to date?

(e) *Convenience.* Is the sampling frame readily accessible?

(f) *Non-duplication.* Does each member of the population appear on the list only once?

8.8 Two readily available sampling frames for the human population of Great Britain are the council tax register (list of dwellings) and the electoral register (list of individuals).

Random number tables

8.9 Assuming that a sampling frame can be drawn up, then a random sample can be picked from it by one of the following methods.

(a) The lottery method, which amounts to picking numbered pieces of paper out of a box

(b) The use of random number tables

8.10 Set out below is part of a typical random number table.

93716	16894	98953	73231
32886	59780	09958	18065
92052	06831	19640	99413
39510	35905	85244	35159
27699	06494	03152	19121
92962	61773	22109	78508
10274	12202	94205	50380
75867	20717	82037	10268
85783	47619	87481	37220

You should note the following points.

(a) The sample is found by selecting groups of random numbers with the number of digits depending on the total population size, as follows.

Total population size	*Number of random digits*
1– 10	1
1– 100	2
1–1,000	3

The items selected for the sample are those corresponding to the random numbers selected.

(b) The starting point on the table should be selected at random. After that, however, numbers must be selected in a consistent manner. In other words, you should use the table row by row or column by column. By jumping around the table from place to place, personal bias may be introduced.

(c) In many practical situations it is more convenient to use a computer to generate a list of random numbers, especially when a large sample is required.

EXAMPLE: RANDOM NUMBER TABLES

An investigator wishes to select a random sample from a population of 800 people, who have been numbered 000, 001, ..., 799. As there are three digits in 799 the random numbers will be selected in groups of three. Working along the first line of the table given earlier, the first few groups are as follows.

937 161 689 498 953 732

Numbers over 799 are discarded. The first four people in the sample will therefore be those numbered 161, 689, 498 and 732.

NOTES

Drawbacks of random sampling

8.11 (a) The selected items are subject to the full range of variation inherent in the population.

(b) An unrepresentative sample may result.

(c) The members of the population selected may be scattered over a wide area, adding to the cost and difficulty of obtaining the data.

(d) An adequate sampling frame might not exist.

(e) The numbering of the population might be laborious.

Quasi- and non-random sampling

8.12 In many situations it might be too expensive to obtain a random sample, in which case quasi-random sampling is necessary, or else it may not be possible to draw up a sampling frame. In such cases, non-random sampling has to be used.

9 QUASI-RANDOM SAMPLING

9.1 Quasi-random sampling, which provides a good approximation to random sampling, necessitates the existence of a sampling frame.

The main methods of quasi-random sampling are as follows.

(a) Systematic sampling

(b) Stratified sampling

(c) Multistage sampling

Systematic sampling

9.2 Systematic sampling may provide a good approximation to random sampling. It works by selecting every nth item after a random start. For example, if it was decided to select a sample of 20 from a population of 800, then every 40th (800 ÷ 20) item after a random start in the first 40 should be selected. The starting point could be found using the lottery method or random number tables. If (say) 23 was chosen, then the sample would include the 23rd, 63rd, 103rd, 143rd, ..., 783rd items.

The gap of 40 is known as the sampling interval.

The investigator must ensure that there is no regular pattern to the population which, if it coincided with the sampling interval, might lead to a biased sample. In practice, this problem is often overcome by choosing multiple starting points and using varying sampling intervals whose size is selected at random.

9.3 If the sampling frame is in random order (such as an alphabetical list of students) a systematic sample is essentially the same as a simple random sample.

A systematic sample does not fully meet the criterion of randomness since some samples of the given size have zero probability of being chosen. However, the method is easy and cheap, and hence is widely used.

Stratified sampling

9.4 In many situations stratified sampling is the best method of choosing a sample. The population must be divided into strata or categories.

If we took a random sample of all cost and management accountants in the country, it is conceivable that the entire sample might consist of members of the CIMA working in public companies. Stratified sampling removes this possibility as random samples could be taken from each type of employment, the number in each sample being proportional to the total number of cost and management accountants in each type (for example those in partnerships, those in public companies and those in private companies).

EXAMPLE: STRATIFIED SAMPLING

The number of accountants in each type of work in a particular country are as follows.

Partnerships	500
Public companies	500
Private companies	700
Public practice	800
	2,500

If a sample of 20 was required the sample would be made up as follows.

		Sample
Partnerships	$\frac{500}{2,500} \times 20$	4
Public companies	$\frac{500}{2,500} \times 20$	4
Private companies	$\frac{700}{2,500} \times 20$	6
Public practice	$\frac{800}{2,500} \times 20$	6
		20

9.5 The strata frequently involve multiple classifications. In social surveys, for example, there is usually stratification by age, sex and social class. This implies that the sampling frame must contain information on these three variables before the threefold stratification of the population can be made.

9.6 Advantages of stratification are as follows.

(a) It ensures a representative sample since it guarantees that every important category will have elements in the final sample.

(b) The structure of the sample will reflect that of the population if the same proportion of individuals is chosen from each stratum.

(c) Each stratum is represented by a randomly chosen sample and therefore inferences can be made about each stratum.

NOTES

(d) Precision is increased. Sampling takes place within strata and, because the range of variation is less in each stratum than in the population as a whole and variation between strata does not enter as a chance effect, higher precision is obtainable. (For this to occur, the items in each stratum must be as similar as possible and the difference between the individual strata must be as great as possible.)

9.7 Note, however, that stratification requires prior knowledge of each item in the population. Sampling frames do not always contain this information. Stratification from the electoral register as to age structure would not be possible because the electoral register does not contain information about age.

Multistage sampling

9.8 Multistage sampling is normally used to cut down the number of investigators and the costs of obtaining a sample. An example will show how the method works.

EXAMPLE: MULTISTAGE SAMPLING

A survey of spending habits is being planned to cover the whole of Britain. It is obviously impractical to draw up a sampling frame, so random sampling is not possible and multistage sampling is to be used instead.

The country is divided into a number of areas and a small sample of these is selected at random. Each of the areas selected is subdivided into smaller units and again a smaller number of these is selected at random. This process is repeated as many times as necessary and, finally, a random sample of the relevant people living in each of the smallest units is taken. A fair approximation to a random sample can be obtained.

Thus, we might choose a random sample of eight areas, and from each of these areas, select a random sample of five towns. From each town, a random sample of 200 people might be selected so that the total sample size is $8 \times 5 \times 200 = 8{,}000$ people.

9.9 The main advantage of this method is one of cost saving but there are a number of disadvantages.

(a) There is the possibility of bias if, for example, only a small number of regions are selected.

(b) The method is not truly random as once the final sampling areas have been selected the rest of the population cannot be in the sample.

(c) If the population is heterogeneous, the areas chosen should reflect the full range of the diversity. Otherwise, choosing some areas and excluding others (even if it is done randomly) will result in a biased sample.

9.10 The sampling methods looked at so far have necessitated the existence of a sampling frame (or in multistage sampling, sampling frames of areas, sub-areas and items within selected sub-areas). It is often impossible to identify a satisfactory sampling frame and, in such instances, other sampling methods have to be employed.

NOTES

10 NON-RANDOM SAMPLING

10.1 There are two main methods of non-random sampling, used when a sampling frame cannot be established.

(a) Quota sampling

(b) Cluster sampling

Quota sampling

10.2 In quota sampling, randomness is forfeited in the interests of cheapness and administrative simplicity. Investigators are told to interview all the people they meet up to a certain quota. A large degree of bias could be introduced accidentally. For example, an interviewer in a shopping centre may fill her quota by meeting only people who can go shopping during the week. In practice, this problem can be partly overcome by subdividing the quota into different types of people, for example on the basis of age, sex and income, to ensure that the sample mirrors the structure or stratification of the population. The interviewer is then told to interview, for example, 30 males between the ages of 30 and 40 from social class C1. The actual choice of the individuals to be interviewed, within the limits of the *quota controls*, is left to the field worker.

Advantages of quota sampling

10.3 (a) It is cheap and administratively easy.

(b) A much larger sample can be studied, and hence more information can be gained at a faster speed for a given outlay than when compared with a fully randomised sampling method.

(c) Although a fairly detailed knowledge of the characteristics of a population is required, no sampling frame is necessary because the interviewer questions every person she meets up to the quota.

(d) Quota sampling may be the only possible approach in certain situations, such as television audience research.

(e) Given suitable, trained and properly briefed field workers, quota sampling yields enough accurate information for many forms of commercial market research.

Disadvantages of quota sampling

10.4 (a) The method can result in certain biases (although these can often be allowed for or may be unimportant for the purpose of the research).

(b) The non-random nature of the method rules out any valid estimate of the sampling error (a concept you will meet later in this Study Guide) in estimates derived from the sample.

Conclusion

10.5 Quota sampling cannot be regarded as ultimately satisfactory in research where it is important that theoretically valid results should be obtained. It can be argued, however, that when other large sources of error, such as non-response, exist, it is pointless to worry too much about sampling error.

NOTES

EXAMPLE: QUOTA SAMPLING

Consider the figures in the stratified sampling example above, but with the following additional information relating to the sex of the accountants.

	Male	*Female*
Partnerships	300	200
Public companies	400	100
Private companies	300	400
Public practice	300	500

An investigator's quotas might be as follows.

	Male	*Female*	*Total*
Partnerships	30	20	50
Public companies	40	10	50
Private companies	30	40	70
Public practice	30	50	80
			250

Using quota sampling, the investigator would interview the first 30 male cost and management accountants in partnerships that he met, the first 20 female cost and management accountants in partnerships that he met and so on.

Cluster sampling

10.6 Cluster sampling involves selecting one definable subsection of the population as the sample, that subsection taken to be representative of the population in question. The pupils of one school might be taken as a cluster sample of all children at school in one county.

Cluster sampling benefits from low costs in the same way as multistage sampling.

10.7 The advantages of cluster sampling are that it is a good alternative to multistage sampling if a satisfactory sampling frame does not exist and it is inexpensive to operate because little organisation or structure is involved. There is, however, the potential for considerable bias.

Activity 5

Describe four methods a brewery could employ to test the market for a new canned beer. Discuss the relative advantages and disadvantages of each method chosen.

11 THE SIZE OF A SAMPLE

11.1 As well as deciding on the appropriateness of a particular sampling method for a given situation, the size of the sample actually selected must also be given consideration.

11.2 Although, in certain circumstances, statistical processes can be used to calculate sample sizes, there is no universal law for determining the size of the sample. Two general considerations should, however, be borne in mind.

(a) The larger the size of the sample, the more accurate the results.

(b) There reaches a point after which there is little to be gained from increasing the size of the sample.

11.3 Despite these principles other, more administration-type factors, play a role in determining sample size.

(a) *Money and time available.*

(b) *Degree of precision required.* A survey may have the aim of discovering residents' reaction to a road widening scheme and hence a fairly small sample, producing imprecise results, would be acceptable. An enquiry into the safety of a new drug would, on the other hand, require an extremely large sample so that the information gained was as precise as possible.

(c) *Number of subsamples required.* If a complicated sampling method such as stratified sampling is to be used, the overall sample size will need to be large so as to ensure adequate representation of each subgroup (in this case, each stratum).

Chapter roundup

- This chapter has concentrated on the practical problems of collecting data.
- An attribute is something an object has either got or not got. It cannot be measured. A variable is something which can be measured.
- Variables can be discrete (may take specific values) or continuous (may take any value).
- Data may be primary (collected specifically for the current purpose) or secondary (collected already).
- Examples of secondary data include published statistics and historical records.
- Primary data can be collected using surveys. There are two main types of survey: interviews and postal questionnaires. Interviews can be face to face or performed over the telephone.
- Questionnaire design involves considering question content, question phrasing, types of response format, questions required and layout. Questionnaires should be pretested.
- Data are often collected from a sample rather than from a population. A sample can be selected using random sampling (using random number tables or the lottery method), quasi-random sampling (systematic, stratified and multistage sampling) or non-random sampling (quota and cluster sampling). Ensure that you know the characteristics, advantages and disadvantages of each sampling method.
- Once data have been collected they need to be presented and analysed. It is important to remember that if the data have not been collected properly, no amount of careful presentation or interpretation can remedy the defect.

NOTES

Quick quiz

1 What is a discrete variable?

2 What are secondary data?

3 List some of the UK sources of published statistics.

4 What types of error can appear in survey methods of collecting data?

5 What factors relating to question sequence should be considered when designing a questionnaire?

6 What are the advantages and disadvantages of personal interviews?

7 List the arguments in favour of using a sample.

8 What is a simple random sample?

9 What is stratified sampling?

10 List three administrative factors which may affect the size of a sample.

Answers to activities

1 (a) The number of diagrams in a textbook is a discrete variable, because it can only be counted in whole number steps. You cannot, for example, have 26¼ diagrams or 47.32 diagrams in a book.

(b) Whether or not a can possesses a sticker is an attribute. It is not something which can be measured. A can either possesses the attribute or it does not.

(c) How long an athlete takes to run a mile is a continuous variable, because the time recorded can, in theory, take any value, for example 4 minutes 2.0643 seconds.

(d) The height of a telegraph pole is a continuous variable.

2 'Do you go to the cinema (a) once a week, (b) once a month, (c) twice a year?'

3 'Do you think that people go to the pub simply to get drunk?'

4 Here are some ideas. You may have thought of others.

(a) Capturing a full range of possible responses to a question such as 'In which store do you buy the majority of your clothes?' can be impractical.

This problem can be overcome by listing the most popular stores and using an 'other (please specify)' option

(b) The position of the alternative responses may introduce bias.

This problem can be overcome (but not entirely) by producing different versions of the questionnaire.

(c) An unbalanced set of alternative responses could be provided such as the following.

Q: What do you think of TV programme 'XXX'?

A: 1	2	3
Too boring	Very dull	Indifferent

Obviously such response sets should not be used.

5 (a) The brewery could try to supply the beer to a random sample of beer drinkers, and then ask for their views. Such samples are taken in such a way that every member of the population (in this case, all beer drinkers and perhaps all potential beer drinkers) has an equal chance of being selected for the sample. The main advantage of random sampling is that it allows mathematical analysis of the data to be carried out. The main disadvantage is that a random sample can be difficult and expensive to collect. The brewery may well find that it is impossible to compile a list of all beer drinkers from which to select a sample.

(b) Stratified sampling may well be appropriate. The population would first be divided into groups, perhaps by age or by weekly beer consumption, and then samples would be selected from each group (reflecting the proportion of the population in the group). The main advantage of stratified sampling is that it ensures that each group is represented in the sample. The main disadvantage is that preliminary work is needed to determine which groupings are likely to be useful and the proportion of the population in each group.

(c) Cluster sampling may well be a practical alternative, giving some of the benefits of both random sampling and stratified sampling. The population could be divided geographically into beer drinkers at public houses in different regions of the country and beer purchasers at off-licences within these regions. A sample of regions could be selected, and a sample of public houses and off-licences in each selected region could be chosen. All consumers at the chosen public houses and off-licences would then form the sample. The main advantage of cluster sampling is its relative cheapness. The main disadvantage is that the sample obtained will not be truly random, so some forms of statistical analysis will not be possible.

(d) Quota sampling has the advantage of being even cheaper than cluster sampling, but the disadvantage of producing a sample which is even further from being random. Researchers would simply visit a selection of public houses and off-licences and interview the first beer drinkers they met until they had fulfilled some quota (say ten men and ten women).

Further question practice

Now try the following practice questions at the end of this text.

Multiple choice questions **11–15**

Exam style question **2**

Chapter 3

DATA PRESENTATION

Introduction

You now know how to collect data. So what do you do with them next? You have to present the data you have collected so that they can be of use. This chapter begins by looking at how data can be presented in tables and charts. Such methods are helpful in presenting key data in a concise and easy to understand way. They are, however, purely descriptive and offer little opportunity for further detailed numerical analysis of a situation.

Data that are a mass of numbers can usefully be summarised into a frequency distribution (effectively a table which details the frequency with which a particular value occurs). Histograms and ogives are the pictorial representation of grouped and cumulative frequency distributions and provide the link between the purely descriptive approach to data analysis and the numerical approach covered in Chapter 5.

Data recorded over time can be presented as time series graphs. Z charts and semi-logarithmic graphs are special types of time series graph.

Your objectives

After completing this chapter you should:

(a) be able to present data using tables, pie charts and bar charts;

(b) be able to construct frequency distributions;

(c) be able to prepare histograms;

(d) be able to draw ogives, time series graphs, Z charts and semi-logarithmic graphs;

(e) know the circumstances in which each data presentation format should be used.

1 TABLES

Definition

A *table* is a matrix of data in rows and columns, with the rows and the columns having titles.

1.1 Raw data (the list of results from a survey) need to be summarised and analysed, to give them meaning. This chapter is concerned with several different ways of presenting data to convey their meaning. We will start with one of the most basic ways, the preparation of a table.

1.2 Tabulation means putting data into tables.

1.3 Since a table is two-dimensional, it can only show two variables. For example, the resources required to produce items in a factory could be tabulated, with one dimension (rows or columns) representing the items produced and the other dimension representing the resources.

Resources for production: all figures in pounds

		Product items			
	A	*B*	*C*	*D*	*Total*
Resources					
Direct material A	X	X	X	X	X
Direct material B	X	X	X	X	X
Direct labour grade 1	X	X	X	X	X
Direct labour grade 2	X	X	X	X	X
Supervision	X	X	X	X	X
Machine time	X	X	X	X	X
Total	X	X	X	X	X

1.4 To tabulate data, you need to recognise what the two dimensions should represent, prepare rows and columns accordingly with suitable titles, and then insert the data into the appropriate places in the table.

Guidelines for tabulation

1.5 The table in Paragraph 1.3 illustrates certain guidelines which you should apply when presenting data in tabular form. These are as follows.

(a) The table should be given a clear title.

(b) All columns should be clearly labelled.

(c) Where appropriate, there should be clear sub-totals.

(d) A total column may be presented; this is usually the right-hand column.

(e) A total figure is often advisable at the bottom of each column of figures.

(f) Tables should not be packed with so much data that reading the information is difficult.

(g) Eliminate non-essential information, rounding large numbers to two or three significant figures.

(h) Do not hide important figures in the middle of the table. Consider ordering columns or rows by order of importance or magnitude.

NOTES

EXAMPLE: TABLES

The total number of employees in a certain trading company is 1,000. They are employed in three departments: production, administration and sales. There are 600 people employed in the production department and 300 in administration. There are 110 male juveniles in employment, 110 female juveniles, and 290 adult females. The remaining employees are adult males.

In the production department there are 350 adult males, 150 adult females and 50 male juveniles, whilst in the administration department there are 100 adult males, 110 adult females and 50 juvenile males.

Required

Draw up a table to show all the details of employment in the company and its departments and provide suitable secondary statistics to describe the distribution of people in departments.

Solution

The basic table required has the following two dimensions.

(a) Departments

(b) Age/sex analysis

Secondary statistics (not the same thing as secondary data) are supporting figures that are supplementary to the main items of data, and which clarify or amplify the main data. A major example of secondary statistics is percentages. In this example, we could show one of the following.

(a) The percentage of the total work force in each department belonging to each age/sex group

(b) The percentage of the total of each age/sex group employed in each department

In this example, (a) has been selected but you might consider that (b) would be more suitable. Either could be suitable, depending of course on what purposes the data are being collected and presented for.

Analysis of employees

	Department							
	Production		*Administration*		*Sales*		*Total*	
	No	*%*	*No*	*%*	*No*	*%*	*No*	*%*
Adult males	350	58.4	100	33.3	**40	40	*490	49
Adult females	150	25.0	110	36.7	**30	30	290	29
Male juveniles	50	8.3	50	16.7	**10	10	110	11
Female juveniles	*50	8.3	* 40	13.3	**20	20	110	11
Total	600	100.0	300	100.0	100	100	1,000	100

* Balancing figure to make up the column total

** Balancing figure then needed to make up the row total

Rounding errors

1.6 Rounding errors may become apparent when, for example, a percentages column does not add up to 100%. Any rounding should therefore be to the nearest unit and the potential size of errors should be kept to a tolerable level by rounding to a small enough unit (for example to the nearest £10, rather than to the nearest £1,000).

2 CHARTS

2.1 Instead of presenting data in a table, it might be preferable to give a visual display in the form of a chart.

2.2 The purpose of a chart is to convey the data in a way that will demonstrate its meaning or significance more clearly than a table of data would. Charts are not always more appropriate than tables, and the most suitable way of presenting data will depend on the following.

(a) What the data are intended to show. Visual displays usually make one or two points quite forcefully, whereas tables usually give more detailed information.

(b) Who is going to use the data. Some individuals might understand visual displays more readily than tabulated data.

Pie charts

Definition

A *pie chart* is used to show pictorially the relative sizes of component elements of a total.

2.3 Such charts are called pie charts because they are circular, and so have the shape of a pie in a round pie dish and because the 'pie' is then cut into slices. Each slice represents a part of the total.

2.4 Pie charts have sectors of varying sizes, and you need to be able to draw sectors fairly accurately. To do this, you need a protractor. Working out sector sizes involves converting parts of the total into equivalent degrees of a circle.

EXAMPLE: PIE CHARTS

The costs of production at Factory A and Factory B during March 19X2 were as follows.

	Factory A		*Factory B*	
	£'000	%	£'000	%
Direct materials	70	35	50	20
Direct labour	30	15	125	50
Production overhead	90	45	50	20
Office costs	10	5	25	10
	200	100	250	100

Required

Show the costs for the factories in pie charts.

Solution

To convert the components into degrees of a circle, we can use either the percentage figures or the actual cost figures.

(a) Using the percentage figures, the total percentage is 100%, and the total number of degrees in a circle is 360°. To convert from one to the other, we multiply each percentage value by 360/100 = 3.6.

NOTES

EXAMPLE *continued*

	Factory A %	*Factory A* Degrees	*Factory B* %	*Factory B* Degrees
Direct materials	35	126	20	72
Direct labour	15	54	50	180
Production overhead	45	162	20	72
Office costs	5	18	10	36
	100	360	100	360

(b)Using the actual cost figures, we would multiply each cost by

	Factory A	*Factory B*
$\frac{\text{Number of degrees}}{\text{Total cost}}$	$\frac{360}{200} = 1.8$	$\frac{360}{250} = 1.44$

	Factory A £'000	*Factory A* Degrees	*Factory B* £'000	*Factory B* Degrees
Direct materials	70	126	50	72
Direct labour	30	54	125	180
Production overhead	90	162	50	72
Office costs	10	18	25	36
	200	360	250	360

A pie chart could be drawn for each factory, as follows. A protractor is used to measure the degrees accurately to obtain the correct sector sizes.

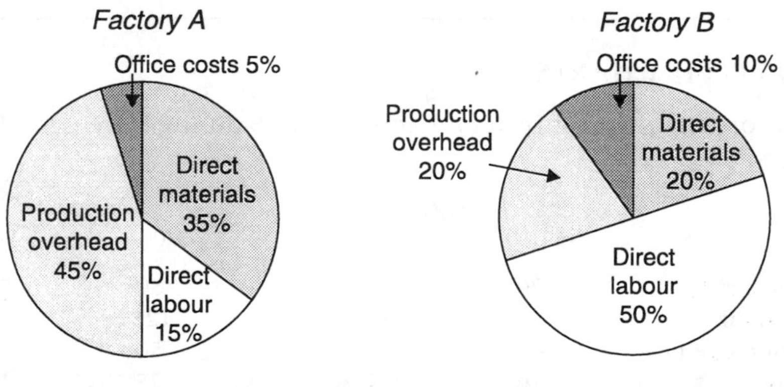

2.5 The advantages of pie charts are as follows.

(a) They give a simple pictorial display of the relative sizes of elements of a total.

(b) They show clearly when one element is much bigger than others.

(c) They can sometimes clearly show differences in the elements of two different totals. In the example above, the pie charts for factories A and B show how factory A's costs mostly consist of production overhead and direct materials, whereas at factory B, direct labour is the largest cost element.

2.6 The disadvantages of pie charts are as follows.

(a) They show only the relative sizes of elements. In the example of the two factories, for instance, the pie charts do not show that costs at Factory B were £50,000 higher in total than at Factory A.

(b) They involve calculating degrees of a circle and drawing sectors accurately, and this can be time consuming.

(c) It is sometimes difficult to compare sector sizes accurately by eye.

NOTES

Bar charts

Definition

A *bar chart* is a chart in which quantities are shown in the form of bars.

2.7 The bar chart is one of the most common methods of presenting data in a visual form.

2.8 There are three main types of bar chart.

(a) Simple bar charts

(b) Component bar charts, including percentage component bar charts

(c) Multiple (or compound) bar charts

Simple bar charts

2.9 A simple bar chart is a chart consisting of one or more bars, in which the length of each bar indicates the magnitude of the corresponding data item.

EXAMPLE: A SIMPLE BAR CHART

A company's total sales for the years from 19X1 to 19X6 are as follows.

Year	*Sales* *£'000*
19X1	800
19X2	1,200
19X3	1,100
19X4	1,400
19X5	1,600
19X6	1,700

The data could be shown on a simple bar chart as follows.

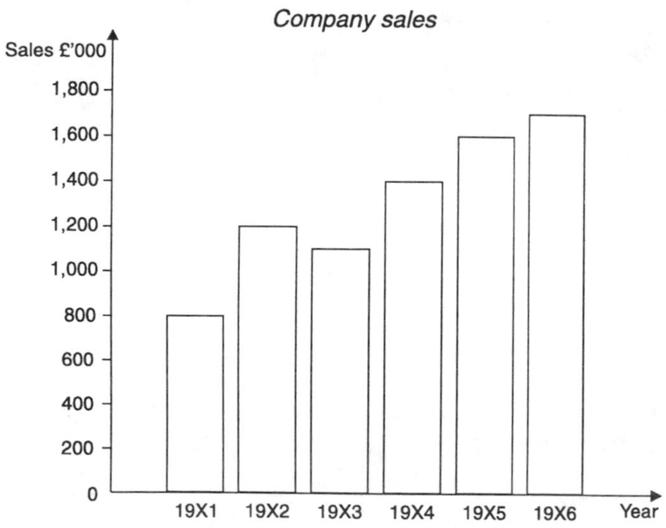

Each axis of the chart must be clearly labelled, and there must be a scale to indicate the magnitude of the data. Here, the y axis includes a scale for the amount of sales, and so readers of the bar chart can see not only that sales have been rising year by year (with 19X3 being an exception) but also what the actual sales have been each year.

NOTES

2.10 Simple bar charts serve two purposes.

(a) They show the actual magnitude of each item.

(b) They enable one to compare magnitudes, by comparing the lengths of bars on the chart.

Component bar charts

2.11 A component bar chart is a bar chart that gives a breakdown of each total into its components.

EXAMPLE: A COMPONENT BAR CHART

Charbart plc's sales for the years from 19X7 to 19X9 are as follows.

	19X7	*19X8*	*19X9*
	£'000	*£'000*	*£'000*
Product A	1,000	1,200	1,700
Product B	900	1,000	1,000
Product C	500	600	700
Total	2,400	2,800	3,400

A component bar chart would show the following.

(a) How total sales have changed from year to year

(b) The components of each year's total

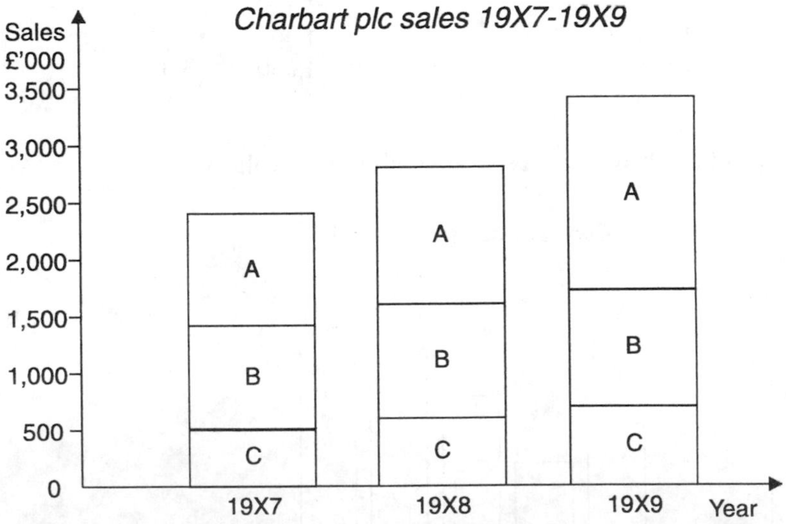

In this diagram the growth in sales is illustrated and the significance of growth in product A sales as the reason for the total sales growth is also fairly clear. The growth in product A sales would have been even clearer if product A had been drawn as the bottom element in each bar instead of the top one.

Percentage component bar charts

2.12 The difference between a component bar chart and a percentage component bar chart is that with a component bar chart, the total length of each bar (and the length of each component in it) indicates magnitude. A bigger amount is shown by a longer bar. With a percentage component bar chart, total magnitudes are not shown. If two or more bars are drawn on the chart, the total length of each bar is the same. The only varying lengths in a percentage component bar chart are the lengths of the sections of a bar, which vary according to the relative sizes of the components.

NOTES

EXAMPLE: A PERCENTAGE COMPONENT BAR CHART

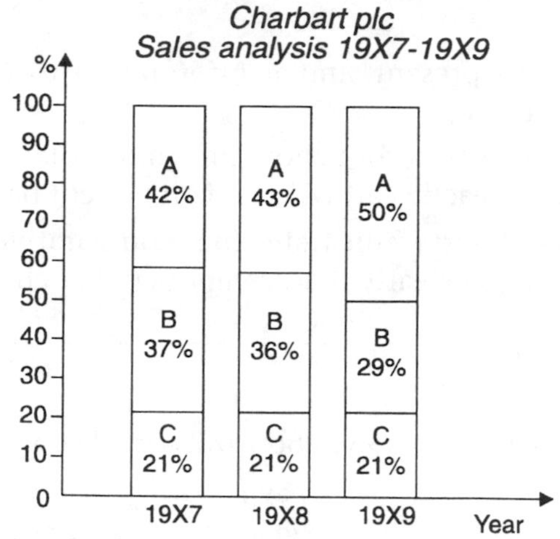

The information in the previous example of sales of Charbart plc could have been shown in a percentage component bar chart as follows.

Working	*19X7*		*19X8*		*19X9*	
	£'000	*%*	*£'000*	*%*	*£'000*	*%*
Product A	1,000	42	1,200	43	1,700	50
Product B	900	37	1,000	36	1,000	29
Product C	500	21	600	21	700	21
Total	2,400	100	2,800	100	3,400	100

This chart shows that sales of C have remained a steady proportion of total sales, but the proportion of A in total sales has gone up quite considerably, while the proportion of B has fallen correspondingly.

Multiple bar charts (compound bar charts)

2.13 A multiple bar chart (or compound bar chart) is a bar chart in which two or more separate bars are used to present sub-divisions of data.

EXAMPLE: A MULTIPLE BAR CHART

The data on Charbart plc's sales could be shown in a multiple bar chart as follows.

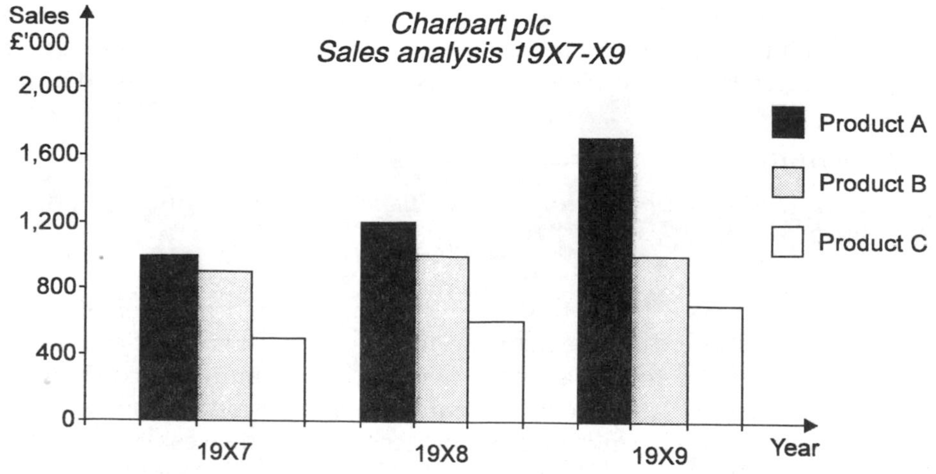

NOTES

2.14 A multiple bar chart uses several bars for each total. In the above example, the sales in each year are shown as three separate bars, one for each product, A, B and C.

Multiple bar charts are sometimes drawn with the bars horizontal instead of vertical.

2.15 Multiple bar charts present similar information to component bar charts, except for the following.

(a) Multiple bar charts do not show the grand total (in the above example, the total output each year) whereas component bar charts do.

(b) Multiple bar charts illustrate the comparative magnitudes of the components more clearly than component bar charts.

Activity 1

Income for Lemmi Bank in 19X0, 19X1 and 19X2 is made up as follows.

	19X0	*19X1*	*19X2*
	£'000	*£'000*	*£'000*
Interest income	3,579	2,961	2,192
Commission income	857	893	917
Other income	62	59	70

Required

Using the above data, draw the following.

(a) A simple bar chart

(b) A component bar chart

(c) A percentage component bar chart

(d) A compound bar chart

3 FREQUENCY DISTRIBUTIONS

3.1 Frequently the data collected from a statistical survey or investigation are simply a mass of numbers.

65	69	70	71	70	68	69	67	70	68
72	71	69	74	70	73	71	67	69	70

3.2 The raw data above yield little information as they stand; imagine how much more difficult it would be if there were hundreds or even thousands of data items. The data could, of course, be arranged in order size (an array) and the lowest and highest data items, as well as typical items, could be identified.

Definitions

A *frequency distribution* (or *frequency table*) records the number of times each value occurs (the *frequency*).

3.3 Many sets of data, however, contain a limited number of data values, even though there may be many occurrences of each value. It can therefore be useful to organise the data into a frequency distribution recording the number of times each value occurs. A frequency distribution for the data in Paragraph 3.1 (the output in units of 20 employees during one week) is as follows.

Output of employees in one week in units

Output Units	*Number of employees (frequency)*
65	1
66	0
67	2
68	2
69	4
70	5
71	3
72	1
73	1
74	1
	20

3.4 When the data are arranged in this way it is immediately obvious that 69 and 70 units are the most common volumes of output per employee per week.

Grouped frequency distributions

3.5 If there is a large set of data or if every (or nearly every) data item is different, it is often convenient to group frequencies together into bands or classes. For example, suppose that the output produced by another group of 20 employees during one week was as follows, in units.

1,087	850	1,084	792
924	1,226	1,012	1,205
1,265	1,028	1,230	1,182
1,086	1,130	989	1,155
1,134	1,166	1,129	1,160

3.6 The range of output from the lowest to the highest producer is 792 to 1,265, a range of 473 units. This range could be divided into classes of say, 100 units (the class width or class interval), and the number of employees producing output within each class could then be grouped into a single frequency, as follows.

Output Units	*Number of employees (frequency)*
700 – 799	1
800 – 899	1
900 – 999	2
1,000 – 1,099	5
1,100 – 1,199	7
1,200 – 1,299	4
	20

3.7 Note, however, that once items have been 'grouped' in this way their individual values are lost.

Grouped frequency distributions of continuous variables

3.8 As well as being used for discrete variables (as above), grouped frequency distributions (or grouped frequency tables) can be used to present data for continuous variables.

NOTES

EXAMPLE: A GROUPED FREQUENCY DISTRIBUTION FOR A CONTINUOUS VARIABLE

Suppose we wish to record the heights of 50 different individuals. The information might be presented as a grouped frequency distribution, as follows.

Height (cm)	*Number of individuals (frequency)*
Up to and including 154	1
Over 154, up to and including 163	3
Over 163, up to and including 172	8
Over 172, up to and including 181	16
Over 181, up to and including 190	18
Over 190	4
	50

Note the following points.

(a) It would be wrong to show the ranges as 0–154, 154–163, 163–172 and so on, because 154 cm and 163 cm would then be values in two classes, which is not permissible. Although each value should only be in one class, we have to make sure that each possible value can be included. Classes such as 154–162, 163–172 would not be suitable since a height of 162.5 cm would not belong in either class. Such classes could be used for discrete variables, however.

(b) There is an *open-ended* class at each end of the range. This is because heights up to 154 cm and over 190 cm are thought to be uncommon, so that a single 'open-ended' class is used to group all the frequencies together.

Preparing grouped frequency distributions

3.9 To prepare a grouped frequency distribution, a decision must be made about how wide each class should be. In an examination, you might be told how many classes to use, or what the class interval should be. You should, however, generally observe the following guidelines.

(a) The size of each class should be appropriate to the nature of the data being recorded, and the most appropriate class interval varied according to circumstances.

(b) The upper and lower limits of each class interval should be suitable 'round' numbers for class intervals which are in multiples of 5, 10, 100, 1,000 and so on. For example, if the class interval is 10, and data items range in value from 23 to 62 (discrete values), the class intervals should be 20–29, 30–39, 40–49, 50–59 and 60–69, rather than 23–32, 33–42, 43–52 and 53–62.

(c) With continuous variables, either:

(i) the upper limit of a class should be 'up to and including ...' and the lower limit of the next class should be 'over ...'; or

(ii) the upper limit of a class should be 'less than...', and the lower limit of the next class should be 'at least ...'.

Activity 2

The commission earnings for May 19X3 of the assistants in a department store were as follows (in pounds).

60	35	53	47	25	44	55	58	47	71
63	67	57	44	61	48	50	56	61	42
43	38	41	39	61	51	27	56	57	50
55	68	55	50	25	48	44	43	49	73
53	35	36	41	45	71	56	40	69	52
36	47	66	52	32	46	44	32	52	58
49	41	45	45	48	36	46	42	52	33
31	36	40	66	53	58	60	52	66	51
51	44	59	53	51	57	35	45	46	54
46	54	51	39	64	43	54	47	60	45

Required

Prepare a grouped frequency distribution classifying the commission earnings into categories of £5 commencing with '£25 and under £30'.

3.10 You should be able to interpret a grouped frequency distribution and express an interpretation in writing. In the example following Paragraph 3.8, an interpretation of the data is fairly straightforward.

(a) Most heights fell between 154 cm and 190 cm.

(b) Most heights were in the middle of this range, with few people having heights in the lower and upper ends of the range.

Cumulative frequency distributions

Definition

A *cumulative frequency distribution* (or *cumulative frequency table*) can be used to show the total number of times that a value above or below a certain amount occurs.

3.11 There are two possible cumulative frequency distributions for the grouped frequency distribution in Paragraph 3.6.

	Cumulative frequency		*Cumulative frequency*
≥ 700	20	< 800	1
≥ 800	19	< 900	2
≥ 900	18	<1,000	4
≥1,000	16	<1,100	9
≥1,100	11	<1,200	16
≥1,200	4	<1,300	20

Notes

(a) The symbol > means 'greater than' and ≥ means 'greater than or equal to'. The symbol < means 'less than' and ≤ means 'less than or equal to'. These symbols provide a convenient method of stating classes.

(b) The first cumulative frequency distribution shows that of the total of 20 employees, 19 produced 800 units or more, 18 produced 900 units or more, 16 produced 1,000 units or more and so on.

(c) The second cumulative frequency distribution shows that, of the total of 20 employees, one produced under 800 units, two produced under 900 units, four produced under 1,000 units and so on.

NOTES

4 HISTOGRAMS

Definitions

A *histogram* is the pictorial representation of a frequency distribution.

4.1 It is often simpler to interpret data after they have been presented pictorially rather than as a table of figures. A frequency distribution can be represented pictorially by means of a histogram. Histograms look rather like bar charts except that the bars are joined together and whereas frequencies are represented by the height of bars on a bar chart, frequencies are represented by the *area* covered by bars on a histogram.

Histograms of frequency distributions with equal class intervals

4.2 If all the class intervals are the same, as in the frequency distribution in Paragraph 3.6, the bars of the histogram all have the same width and the heights will be proportional to the frequencies. The histogram looks almost identical to a bar chart except that the bars are joined together. Because the bars are joined together, when presenting discrete data the data must be treated as continuous so that there are no gaps between class intervals. For example, for a cricketer's scores in various games the classes would have to be ≥0 but <10, ≥10 but <20 and so on, instead of 0–9, 10–19 and so on.

4.3 A histogram of the distribution in Paragraph 3.6 would be drawn as follows.

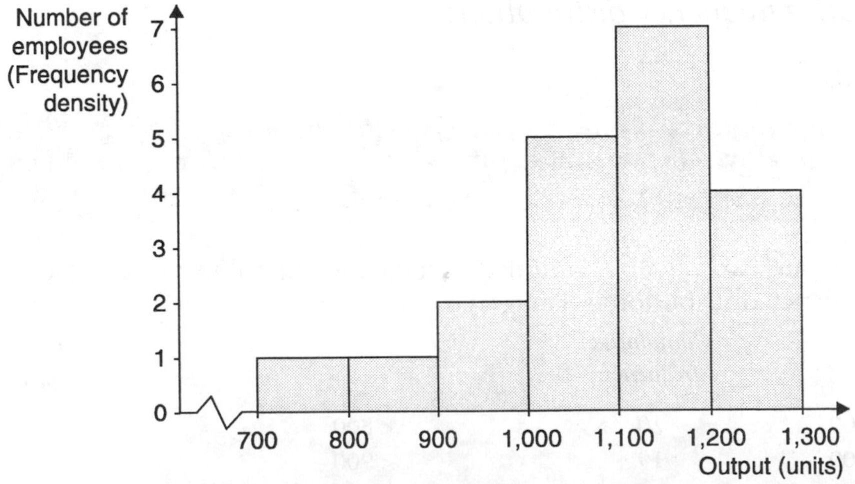

4.4 Note that the discrete data have been treated as continuous, the intervals being changed to >700 but ≤800, >800 but ≤900 and so on.

Histograms of frequency distributions with unequal class intervals

4.5 If a distribution has unequal class intervals, the heights of the bars have to be adjusted for the fact that the bars do not have the same width.

EXAMPLE: A HISTOGRAM WITH UNEQUAL CLASS INTERVALS

The weekly wages of employees of Salt Lake Ltd are as follows.

Wages per employee	*Number of employees*
Up to and including £60	4
>£60 ≤ £80	6
>£80 ≤ £90	6
>£90 ≤ £120	6
>£120	3

The class intervals for wages per employee are not all the same, and range from £10 to £30.

A histogram is drawn as follows.

(a) The width of each bar on the chart must be proportionate to the corresponding class interval. In other words, the bar representing wages of >£60 ≤ £80, a range of £20, will be as wide as the bar representing wages of >£80 ≤ £90, a range of only £10.

(b) A standard width of bar must be selected. This should be the size of class interval which occurs most frequently. In our example, class intervals £10, £20 and £30 each occur once. An interval of £20 will be selected as the standard width.

(c) Open-ended classes must be closed off. It is usual for the width of such classes to be the same as that of the adjoining class. In this example, the class 'up to and including £60' will become>£40 ≤ £60 and the class 'more than £120' will become>£120 ≤ £150.

(d) Each frequency is then multiplied by (standard class width ÷ actual class width) to obtain the height of the bar in the histogram.

(e) The height of bars no longer corresponds to *frequency* but rather to *frequency density* and hence the vertical axis should be labelled frequency density.

(f) Note that the data is considered to be continuous since the gap between, for example, £79.99 and £80.00 is so small.

Class interval	*Size of interval*	*Frequency*	*Adjustment*	*Height of bar*
>£40 ≤ £60	20	4	× 20/20	4
>£60 ≤ £80	20	6	× 20/20	6
>£80 ≤ £90	10	6	× 20/10	12
>£90 ≤ £120	30	6	× 20/30	4
>£120 ≤ £150	30	3	× 20/30	2

(a) The first two bars will be of normal height.

(b) The third bar will be twice as high as the class frequency (6) would suggest, to compensate for the fact that the class interval, £10, is only half the standard size.

(c) The fourth and fifth bars will be two thirds as high as the class frequencies (6 and 3) would suggest, to compensate for the fact that the class interval, £30, is 150% of the standard size.

NOTES

EXAMPLE *continued*

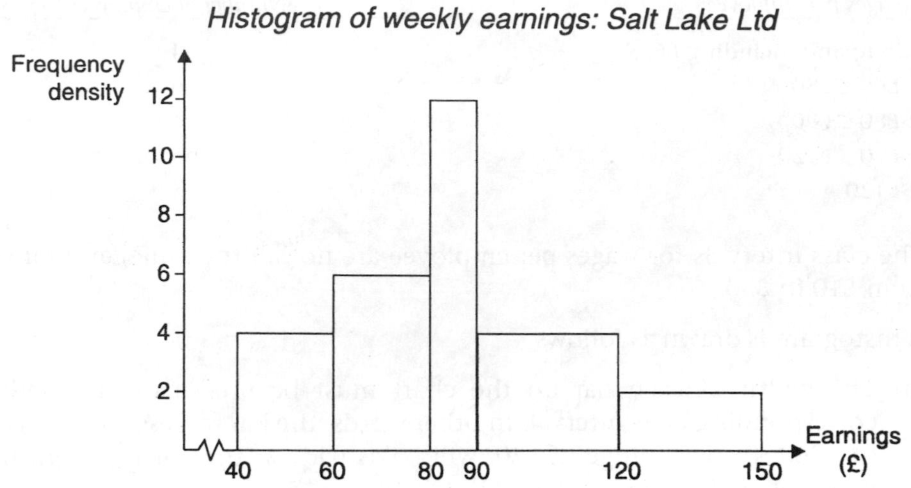

Activity 3

The sales force of a company have just completed a successful sales campaign. The performances of individual sales staff have been analysed as follows, into a grouped frequency distribution.

Sales	*Number of sales staff*
Up to £10,000	1
>£10,000 ≤ £12,000	10
>£12,000 ≤ £14,000	12
>£14,000 ≤ £18,000	8
>£18,000 ≤ £22,000	4
>£22,000	1

Required

Draw a histogram from this information.

Frequency polygons

4.6 A histogram is not a particularly accurate method of presenting a frequency distribution because, in grouping frequencies together in a class interval, it is assumed that these frequencies occur evenly throughout the class interval, which is unlikely. To overcome this criticism, we can convert a histogram into a frequency polygon, which is drawn on the assumption that, within each class interval, the frequency of occurrence of data items is not evenly spread. There will be more values at the end of each class interval nearer the histogram's peak (if any), and so the flat top on a histogram bar should be converted into a rising or falling line.

4.7 A frequency polygon is drawn from a histogram, in the following way.

(a) Mark the mid-point of the top of each bar in the histogram.

(b) Join up all these points with straight lines.

4.8 The ends of the diagram (the mid-points of the two end bars) should be joined to the base line at the mid-points of the next class intervals outside the range of observed data. These intervals should be taken to be of the same size as the last class intervals for observed data.

EXAMPLE: A FREQUENCY POLYGON

The following grouped frequency distribution relates to the number of occasions during the past 40 weeks that a particular cost has been a given amount.

Cost £	*Number of occasions*
> 800 ≤ 1,000	4
>1,000 ≤ 1,200	10
>1,200 ≤ 1,400	12
>1,400 ≤ 1,600	10
>1,600 ≤ 1,800	4
	40

Required

Prepare a frequency polygon.

Solution

A histogram is first drawn, in the way described earlier. All classes are of the same width.

The mid-points of the class intervals outside the range of observed data are 700 and 1,900.

Histogram of frequency of particular costs

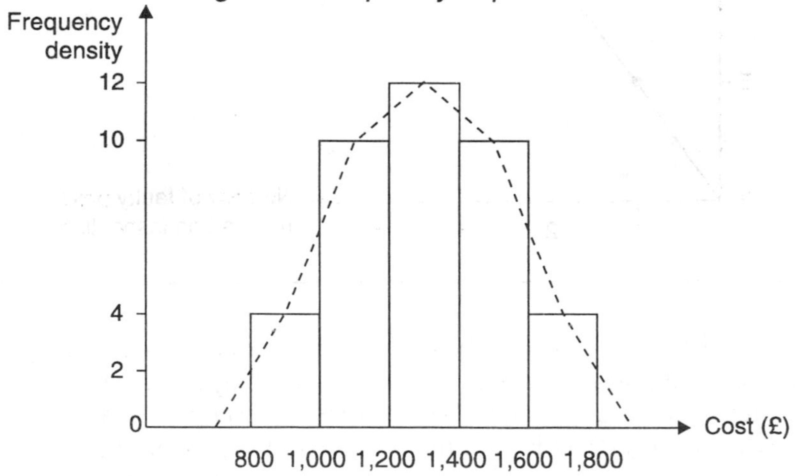

Frequency curves

4.9 Because a frequency polygon has straight lines between points, it too can be seen as an inaccurate way of presenting data. One method of obtaining greater accuracy would be to make the class intervals smaller. If the class intervals of a distribution were made small enough the frequency polygon would become very smooth. It would become a curve.

NOTES

5 OGIVES

Definition

An *ogive* shows the cumulative number of items with a value less than or equal to, or alternatively greater than or equal to, a certain amount.

5.1 Just as a grouped frequency distribution can be graphed as a histogram, a cumulative frequency distribution can be graphed as an ogive.

EXAMPLE: OGIVES

Consider the following frequency distribution.

Number of faulty units rejected on inspection	*Frequency*	*Cumulative frequency*
$>0 \leq 1$	5	5
$>1 \leq 2$	5	10
$>2 \leq 3$	3	13
$>3 \leq 4$	1	14
	14	

An ogive would be drawn as follows.

Ogive of rejected items

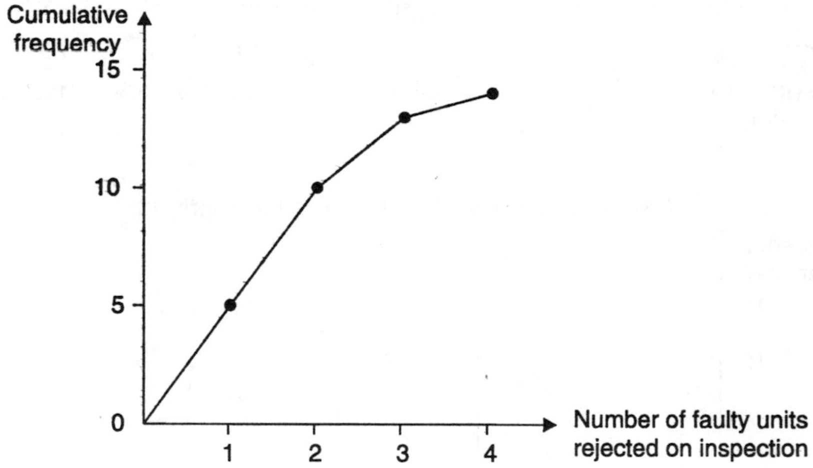

5.2 The ogive is drawn by plotting the cumulative frequencies on the graph, and joining them with straight lines. Although many ogives are more accurately curved lines, you can use straight lines in drawing an ogive in an examination. An ogive drawn with straight lines may be referred to as a cumulative frequency *polygon* (or cumulative frequency *diagram*) whereas one drawn as a curve may be referred to as a cumulative frequency *curve*.

5.3 For grouped frequency distributions, where we work up through values of the variable, the cumulative frequencies are plotted against the *upper* limits of the classes. For example, for the class 'over 2, up to and including 3', the cumulative frequency should be plotted against 3.

NOTES

Activity 4

A grouped frequency distribution for the volume of output produced at a factory over a period of 40 weeks is as follows.

Output (units)	*Number of times output achieved*
>0 ≤ 200	4
>200 ≤ 400	8
>400 ≤ 600	12
>600 ≤ 800	10
>800 ≤ 1,000	6
	40

Required

Draw an appropriate ogive, and estimate the number of weeks in which output was 550 units or less.

5.4 We can also draw ogives to show the cumulative number of items with values greater than or equal to some given value.

EXAMPLE: DOWNWARD-SLOPING OGIVES

Output at a factory over a period of 80 weeks is shown by the following frequency distribution.

Output per week Units	*Number of times output achieved*
> 0 ≤ 100	10
>100 ≤ 200	20
>200 ≤ 300	25
>300 ≤ 400	15
>400 ≤ 500	10
	80

If we want to draw an ogive to show the number of weeks in which output exceeded a certain value, the cumulative total should begin at 80 and drop to 0. In drawing an ogive when we work down through values of the variable, the descending cumulative frequency should be plotted against the lower limit of each class interval.

Lower limit of interval	*Frequency*	*Cumulative ('more than') frequency*
0	10	80
100	20	70
200	25	50
300	15	25
400	10	10
500	0	0

NOTES

EXAMPLE *continued*

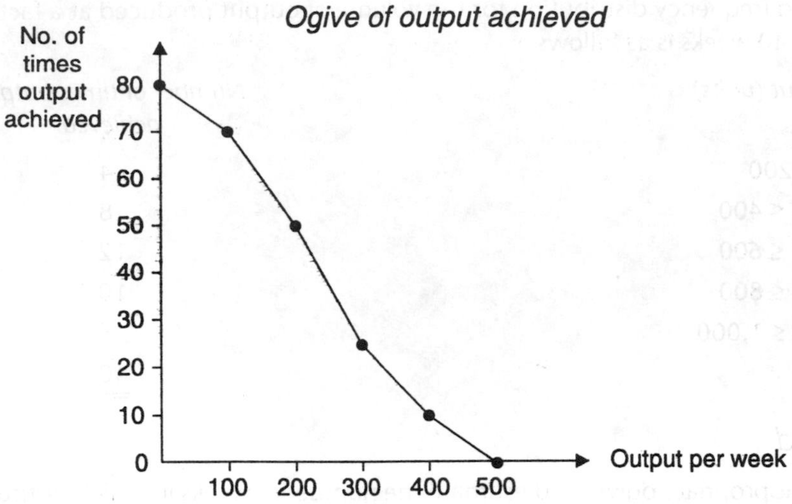

Make sure that you understand what this curve shows.

For example, 350 on the x axis corresponds with about 18 on the y axis. This means that output of 350 units or more was achieved 18 times out of the 80 weeks.

Activity 5

If you wanted to produce an ogive showing the cumulative number of students in a class with an exam mark of 55% or more, would you need an upward-sloping or a downward-sloping ogive?

6 TIME SERIES GRAPHS

Definitions

A *time series* is a series of figures or values recorded over time such as monthly sales over the last two years. A graph of a time series is called a *historigram*. (Note the 'ri'; this is not the same as a histogram).

6.1 The horizontal axis of a historigram is always chosen to represent time and the vertical axis represents the values of the data recorded. The graph will give some indication of the trend in the data over time.

6.2 A *component time series* is data in which various classifications (for example sales in the four branches of a retail organisation each month) can be thought of as the components of a meaningful total (the total monthly sales of the retail organisation). A *multiple time series*, on the other hand, is data which have classifications for each time period which cannot be added to form meaningful totals. An example would be prices of selected food items (such as tea (per packet), bread (per loaf) and caviare (per jar)).

EXAMPLE: TIME SERIES

The following data show the sales of a product in the period 19X6–X8.

Year	*Quarter 1* '000	*Quarter 2* '000	*Quarter 3* '000	*Quarter 4* '000
19X6	86	42	57	112
19X7	81	39	55	107
19X8	77	35	52	99

Required

Plot a time series of the above data.

Solution

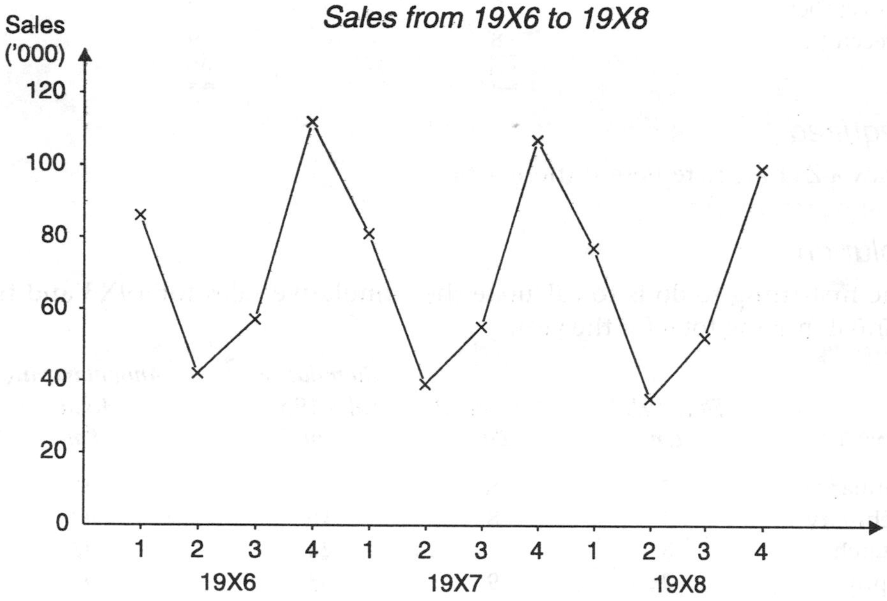

We will be looking at time series analysis in some detail in Chapter 10.

7 Z CHARTS

Definition

A *Z chart* is a form of time series graph.

7.1 A Z chart can be very useful for presenting business data. It shows the following.

(a) The value of a variable plotted against time over the year

(b) The cumulative sum of values for that variable over the year to date

(c) The annual moving total for that variable

The annual moving total is the sum of values of the variable for the 12-month period up to the end of the month under consideration.

NOTES

EXAMPLE: Z CHARTS

The sales figures for a company for 19X2 and 19X3 are as follows.

	19X2 sales	*19X3 sales*
	£m	*£m*
January	7	8
February	7	8
March	8	8
April	7	9
May	9	8
June	8	8
July	8	7
August	7	8
September	6	9
October	7	6
November	8	9
December	8	9
	90	97

Required

Draw a Z chart to represent these data.

Solution

The first thing to do is to calculate the cumulative sales for 19X3 and the annual moving total for the year.

	Sales 19X2	*Sales 19X3*	*Cumulative sales 19X3*	*Annual moving total*
	£m	*£m*	*£m*	*£m*
January	7	8	8	91
February	7	8	16	92
March	8	8	24	92
April	7	9	33	94
May	9	8	41	93
June	8	8	49	93
July	8	7	56	92
August	7	8	64	93
September	6	9	73	96
October	7	6	79	95
November	8	9	88	96
December	8	9	97	97

The first figure in the annual moving total is arrived at by taking the sales for the year ended December 19X2, adding those for January 19X3 and subtracting those for January 19X2. This gives the sales for a 12-month period to the end of January 19X3 as $90 + 8 - 7 = 91$.

A similar approach is used for the rest of the year, by adding on the new 19X3 month and deducting the corresponding 19X2 month.

EXAMPLE *continued*

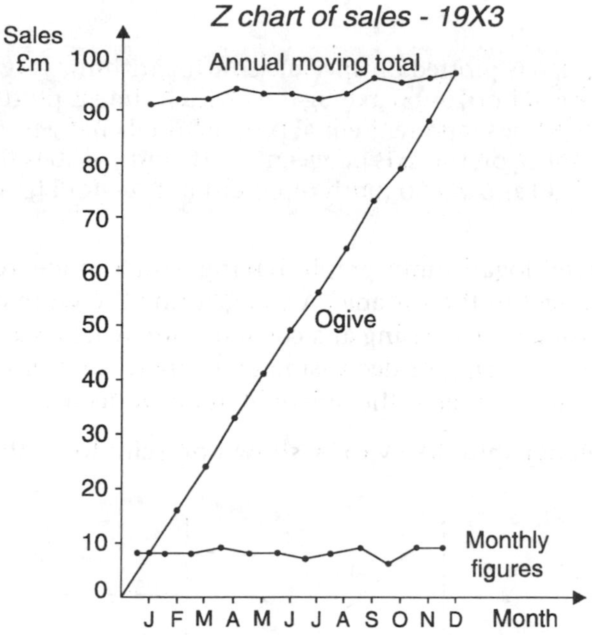

You will notice that while the values of the annual moving total and the cumulative values are plotted on month-end positions, the values for the current monthly figures are plotted on mid-month positions. This is because the monthly figures represent achievement over a particular month whereas the annual moving totals and the cumulative values represent achievement up to a particular month end.

The interpretation of Z charts

7.2 The popularity of Z charts in practical applications derives from the wealth of information which they can contain.

(a) *Monthly totals* show the monthly results at a glance, together with any seasonal variations.

(b) *Cumulative totals* show the performance to date, and can be easily compared with planned or budgeted performance by superimposing a budget line.

(c) *Annual moving totals* compare the current levels of performance with those of the previous year. If the line is rising then this year's monthly results are better than the results of the corresponding month last year. The opposite applies if the line is falling. The annual moving total line indicates the long-term trend in values of the variable, whether rising, falling or steady.

7.3 You should note that Z charts do not have to cover 12 months of a year. They could also be drawn for (for example) four quarters of a year, or seven days of a week. The method would be exactly the same.

Activity 6

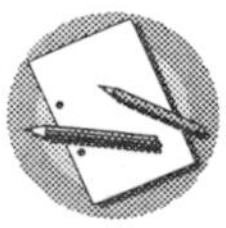

Why does the annual moving total line on a Z chart show the long-term trend, unaffected by seasonal effects such as sales being higher in summer than winter?

NOTES

8 SEMI-LOGARITHMIC GRAPHS

8.1 A variation of the time series graph is the semi-logarithmic graph.

Definition

A *semi-logarithmic graph* is plotted on special semi-logarithmic (log-linear) graph paper. This has a normal horizontal axis against which time is plotted but, on the vertical axis, equal intervals represent equal proportional changes in the variable. For example, the distance on the axis between y = 10 and y = 30 is the same as the distance between y = 30 and y = 90 (both represent a three-fold increase).

8.2 Sections of a semi-logarithmic graph having equal slope represent equal proportional changes in the variable. A straight line therefore indicates that a variable is increasing or decreasing at a constant rate whereas a curve indicates that a variable is increasing or decreasing at an increasing or decreasing rate. The steeper the line, the higher the rate of increase or decrease.

8.3 The principal relationships likely to be shown on semi-logarithmic graphs are as follows.

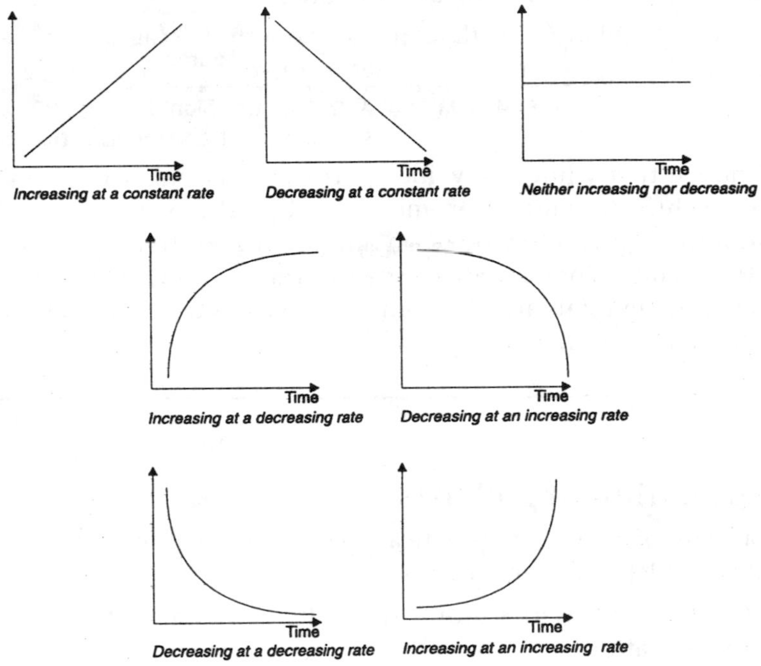

Figure 3.1 Semi-logarithmic graphs

8.4 An alternative to using semi-logarithmic paper is to plot the logarithms of the values of the variable on the vertical axis against time on the horizontal axis.

8.5 Because only proportional changes are of interest, time series measured in different units can be compared on the same semi-logarithmic graph.

8.6 Such graphs are also useful in situations where the dependent variable covers a great range of values. In such a case, use of an ordinary graph would require such a small scale on the vertical axis that significant changes would be obscured.

8.7 Although semi-logarithmic graphs can be useful, they do have a number of disadvantages. Any variables having zero or negative values cannot be plotted. Perhaps more importantly, however, most people are used to interpreting normal graphs and may therefore misread semi-logarithmic graphs. It must therefore be clear if graphs have been drawn on a logarithmic basis. There is a case for not actually labelling the vertical axis since it is the slope of lines that are important, not values.

NOTES

EXAMPLE: SEMI-LOGARITHMIC GRAPHS

The annual production volumes of a particular company over the last ten years are shown below.

Year	*Production volume*	*Log*	*Year*	*Production volume*	*Log*
1	1,014	3.0060	6	10,630	4.0265
2	1,622	3.2101	7	17,009	4.2307
3	2,595	3.4141	8	27,214	4.4348
4	4,152	3.6183	9	43,543	4.6389
5	6,644	3.8224	10	69,669	4.8430

(a) The production volumes cover a very large range. To plot them on a conventional graph would require such a small scale as to make changes in early years impossible to decipher.

(b) It is difficult to determine how production volumes have changed over the period simply by looking at the figures.

If we plot the logarithms of the production volumes against time (as in diagram (a) below) or plot the volumes against time on semi-logarithmic graph paper (as in diagram (b) below) we are able to view changes in volume across the entire 10 year period, and ascertain that the production volume has been increasing at a fairly constant rate.

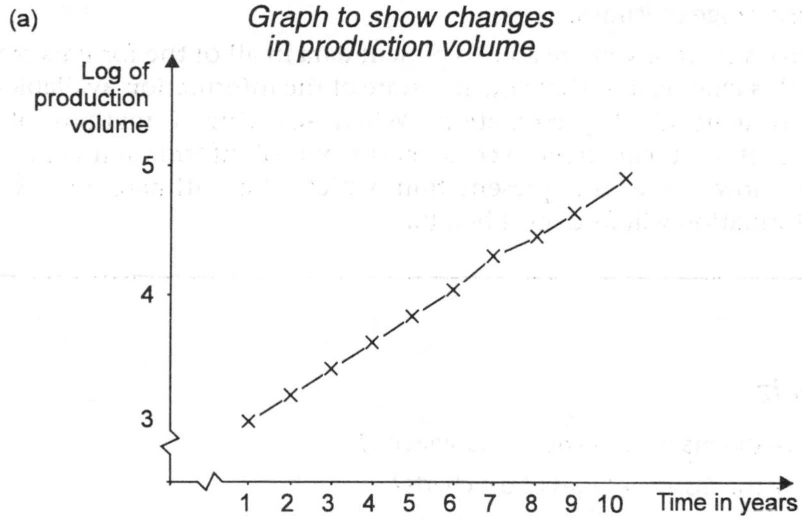

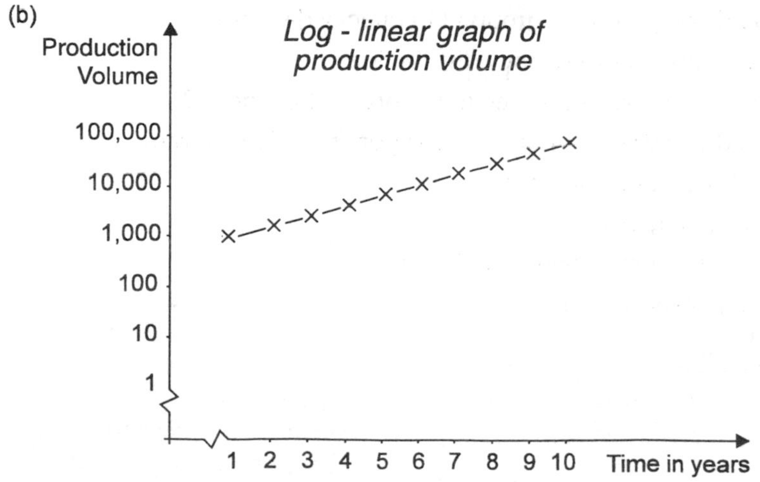

NOTES

Chapter roundup

- This chapter has considered a number of ways of presenting data.
- Tables are a simple way of presenting information about two variables.
- Charts often convey the meaning or significance of data more clearly than would a table.
- There are three main types of bar chart: simple, component (including percentage component) and multiple (or compound).
- Frequency distributions are used if values of particular variables occur more than once. Make sure that you know the difference between grouped frequency and cumulative frequency distributions.
- A frequency distribution can be represented pictorially by means of a histogram. The number of observations in a class is represented by the area covered by the bar, rather than by its height. Frequency polygons and frequency curves are perhaps more accurate methods of data presentation than the standard histogram.
- An ogive shows the cumulative number of items with a value less than or equal to, or alternatively greater than or equal to, a certain amount.
- The graph of a time series is called a historigram.
- A Z chart shows the value of a variable plotted against time over the period, the cumulative sum of values for that variable over the period to date and the period moving total for that variable.
- Semi-logarithmic graphs are useful if the dependent variable covers a great range of values.
- Make sure that you are able to present data in all of the formats covered in this chapter and that you are aware of the information available from each method of presentation. When selecting a method of data presentation remember to consider the type of information which must be shown and the presentation which the ultimate user of the information will find most helpful.

Quick quiz

1 What are the main guidelines for tabulation?
2 What are the disadvantages of pie charts?
3 Name the three main types of bar chart.
4 How would you prepare a grouped frequency distribution?
5 What is a cumulative frequency distribution?
6 What are the computations needed to draw a histogram?
7 How would you draw a frequency polygon from a histogram?
8 How would you draw an ogive?
9 What is a historigram?
10 What three lines are drawn on a Z chart?
11 What is log-linear paper?

NOTES

Answers to activities

1 (a)

19X0	*19X1*	*19X2*
£'000	£'000	£'000
3,579	2,961	2,192
857	893	917
62	59	70
4,498	3,913	3,179

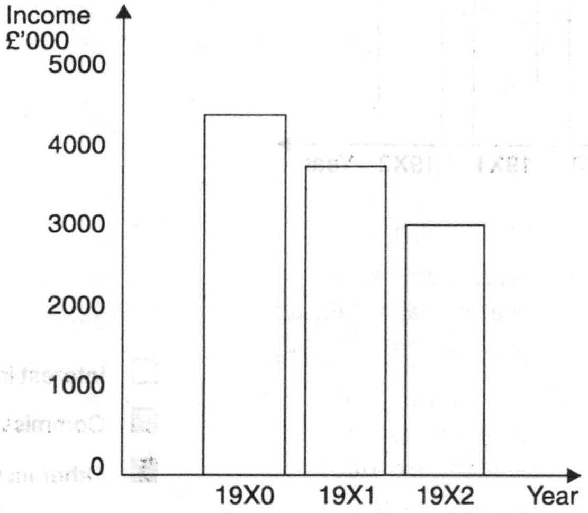

(b)

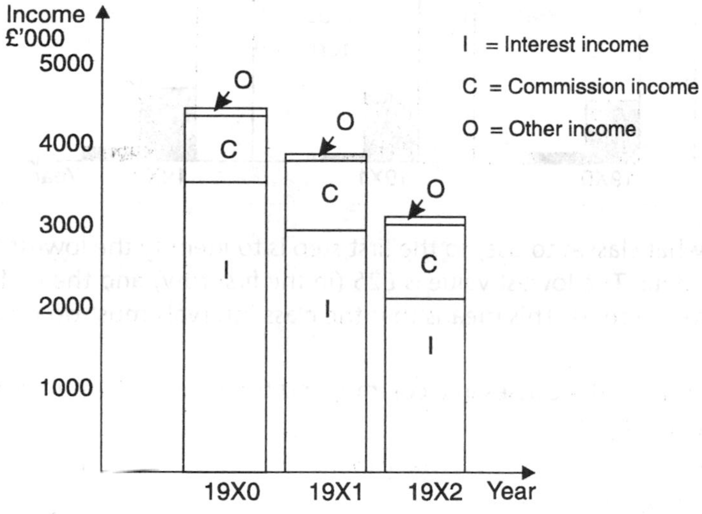

(c)

19X0		*19X1*		*19X2*	
£'000	%	£'000	%	£'000	%
3,579	80	2,961	76	2,192	69
857	19	893	23	917	29
62	1	59	1	70	2
4,498	100	3,913	100	3,179	100

NOTES

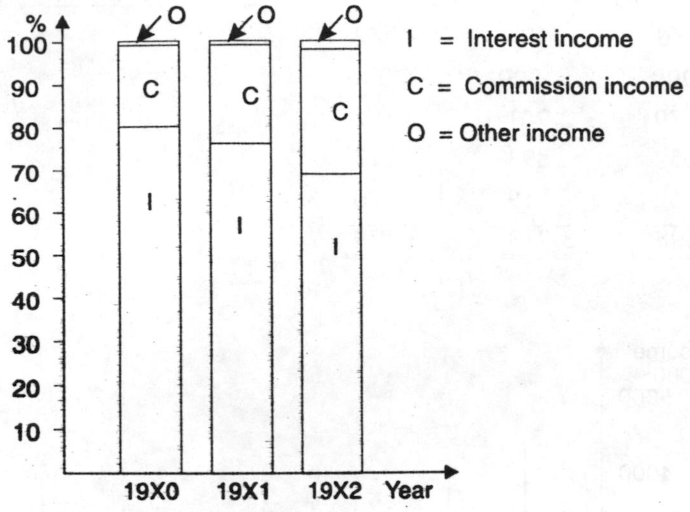

(d)

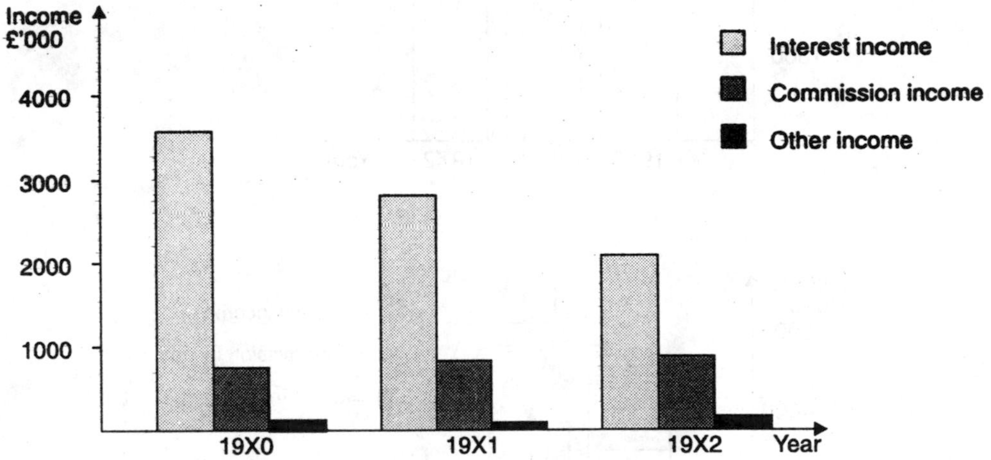

2 We are told what classes to use, so the first step is to identify the lowest and highest values in the data. The lowest value is £25 (in the first row) and the highest value is £73 (in the fourth row). This means that the class intervals must go up to '£70 and under £75'.

We can now set out the classes in a column, and then count the number of items in each class using tally marks.

Class interval	Tally marks	Total
£25 and less than £30	///	3
£30 and less than £35	////	4
£35 and less than £40	~~////~~ ~~////~~	10
£40 and less than £45	~~////~~ ~~////~~ ~~////~~	15
£45 and less than £50	~~////~~ ~~////~~ ~~////~~ ///	18
£50 and less than £55	~~////~~ ~~////~~ ~~////~~ ~~////~~	20
£55 and less than £60	~~////~~ ~~////~~ ///	13
£60 and less than £65	~~////~~ ///	8
£65 and less than £70	~~////~~ /	6
£70 and less than £75	///	3
	Total	100

NOTES

3 Before drawing the histogram, we must decide on the following.

(a) A standard class width: £2,000 will be chosen.

(b) An open-ended class width. In this example, the open-ended class width will therefore be £2,000 for class '≤£10,000' and £4,000 for the class '>£22,000'.

Class interval	*Size of width* £	*Frequency*	*Adjustment*	*Height of block*
≤£10,000	2,000	1	× 2/2	1
>£10,000 ≤ £12,000	2,000	10	× 2/2	10
>£12,000 ≤ £14,000	2,000	12	× 2/2	12
>£14,000 ≤ £18,000	4,000	8	× 2/4	4
>£18,000 ≤ £22,000	4,000	4	× 2/4	2
>£22,000	4,000	1	× 2/4	½

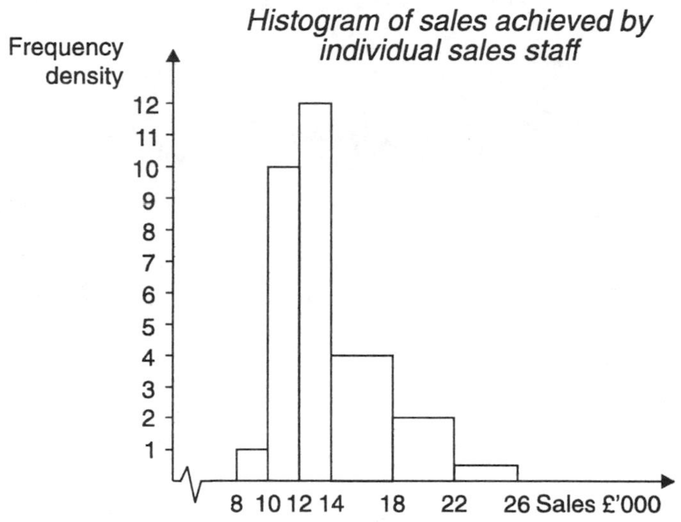

4

Upper limit of interval	*Frequency*	*Cumulative frequency*
200	4	4
400	8	12
600	12	24
800	10	34
1,000	6	40

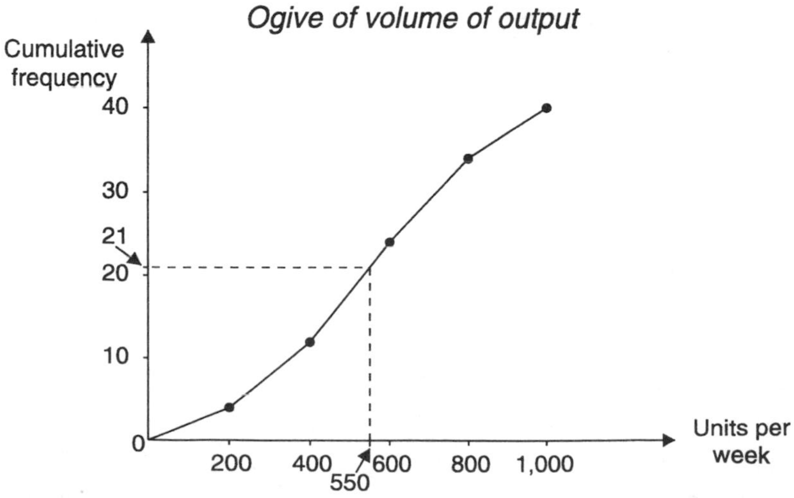

The dotted lines indicate that output of up to 550 units was achieved in 21 out of the 40 weeks.

NOTES

5 A downward-sloping ogive

6 One example of each month is included in the annual moving total. Thus although July might be a very good month, but January a very bad month, there will be one July and one January in the total, balancing each other.

Further question practice

Now try the following practice questions at the end of this text.

Multiple choice questions	**16–21**
Exam style question	**3**

Chapter 4

INDEX NUMBERS

Introduction

A number of methods of data presentation looked at in Chapter 3 can be used to identify visually the trends in data over a period of time. It may also be useful, however, to identify trends using statistical rather than visual means. This is frequently achieved by constructing a set of index numbers.

Index numbers provide a standardised way of comparing the values, over time, of prices, wages, volume of output and so on. They are used extensively in business, government and commerce.

No doubt you will be aware of some index numbers – the RPI, the Financial Times All Share Index and so on. This chapter will explain to you how to construct indices and will look at associated issues such as their limitations.

Your objectives

After completing this chapter, you should:

(a) understand the terminology associated with index numbers;

(b) be able to construct simple indices, index relatives and composite index numbers;

(c) know the difference between weighted means of relatives indices and weighted aggregate indices;

(d) be able to construct Laspeyre and Paasche indices and know when each should be used;

(e) be able to deal with the practical issues associated with index numbers;

(f) have an awareness of the Retail Prices Index.

1 BASIC TERMINOLOGY

Definition

An *index* is a measure, over time, of the average changes in the values (prices or quantities) of a group of items. An index comprises a series of index numbers.

1.1 Although it is possible to prepare an index for a single item, for example the price of an ounce of gold, such an index would probably be unnecessary. It is only when there is a group of items that a simple list of changes in their values over time becomes rather hard to interpret, and an index provides a useful single measure of comparison.

Price indices and quantity indices

Definitions

A *price index* measures the change in the money value of a group of items over time.

A *quantity index* (also called a volume index) measures the change in the non-monetary values of a group of items over time.

1.2 An index may be a price index or a quantity index. Perhaps the best known price index in the UK is the Retail Prices Index (RPI) which measures changes in the costs of items of expenditure of the average household. An example of a quantity index is a productivity index, which measures changes in the productivity of various departments or groups of workers.

Index points

1.3 The term 'points' refers to the difference between the index values in two years. For example, suppose that the index of food prices in 19X1–19X6 was as follows.

19X1	180
19X2	200
19X3	230
19X4	250
19X5	300
19X6	336

The index has risen 156 points between 19X1 and 19X6. This is an increase of $(156/180) \times 100 = 86.7\%$.

Similarly, the index rose 36 points between 19X5 and 19X6, a rise of 12%.

The base period, or base year

1.4 Index numbers normally take the value for a base date, usually the starting point of the series though it could be part way through the series, as 100.

NOTES

2 SIMPLE INDICES

2.1 When one commodity only is under consideration, we have the following formulae.

(a) Price index = $100 \times \frac{P_1}{P_0}$

where P_1 is the price for the period under consideration and P_0 is the price for the base period.

(b) Quantity index = $100 \times \frac{Q_1}{Q_0}$

where Q_1 is the quantity for the period under consideration and Q_0 is the quantity for the base period.

EXAMPLE: SINGLE-ITEM INDICES

If the price of a cup of coffee was 40p in 19X0, 50p in 19X1 and 76p in 19X2, then using 19X0 as a base year the price index numbers for 19X1 and 19X2 would be as follows:

$$19X1 \text{ price index} = 100 \times \frac{50}{40} = 125$$

$$19X2 \text{ price index} = 100 \times \frac{76}{40} = 190$$

If the number of cups of coffee sold in 19X0 was 500,000, in 19X1 700,000 and in 19X2 600,000, then using 19X0 as a base year, the quantity index numbers for 19X1 and 19X2 would be as follows

$$19X1 \text{ quantity index} = 100 \times \frac{700{,}000}{500{,}000} = 140$$

$$19X2 \text{ quantity index} = 100 \times \frac{600{,}000}{500{,}000} = 120$$

3 INDEX RELATIVES

Definition

An *index relative* (sometimes just called a *relative*) is the name given to an index number which measures the change in a single distinct commodity.

3.1 A price relative is calculated as $100 \times P_1/P_0$. We calculated price relatives for a cup of coffee in the example following paragraph 2.1.

3.2 A quantity relative is calculated as $100 \times Q_1/Q_0$. We calculated quantity relatives for cups of coffee in the example following paragraph 2.1.

Time series of relatives

3.3 Given the values of some commodity over time (a time series), there are two ways in which index relatives can be calculated.

3.4 In the *fixed base method*, a base year is selected (index 100), and all subsequent changes are measured against this base. Such an approach should only be used if the basic nature of the commodity is unchanged over time.

3.5 In the *chain base method*, changes are calculated with respect to the value of the commodity in the period immediately before. This approach can be used for any set of commodity values but must be used if the basic nature of the commodity is changing over time.

EXAMPLE: FIXED BASE AND CHAIN METHODS

The price of commodity was £2.70 in 19X0, £3.11 in 19X1, £3.42 in 19X2 and £3.83 in 19X3. Construct both a chain base index and a fixed base index for the years 19X0 to 19X3 using 19X0 as the base year.

Solution

Chain base index	19X0	100	
	19X1	115	(3.11/2.70 × 100)
	19X2	110	(3.42/3.11 × 100)
	19X3	112	(3.83/3.42 × 100)
Fixed base index	19X0	100	
	19X1	115	
	19X2	127	(3.42/2.70 × 100)
	19X3	142	(3.83/2.70 × 100)

The chain base relatives show the rate of change in prices from year to year, whereas the fixed base relatives show changes relative to prices in the base year.

Changing the base of fixed base relatives

3.6 It is sometimes necessary to change the base of a time series of fixed base relatives, perhaps because the base time point is too far in the past. The following time series has a base date of 1970 which would probably be considered too out of date.

	1990	*1991*	*1992*	*1993*	*1994*	*1995*
Index (1970 = 100)	451	463	472	490	499	505

To change the base date (to *rebase*), divide each relative by the relative corresponding to the new base time point and multiply the result by 100.

Activity 1

Rebase the index in Paragraph 3.6 to 1993.

Comparing sets of fixed base relatives

3.7 You may be required to compare two sets of time series relatives. For example, an index of the annual number of advertisements placed by an organisation in the press and the index of the number of the organisation's product sold per annum might be compared. If the base years of the two indices differ, however, comparison is extremely difficult (as the illustration below shows).

	19W8	19W9	19X0	19X1	19X2	19X3	19X4
Number of advertisements placed (19X0 = 100)	90	96	100	115	128	140	160
Volumes of sales (19W0 = 100)	340	347	355	420	472	515	572

3.8 From the figures above it is impossible to determine whether sales are increasing at a greater rate than the number of advertisements placed, or vice versa. This difficulty can be overcome by rebasing one set of relatives so that the base dates are the same. For example, we could rebase the index of volume of sales to 19X0.

	19W8	19W9	19X0	19X1	19X2	19X3	19X4
Number of advertisements placed (19X0 = 100)	90	96	100	115	128	140	160
Volumes of sales (19X0 = 100)	96	98*	100	118	133**	145	161

* 347/355 × 100

** 472/355 × 100

3.9 The two sets of relatives are now much easier to compare. They show that volume of sales is increasing at a slightly faster rate, in general, than the number of advertisements placed.

Time series deflation

3.10 The real value of a commodity can only be measured in terms of some 'indicator' such as the rate of inflation (normally represented by the Retail Prices Index) or the Index of Output of Production Industries. For example the cost of a commodity may have been £10 in 19X0 and £11 in 19X1, representing an increase of 10%. However, if we are told the prices in general (as measured by the RPI) increased by 12% between 19X0 and 19X1, we can argue that the real cost of the commodity has decreased.

EXAMPLE: DEFLATION

Mack Johnson works for Pound of Flesh Ltd. Over the last five years he has received an annual salary increase of £500. Despite his employer assuring him that £500 is a reasonable annual salary increase, Mack is unhappy because, although he agrees £500 is a lot of money, he finds it difficult to maintain the standard of living he had when he first joined the company.

Consider the figures below.

	(a)	*(b)*	*(c)*	*(d)*
Year	*Wages £*	*RPI*	*Real wages £*	*Real wages index*
1	12,000	250	12,000	100.0
2	12,500	260	12,019	100.2
3	13,000	275	11,818	98.5
4	13,500	295	11,441	95.3
5	14,000	315	11,111	92.6

(a) This column shows Mack's wages over the five-year period.

(b) This column shows the current RPI.

(c) This column shows what Mack's wages are worth taking prices, as represented by the RPI, into account. The wages have been deflated relative to the new base period (year 1). Economists call these deflated wage figures real wages. The real wages for years 2 and 4, for example, are calculated as follows.

Year 2: £12,500 × 250/260 = £12,019

Year 4: £13,500 × 250/295 = £11,441

EXAMPLE *continued*

(d) This column is calculated by dividing the entries in column (c) by £12,000

$$\text{Real index} = \frac{\text{current value}}{\text{base value}} \times \frac{\text{base indicator}}{\text{current indicator}}$$

So, for example, the real wage index in year 4 = $\frac{13,500}{12,000} \times \frac{250}{295} \times 100 = 95.3$

The real wages index shows that the real value of Mack's wages has fallen by 7.4% over the five-year period. In real terms he is now earning £11,111 compared to £12,000 in year 1. He is probably justified, therefore, in being unhappy.

Activity 2

The mean weekly take-home pay of the employees of Staples Ltd and a price index for the 11 years from 19X0 to 19Y0 are as follows.

Year	*Weekly wage*	*Price index (19X0 = 100)*
	£	
19X0	150	100
19X1	161	103
19X2	168	106
19X3	179	108
19X4	185	109
19X5	191	112
19X6	197	114
19X7	203	116
19X8	207	118
19X9	213	121
19Y0	231	123

Required

Construct a time series of real wages for 19X0 to 19Y0 using a price index with 19X6 as the base year.

4 COMPOSITE INDEX NUMBERS

4.1 Most practical indices cover more than one item and are hence termed composite index numbers. The RPI, for example, considers components such as food, alcoholic drink, tobacco and housing. An index of motor car costs might consider components such as finance payments, service costs, repairs, insurance and so on.

4.2 Suppose that the cost of living index is calculated from only three commodities: bread, tea and caviare, and that the prices for 19X1 and 19X2 were as follows.

	19X1	*19X2*
Bread	20p a loaf	40p a loaf
Tea	25p a packet	30p a packet
Caviare	450p a jar	405p a jar

NOTES

4.3 A simple index could be calculated by adding the prices for single items in 19X2 and dividing by the corresponding sum relating to 19X1 (if 19X1 is the base year). In general, if the sum of the prices in the base year is ΣP_0 and the sum of the prices in the new year is ΣP_1, the index is

$$100 \times \frac{\Sigma P_1}{\Sigma P_0}$$

The index, known as a *simple aggregate price index*, would therefore be calculated as follows.

	P_0 *19X1* *£*	P_1 *19X2* *£*
Bread	0.20	0.40
Tea	0.25	0.30
Caviare	4.50	4.05
	ΣP_0 = 4.95	ΣP_1 = 4.75

Year	$\Sigma P_1 / \Sigma P_0$	*Simple aggregate price index*
19X1	4.95/4.95 = 1.00	100
19X2	4.75/4.95 = 0.96	96

4.4 This type of index has a number of disadvantages. It ignores the amounts of bread, tea and caviare consumed (and hence the importance of each item), and the units to which the prices refer. If, for example, we had been given the price of a cup of tea rather than a packet of tea, the index would have been different.

Average relatives indices

4.5 To overcome the problem of different units we consider the changes in prices as ratios rather than absolutes so that all price movements, whatever their absolute values, are treated as equally important.

4.6 Price changes are considered as ratios rather than absolutes by using the *average price relatives index* which is calculated as

$$100 \times \frac{1}{n} \times \Sigma(P_1/P_0)$$

where n is the number of goods. Here, the price relative P_1/P_0 (so called because it gives the new price level of each item relative to the base year price) for a particular commodity will have the same value whatever the unit for which the price is quoted.

4.7 Using the information in Paragraph 4.2, we can construct the average price relatives index as follows.

Commodity	P_0 £	P_1 £	P_1/P_0
Bread	0.20	0.40	2.00
Tea	0.25	0.30	1.20
Caviare	4.50	4.05	0.90
			4.10

Year	$\frac{1}{n}\Sigma(P_1/P_0)$	*Average price relatives index*
19X1	1/3 × 3.00 = 1.00	100
19X2	1/3 × 4.10 = 1.37	137

4.8 There has therefore been an average price increase of 37% between 19X1 and 19X2.

4.9 We could, of course, construct an average quantity relatives index if we had been given information on quantities purchased per time period.

4.10 However, no account has been taken of the relative importance of each item, in this index. Bread is probably more important than caviare. To overcome both the problem of quantities in different units and the need to attach importance to each item, we can use weighting which reflects the importance of each item. To decide the weightings of different items in an index, it is necessary to obtain information, perhaps by market research, about the relative importance of each item. Thus, in our example of a simple cost of living index, it would be necessary to find out how much the average person or household spends each week on each item to determine weightings.

4.11 There are two types of index which give different weights to different items, weighted means of relatives indices and weighted aggregate indices.

Weighted means of relatives indices

4.12 This method of weighting involves calculating index relatives for each of the components and using the weights given to obtain a weighted average of the relatives.

4.13 The general form of a weighted means of relatives index number is

$$\frac{\sum wI}{\sum w}$$

where w is the weighting factor

and I is the index relative.

4.14 Values (price × quantity) relating to some point in time are usually used as weights.

4.15 Note that the weights may be from a year other than the base year. This is the method used for the index of wholesale prices. We could, for example, produce a weighted means of relatives index using 19X4 as base year, 19X6 as the given year and 19X5 values as weights.

4.16 Weighted means of relatives are very important in practice, and the great majority of indices published in the UK are of this type.

NOTES

EXAMPLE: WEIGHTED MEANS OF RELATIVES INDICES

Use both the information in Paragraph 4.2 and the following details about quantities purchased by each household in a week in 19X1 to determine a weighted means of price relatives index number for 19X2 using 19X1 as the base year.

	Quantity
Bread	6
Tea	2
Caviare	0.067

Solution

Price relatives (I)	Bread	40/20 =	2.00
	Tea	30/25 =	1.20
	Caviare	405/450 =	0.90
Weightings (w)	Bread	6×0.20 =	1.20
	Tea	2×0.25 =	0.50
	Caviare	0.067×4.50 =	0.30
	Σw =		2.00
Index	Bread	2×1.2 =	2.40
	Tea	1.2×0.5 =	0.60
	Caviare	0.9×0.3 =	0.27
	ΣwI =		3.27

$$\text{Index number} = \frac{3.27}{2} \times 100 = 163.5$$

Weighted aggregate indices

4.17 This method of weighting involves multiplying each component value by its corresponding weight and adding these products to form an aggregate. This is done for both the base period and the period in question. The aggregate for the period under consideration is then divided by the base period aggregate.

4.18 The general form of a weighted aggregate index is

$$\frac{\sum wv_n}{\sum wv_0}$$

where w is the weighting factor

v_0 is the value of the commodity in the base period

v_n is the value of the commodity in the period in question

4.19 Price indices are usually weighted by quantities and quantity indices are usually weighted by prices.

Activity 3

What are the formulae for calculating price and quantity weighted aggregate indices if base year weights are used?

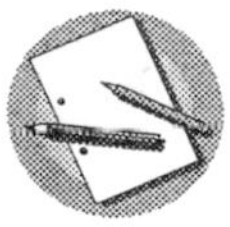

NOTES

EXAMPLE: A PRICE INDEX

In the previous example of the cost of living index, the 19X2 index value could have been calculated as follows.

Item	*Quantity*	*Price in 19X1*		*Price in 19X2*	
	Q_0	P_0	P_0Q_0	P_1	P_1Q_0
Bread	6.000	20	120	40	240
Tea	2.000	25	50	30	60
Caviare	0.067	450	30	405	27
			200		327

$$\text{Index in 19X2} = \frac{327}{200} \times 100 = 163.5$$

EXAMPLE: A QUANTITY INDEX

The Falldown Construction Company uses four items of materials and components in a standard production job.

In 19X0 the quantities of each material or component used per job and their cost were as follows.

	Quantity Units	*Price per unit* £
Material A	20	2
Material B	5	10
Component C	40	3
Component D	15	6

In 19X2 the quantities of materials and components used per job were as follows.

	Quantity Units
Material A	15
Material B	6
Component C	36
Component D	25

Using 19X0 as a base year, calculate the quantity index value in 19X2 for the amount of materials used in a standard job.

Solution

	Price in 19X0	*Quantity used in 19X0*		*Quantity used in 19X2*	
	P_0	Q_0	P_0Q_0	Q_1	P_0Q_1
Material A	£2	20	40	15	30
Material B	£10	5	50	6	60
Component C	£3	40	120	36	108
Component D	£6	15	90	25	150
			300		348

$$\text{Quantity index} = \frac{348}{300} \times 100 = 116$$

This would suggest that the company is using 16% more materials in 19X2 than in 19X0 on a standard job.

5 LASPEYRE AND PAASCHE INDICES

5.1 Laspeyre and Paasche indices are special cases of weighted aggregate indices.

Definition

Laspeyre indices use weights from the base period and are therefore sometimes called *base weighted indices*.

Laspeyre price index

5.2 A Laspeyre price index uses quantities consumed in the base period as weights. In the notation already used it can be expressed as follows.

$$\text{Laspeyre price index} = 100 \times \frac{\Sigma Q_0 P_1}{\Sigma Q_0 P_0}$$

Laspeyre quantity index

5.3 A Laspeyre quantity index uses prices from the base period as weights and can be expressed as follows.

$$\text{Laspeyre quantity index} = 100 \times \frac{\Sigma Q_1 P_0}{\Sigma Q_0 P_0}$$

Definition

Paasche indices use current time period weights. In other words the weights are changed every time period.

Paasche price index

5.4 A Paasche price index uses quantities consumed in the current period as weights and can be expressed as follows.

$$\text{Paasche price index} = 100 \times \frac{\Sigma Q_1 P_1}{\Sigma Q_1 P_0}$$

Paasche quantity index

5.5 A Paasche quantity index uses prices from the current period as weights and can be expressed as follows.

$$\text{Paasche quantity index} = 100 \times \frac{\Sigma Q_1 P_1}{\Sigma Q_0 P_1}$$

NOTES

EXAMPLE: LASPEYRE AND PAASCHE PRICE INDICES

The wholesale price index in Ruritania is made up from the prices of five items. The price of each item, and the average quantities purchased by manufacturing and other companies each week were as follows, in 19X0 and 19X2.

Item	*Quantity 19X0*	*Price per unit 19X0*	*Quantity 19X2*	*Price per unit 19X2*
	'000 units	Roubles	'000 units	Roubles
P	60	3	80	4
Q	30	6	40	5
R	40	5	20	8
S	100	2	150	2
T	20	7	10	10

Required

Calculate the price index in 19X2, if 19X0 is taken as the base year, using the following.

(a) A Laspeyre index

(b) A Paasche index

Solution

Workings

Item					*Laspeyre*		*Paasche*	
	Q_0	P_0	Q_1	P_1	Q_0P_0	Q_0P_1	Q_1P_1	Q_1P_0
P	60	3	80	4	180	240	320	240
Q	30	6	40	5	180	150	200	240
R	40	5	20	8	200	320	160	100
S	100	2	150	2	200	200	300	300
T	20	7	10	10	140	200	100	70
					900	1,110	1,080	950

19X2 index numbers are as follows.

(a) Laspeyre index = $100 \times \dfrac{1,110}{900} = 123.3$

(b) Paasche index = $100 \times \dfrac{1,080}{950} = 113.7$

The Paasche index for 19X2 reflects the decline in consumption of the relatively expensive items R and T since 19X0. The Laspeyre index for 19X2 fails to reflect this change.

Activity 4

A baker has listed the ingredients he used and their prices, in 19X3 and 19X4, as follows.

	Kg used *19X3* '000s	*Price per kg* *19X3* £	*Kg used* *19X4* '000s	*Price per kg* *19X3* £
Milk	3	1.20	4	1.50
Eggs	6	0.95	5	0.98
Flour	1	1.40	2	1.30
Sugar	4	1.10	3	1.14

Required

Calculate the following quantity indices for 19X4 (with 19X3 as the base year).

(a) A Laspeyre index

(b) A Paasche index

Which to use – Paasche or Laspeyre ?

5.6 Patterns of consumption and prices both change and a decision therefore has to be made as to whether a Paasche or a Laspeyre index should be used.

5.7 The following points should be considered when deciding which type of index to use.

(a) A Paasche index requires quantities to be ascertained each year. A Laspeyre index only requires them for the base year. Constructing a Paasche index may therefore cost more.

(b) For the Paasche index the denominator has to be recalculated each year because the quantities/prices must be changed to current year consumption/price levels.

For the Laspeyre index, the denominator is fixed. The Laspeyre index can therefore be calculated as soon as current prices/quantities are known. The Paasche index, on the other hand, cannot be calculated until the end of a period, when information about current quantities/prices becomes available.

(c) The denominator of a Laspeyre index is fixed and therefore the Laspeyre index numbers for several different years can be directly compared. With the Paasche index, on the other hand, comparisons can only be drawn directly between the current year and the base year (although indirect comparisons can be made).

(d) The weights for a Laspeyre index become out of date, whereas those for the Paasche index are updated each year.

(e) A Laspeyre price index implicitly assumes that, whatever the price changes, the quantities purchased will remain the same. In terms of economic theory, no substitution of cheaper alternative goods and services is allowed to take place. Even if goods become relatively more expensive, it assumes that the same quantities are bought. As a result, the index tends to overstate inflation.

(f) The effect of current year weighting when using the Paasche price index means that greater importance is placed on goods that are relatively cheaper now than they were in the base year. As a consequence, the Paasche price index tends to understate inflation.

In practice, it is common to use a Laspeyre index and revise the weights every few years. (Where appropriate, a new base year may be created when the weights are changed.)

6 PRACTICAL ISSUES

What items to include

6.1 The purpose to which the index is to be put must be carefully considered. Once this has been done, the items selected must be as representative as possible, taking into account this purpose. Care must be taken to ensure that the items are unambiguously defined and that their values are readily ascertainable.

6.2 For some indices, the choice of items might be relatively straightforward. For example, the FT Actuaries All-Share Index, compiled jointly by the *Financial Times*, the Institute of Actuaries and the Faculty of Actuaries, is made up of the share prices of approximately 800 companies quoted on the Stock Exchange. The weights are based on the market capitalisations of the companies (the number of shares in issue multiplied by their market value).

6.3 For other indices, the choice of items will be more difficult. The Retail Prices Index provides an excellent example of the problem. It would be impossible to include all items of domestic spending and a selective, representative basket of goods and services must be found, ranging from spending on mortgages and rents, to cars, public transport, food and drink, electricity, gas, telephone, clothing, leisure activities and so on.

Collecting the data

6.4 Data are required to determine the following.

(a) The values for each item

(b) The weight that will be attached to each item

Consider as an example a cost of living index. The prices of a particular commodity will vary from place to place, from shop to shop and from type to type. Also the price will vary during the period under consideration. The actual prices used must obviously be some sort of average. The way in which the average is to be obtained should be clearly defined at the outset.

6.5 When constructing a price index, it is common practice to use the quantities consumed as weights; similarly, when constructing a quantity index, the prices may be used as weights. Care must be taken in selecting the basis for the weighting. For example, in a cost of living index, it may be decided to use the consumption of a typical family as the weights, but it may prove difficult to define a typical family.

The choice of a base year

6.6 The choice of a base date, or base year is not significant, except that it should be representative. In the construction of a price index, the base year must not be one in which there were abnormally high or low prices for any items in the basket of goods making up the index. For example, a year in which there is a potato famine would be unsuitable as a base period for the Retail Prices Index.

NOTES

The limitations and misinterpretation of index numbers

Limitations

6.7 Index numbers are usually only approximations of changes in price or quantity over time, and must be interpreted with care.

(a) As we have seen, weightings become out of date over time. Unless a Paasche index is used, the weightings will gradually cease to reflect current reality.

(b) New products or items may appear, and old ones may cease to be significant. Such changes can make an index out of date.

(c) The data used to calculate index numbers might be incomplete, out of date, or inaccurate. For example, the quantity indices of imports and exports are based on records supplied by traders which may be prone to error or even deliberate falsification.

(d) The base year of an index should be a normal year, but there is probably no such thing as a perfectly normal year. Some error in the index will be caused by atypical values in the base period.

(e) The 'basket of items' in an index is necessarily selective. For example, the Retail Prices Index (RPI) is constructed from a sample of households and from a basket of around 600 items.

(f) A national index may not be very relevant to an individual town or region. For example, if the national index of wages and salaries rises from 100 to 115, we cannot conclude that the wages and salaries of people in, say, Glasgow have gone up by 15%.

(g) An index may exclude important items: for example, the RPI excludes payments of income tax out of gross wages.

Misinterpretation

6.8 You must be careful not to misinterpret index numbers. Several possible mistakes will be explained, using the following example of a retail prices index.

19X0		*19X1*		*19X2*	
January	340.0	January	360.6	January	436.3
		February	362.5	February	437.1
		March	366.2	March	439.5
		April	370.0	April	442.1

(a) It would be wrong to say that prices rose by 2.6% between March and April 19X2. It is correct to say that prices rose 2.6 points, or

$$\frac{2.6}{439.5} = 0.6\%$$

(b) It would be correct to say that the annual rate of price increases (the rate of inflation) fell between March and April 19X2. It would be a mistake, however, to suppose that a fall in the rate of inflation means that prices are falling, therefore the price index is falling.

The rate of price increases has slowed down, but the trend of prices is still upwards.

(i) The annual rate of inflation from March 19X1 to March 19X2 is

$$\left(\frac{439.5-366.2}{366.2}\right) = 20\%$$

(ii) The annual rate of inflation from April 19X1 to April 19X2 is

$$\left(\frac{442.1 - 370.0}{370.0}\right) = 19.5\%$$

Thus the annual rate of inflation has dropped from 20% to 19.5% between March and April 19X2, even though prices went up in the month between March and April 19X2 by 0.6%. (The price increase between March and April 19X1 was over 1%. This is included in the calculation of the rate of inflation between March 19X1 and March 19X2, but is excluded in the comparison between April 19X1 and April 19X2 where it has been replaced by the lower price increase, 0.6%, between March and April 19X2.)

7 THE RETAIL PRICES INDEX FOR THE UNITED KINGDOM (RPI)

7.1 We will conclude our study of index numbers by looking at the construction of the UK Retail Prices Index (RPI).

7.2 On one particular day of each month, data are collected about prices of the following groups of items.

Food
Alcohol
Tobacco
Housing
Fuel and light
Household goods
Clothing and footwear
Motoring expenditure
Leisure services
Household services
Leisure goods
Catering
Personal goods and services
Fares and other travel

7.3 Each group is sub-divided into sections: for example 'food' will be subdivided into bread, butter, potatoes and so on. These sections may in turn be subdivided into more specific items. The groups do not cover every item of expenditure (for example they exclude income tax, pension fund contributions and football pools).

7.4 The weightings given to each group, section and subsection are based on information provided by the *Family Expenditure Survey* which is based on a survey of over 10,000 households, spread evenly over the year.

Each member of the selected households (aged 16 or over) is asked to keep a detailed record of their expenditure over a period of 14 days, and to provide information about longer-term payments (such as insurance premiums). Information is also obtained about their income.

7.5 The weightings used in the construction of the RPI are revised every year, using information in the *Family Expenditure Survey* of the previous year. As well as annual changes to the weights, the items included in the index are changed to reflect changing spending habits. For example, CD's and CD players were added in 1987; in 1994 the shampoo and set was replaced by highlights; in 1996, Doc Marten style boots and charges for aerobics classes were added.

NOTES

Chapter roundup

- An index is a measure, over time, of the average changes in the value (price or quantity) of a group of items relative to the situation at some period in the past.
- An index relative is an index number which measures the change in a single distinct commodity.
- Index relatives can be calculated using the fixed base method or the chain base method.
- In order to compare two time series of relatives, each series should have the same base period and hence one (or both) may need rebasing.
- The real value of a commodity can only be measured in terms of some 'indicator' (such as the RPI).
- Time series deflation is a technique used to obtain a set of index relatives that measure the changes in the real value of some commodity with respect to some given indicator.
- Composite indices cover more than one item.
- Weighting is used to reflect the importance of each item in the index.
- Weighted means of relatives indices are found by calculating indices and then applying weights.
- Weighted aggregate indices are found by applying weights and then calculating the index.
- There are two types of weighted aggregate index, the Laspeyre (which uses quantities/prices from the base period as the weights) and the Paasche (which uses quantities/prices from the current period as weights).
- Index numbers are a very useful way of summarising a large amount of data in a single series of numbers. You should remember, however, that any summary hides some detail and that index numbers should therefore be interpreted with caution.

Quick quiz

1 How are index relatives calculated using the chain base method?

2 How is a time series of relatives rebased?

3 Why must the real value of a commodity be measured in terms of some indicator?

4 What is the general form of

(a) a weighted means of relatives index

(b) a weighted aggregate index?

5 What do Laspeyre indices use as weights?

6 What are the limitations of index numbers?

7 Give some examples of how index numbers might be misinterpreted.

NOTES

Answers to activities

1

	1990	*1991*	*1992*	*1993*	*1994*	*1995*
Index (1993 = 100)	92*	94	96	100**	102***	103

* 451/490 × 100

** 490/490 × 100

*** 499/490 × 100

2 The index number for each year with 19X6 as the base year will be the original index number divided by 1.14, and the real wages for each year will be (money wages × 100)/index number for the year.

Year	*Index*	*Real wage* £
19X0	88	170
19X1	90	179
19X2	93	181
19X3	95	188
19X4	96	193
19X5	98	195
19X6	100	197
19X7	102	199
19X8	104	199
19X9	106	201
19Y0	108	214

3 Price index: $100 \times \dfrac{\Sigma Q_0P_1}{\Sigma Q_0P_0}$

where P_0 represents the prices of items in the base year
P_1 represents the prices of items in the new year
Q_0 represents the quantities of the items consumed in the base year

Quantity index: $100 \times \dfrac{\Sigma P_0Q_1}{\Sigma Q_0P_0}$

where Q_0 represents the quantities consumed in the base year
Q_1 represents the quantities consumed in the new year
P_0 represents the prices in the base year

4 Workings

					Laspeyre		*Paasche*	
	Q_0	P_0	Q_1	P_1	Q_0P_0	Q_1P_0	Q_1P_1	Q_0P_1
Milk	3	1.20	4	1.50	3.60	4.80	6.00	4.50
Eggs	6	0.95	5	0.98	5.70	4.75	4.90	5.88
Flour	1	1.40	2	1.30	1.40	2.80	2.60	1.30
Sugar	4	1.10	3	1.14	4.40	3.30	3.42	4.56
					15.10	15.65	16.92	16.24

Quantity index numbers for 19X4 are as follows.

(a) Laspeyre method $= 100 \times \dfrac{15.65}{15.10} = 103.64$

(b) Paasche method $= 100 \times \dfrac{16.92}{16.24} = 104.19$

NOTES

Further question practice

Now try the following practice questions at the end of this text.

Multiple choice questions	**22–26**
Exam style question	**4**

Chapter 5

AVERAGES AND DISPERSION

Introduction

In Chapter 3 we saw how data can be summarised and presented in tabular, chart and graphical formats. Such formats provide an overview of a situation and show the key features of the data. For example, a bar chart might show that very few people in Ruritania earn less than 100 Ruritanian dollars a month and that very few earn more than 700 Ruritanian dollars a month, the majority earning somewhere between the two extremes. Sometimes you might need more information than diagrammatic representations of data can provide, however. In such circumstances you may need to apply some sort of numerical analysis. A teacher in Ruritania, for example, might want some means of comparing her salary with those of other teachers.

There are two initial measures that we can take from a set of data to help in such a situation: a measure of centrality (an average) and a measure of dispersion (or spread).

An average is a representative figure that is used to give some impression of the size of all the items in the population. The average salary earned in Ruritania will therefore be representative of all salaries in Ruritania. You may have thought that an average is simply 'an average' but there are in fact three main types of average: the mean; the mode; the median.

In the first part of this chapter we will therefore be looking at each of these averages in turn, their calculation, advantages and disadvantages.

Averages are a method of determining the 'location' or central point of a distribution, but they give no information about the dispersion of values in the distribution. Although the mean, modal and median monthly salaries in North Ruritania might be identical to those in South Ruritania, monthly salaries in North Ruritania might vary between 100 and 1,000 Ruritanian dollars whereas those in South Ruritania might vary between 400 and 700 Ruritanian dollars. The spread or dispersion of the distribution of the salaries are therefore different and measures of dispersion, the topic of the second part of the chapter, would provide the teacher we mentioned above with additional means of comparing her salary with those other teachers.

Your objectives

After completing this chapter you should:

(a) understand the difference between the arithmetic mean, mode and median of a set of data and be aware of their advantages and disadvantages;

(b) be able to calculate the arithmetic mean, mode and median of both ungrouped and grouped data;

(c) understand and be able to calculate the range, quartiles, mean deviation, standard deviation and coefficient of variation of a set of data;

(d) be aware of the concept of the skewness of a distribution.

1 THE ARITHMETIC MEAN

Definition

The *arithmetic mean* is calculated from the sum of values of items divided by the number of items. The arithmetic mean of a variable x is shown as $\overline{x}$ ('x bar').

1.1 The arithmetic mean is the best known type of average. For ungrouped data, it is calculated by the formula

$$\text{Arithmetic mean} = \frac{\text{Sum of values of items}}{\text{Number of items}}$$

For example, the mean wage of a work force of ten men is the amount each worker would receive if all their earnings were pooled and then shared out equally among them.

EXAMPLE: THE ARITHMETIC MEAN

The demand for a product on each of 20 days was as follows (in units).

3 12 7 17 3 14 9 6 11 10 1 4 19 7 15 6 9 12 12 8

The arithmetic mean of daily demand is

$$\frac{\text{Sum of demand}}{\text{Number of days}} = \frac{185}{20} = 9.25 \text{ units}$$

1.2 The arithmetic mean of a variable x is shown as $\overline{x}$ ('x bar').

Thus in the above example $\overline{x}$ = 9.25 units.

1.3 In the above example, demand on any one day is never actually 9.25 units. The arithmetic mean is merely an average representation of demand on each of the 20 days.

Finding the arithmetic mean of data in a frequency distribution

1.4 It is more likely in an exam that you will be asked to calculate the arithmetic mean of a frequency distribution. In our previous example, the frequency distribution would be shown as follows.

Daily demand x	*Frequency* f	*Demand × frequency* fx
1	1	1
3	2	6
4	1	4
6	2	12
7	2	14
8	1	8
9	2	18
10	1	10
11	1	11
12	3	36
14	1	14
15	1	15
17	1	17
19	1	19
	20	185

$$\overline{x} = \frac{185}{20} = 9.25$$

NOTES

The summation sign, sigma(Σ)

1.5 The statistical notation for the arithmetic mean of a set of data uses the symbol Σ (sigma). Σ means 'the sum of' and is used as shorthand to mean 'the sum of a set of values'.

Thus, in the previous example:

(a) Σf would mean the sum of all the frequencies, which is 20;

(b) Σfx would mean the sum of all the values of 'frequency multiplied by daily demand', that is, all 14 values of fx, so Σfx = 185.

The symbolic formula for the arithmetic mean of a frequency distribution

1.6 Using the Σ sign, the formula for the arithmetic mean of a frequency distribution is

$$\bar{x} = \frac{\Sigma fx}{n} \text{ or } \frac{\Sigma fx}{\Sigma f}$$

where n is the number of values recorded, or the number of items measured.

Finding the arithmetic mean of grouped data in class intervals

1.7 You might also be asked to calculate (or at least approximate) the arithmetic mean of a frequency distribution, where the frequencies are shown in class intervals.

1.8 Using the example in Paragraph 1.4, the frequency distribution might have been shown as follows.

Daily demand	*Frequency*
$>0 \leq 5$	4
$>5 \leq 10$	8
$>10 \leq 15$	6
$>15 \leq 20$	2
	20

1.9 There is, of course, an extra difficulty with finding the average now; as the data have been collected into classes, a certain amount of detail has been lost and the values of the variables to be used in the calculation of the mean are not clearly specified.

1.10 To calculate the arithmetic mean of grouped data we therefore need to decide on a value which best represents all of the values in a particular class interval.

The mid-point of each class interval is conventionally taken, on the assumption that the frequencies occur evenly over the class interval range. In the example above, the variable is discrete, so the first class includes 1, 2, 3, 4 and 5, giving a mid-point of 3. With a continuous variable (such as quantities of fuel consumed in litres), the mid-points would have been 2.5, 7.5 and so on. Once the value of x has been decided, the mean is calculated in exactly the same way as in Paragraph 1.6.

NOTES

EXAMPLE: THE ARITHMETIC MEAN OF GROUPED DATA

Daily demand	*Mid point* x	*Frequency* f	fx
>0 ≤ 5	3	4	12
>5 ≤ 10	8	8	64
>10 ≤ 15	13	6	78
>15 ≤ 20	18	2	36
		$\Sigma f = 20$	$\Sigma fx = 190$

$$\text{Arithmetic mean } \bar{x} = \frac{\sum fx}{\sum f} = \frac{190}{20} = 9.5 \text{ units}$$

Because the assumption that frequencies occur evenly within each class interval is not quite correct in this example, our approximate mean of 9.5 is not exactly correct, and is in error by 0.25.

As the frequencies become larger, the size of this approximating error should become smaller.

Finding the arithmetic mean of combined data

1.11 Suppose that the mean age of a group of five people is 27 and the mean age of another group of eight people is 32. How would we find the mean age of the whole group of 13 people?

1.12 Remember that the arithmetic mean is calculated as

$$\frac{\text{Sum of values of items}}{\text{Number of items}}$$

The sum of the ages in the first group is $5 \times 27 = 135$

The sum of the ages in the second group is $8 \times 32 = 256$

The sum of all 13 ages is $135 + 256 = 391$

The mean age is therefore $\frac{391}{13} = 30.07$ years.

Activity 1

The mean weight of 10 units at 5 kg, 10 units at 7 kg and 20 units at X kg is 8 kg. What is the value of X?

NOTES

The advantages and disadvantages of the arithmetic mean

1.13 The advantages of the arithmetic mean are as follows.

(a) It is easy to calculate.

(b) It is widely understood.

(c) The value of every item is included in the computation of the mean and so it can be determined with arithmetical precision and is representative of the whole set of data.

(d) It is supported by mathematical theory and is suited to further statistical analysis.

1.14 The disadvantages of the arithmetic mean are as follows.

(a) Its value may not correspond to any actual value. For example, the 'average' family might have 2.3 children, but no family can have exactly 2.3 children.

(b) An arithmetic mean might be distorted by extremely high or low values. For example, the mean of 3, 4, 4 and 6 is 4.25, but the mean of 3, 4, 4, 6 and 15 is 6.4. The high value, 15, distorts the average and in some circumstances the mean would be a misleading and inappropriate figure. (Note that extreme values are not uncommon in economic data.)

Activity 2

For the week ended 15 November, the wages earned by the 69 operators employed in the machine shop of Mermaid Ltd were as follows.

Wages	*Number of Operatives*
≤£60	3
>£60 ≤ £70	11
>£70 ≤ £80	16
>£80 ≤ £90	15
>£90 ≤ £100	10
>£100 ≤ £110	8
>£110	6
	69

Required

Calculate the arithmetic mean wage of the machine operators of Mermaid Ltd for the week ended 15 November.

NOTES

2 THE MODE

2.1 The second type of average is the mode or modal value.

Definition

The *mode* is an average which indicates the most frequently occurring value.

EXAMPLE: THE MODE

The daily demand for stock in a ten-day period is as follows.

Demand Units	*Number of days*
6	3
7	6
8	1
	10

The mode is 7 units, because it is the value which occurs most frequently.

Finding the mode of a grouped frequency distribution

2.2 The mode of a grouped frequency distribution can be calculated from a histogram.

EXAMPLE: FINDING THE MODE FROM A HISTOGRAM

Consider the following grouped frequency distribution.

Value At least	*Less than*	*Frequency*
0	10	0
10	20	50
20	30	150
30	40	100

The modal class (the one with the highest frequency) is 'at least 20, less than 30'. But how can we find a single value to represent the mode?

What we need to do is draw a histogram of the frequency distribution.

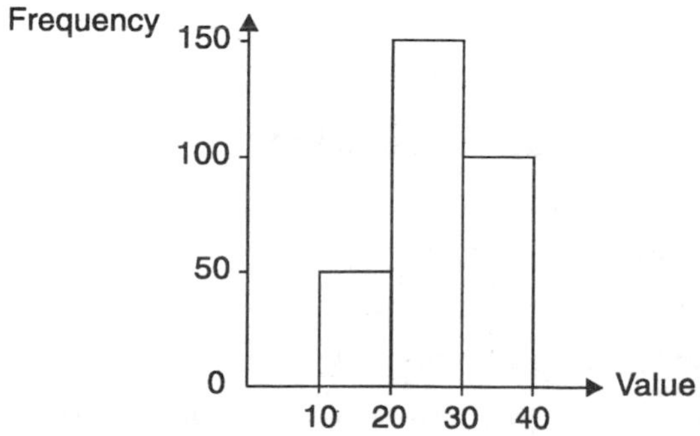

The modal class is always the class with the tallest bar, which may not be the class with the highest frequency if the classes do not all have the same width.

NOTES

EXAMPLE *continued*

We can estimate the mode graphically as follows.

(a) Join with a straight line the top left-hand corner of the bar for the modal class and the top left-hand corner of the next bar to the right.

(b) Join with a straight line the top right-hand corner of the bar for the modal class and the top right-hand corner of the next bar to the left.

Where these two lines intersect, we find the estimated modal value. In this example it is approximately 27.

Histogram showing mode

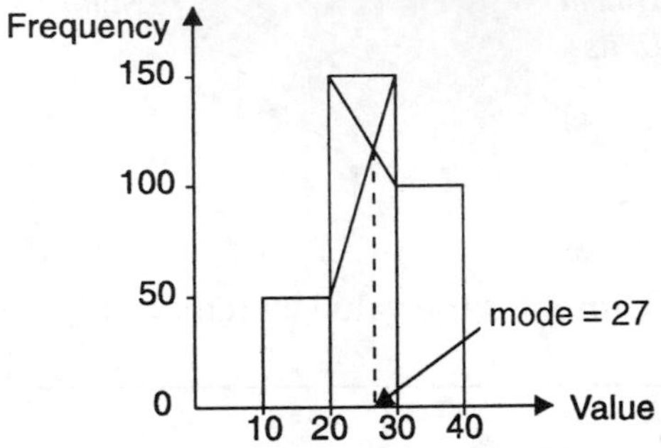

2.3 We are assuming that the frequencies occur evenly within each class interval but this may not always be correct. It is unlikely that the 150 values in the modal class occur evenly. Hence the mode in a grouped frequency distribution is only an estimate.

The advantages and disadvantages of the mode

2.4 The mode is a more appropriate average to use than the mean in situations where it is useful to know the most common value. For example, if a manufacturer wishes to start production in a new industry, it might be helpful to him to know what sort of product made by that industry is most in demand with customers.

2.5 The advantages of the mode are as follows.

(a) It is easy to find.

(b) It is not influenced by a few extreme values.

(c) It can be used for data which are not even numerical (unlike the mean and median).

(d) It can be the value of an actual item in the distribution.

2.6 The mode does have a number of disadvantages.

(a) It may be unrepresentative; it takes no account of a high proportion of the data, only representing the most common value.

(b) It does not take every value into account

(c) There can be two or more modes within a set of data.

(d) If the modal class is only very slightly bigger than another class, just a few more items in this other class could mean a substantially different result, suggesting some instability in the measure.

NOTES

3 THE MEDIAN

3.1 The third type of average is the median.

Definition

The *median* is the value of the middle member of a distribution once all of the items have been arranged in order of magnitude.

3.2 The median of a set of ungrouped data is found by arranging the items in ascending or descending order of value, and selecting the item in the middle of the range. A list of items in order of value is called an array.

EXAMPLE: THE MEDIAN

The median of the following nine values:

8 6 9 12 15 6 3 20 11

is found by taking the middle item (the fifth one) in the array:

3 6 6 8 9 11 12 15 20

The median is 9.

The middle item of an odd number of items is calculated as the $\frac{(n+1)}{2}^{th}$ item.

Consider the following array.

1 2 2 2 3 5 6 7 8 11

The median is 4 because, with an even number of items, we have to take the arithmetic mean of the two middle ones (in this example, (3 + 5)/2 = 4). When there are many items, however, it is not worth doing this.

Activity 3

The following times taken to produce a batch of 100 units of Product X have been noted.

21 min	17 min	24 min	11 min	37 min	27 min
20 min	15 min	17 min	23 min	29 min	30 min
24 min	18 min	17 min	21 min	24 min	20 min

What is the median time?

Finding the median of an ungrouped frequency distribution

3.3 The median of an ungrouped frequency distribution is found in a similar way. Consider the following distribution.

Value x	*Frequency* f	*Cumulative frequency*
8	3	3
12	7	10
16	12	22
17	8	30
19	5	35
	35	

NOTES

The median would be the (35 + 1)/2 = 18th item. The 18th item has a value of 16, as we can see from the cumulative frequencies in the right hand column of the above table.

Finding the median of a grouped frequency distribution

3.4 We can establish the median of a grouped frequency distribution from an ogive.

EXAMPLE: THE MEDIAN FROM AN OGIVE

Construct an ogive of the following frequency distribution and hence establish the median.

Class	*Frequency*	*Cumulative frequency*
£		
≥ 340 < 370	17	17
≥ 370 < 400	9	26
≥ 400 < 430	9	35
≥ 430 < 460	3	38
≥ 460 < 490	2	40
	40	

Solution

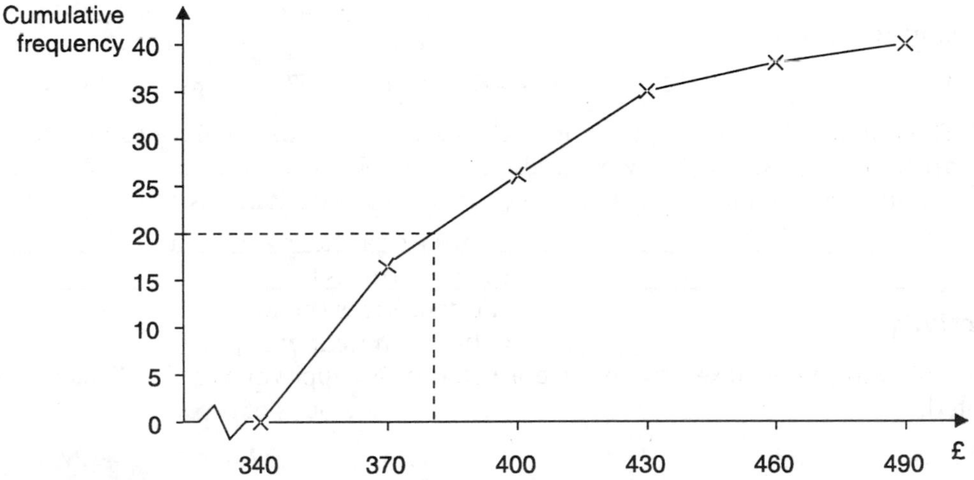

The median is at the ½ × 40 = 20th item. Reading off from the horizontal axis on the ogive, the value of the median is approximately £380.

Note that because we are assuming that the values are spread evenly within each class, the median calculated is only approximate.

The advantages and disadvantages of the median

3.5 The median is only of interest where there is a range of values and the middle item is of some significance. Perhaps the most suitable application of the median is in comparing changes in a 'middle of the road' value over time.

3.6 The median is easy to understand and (like the mode) is unaffected by extremely high or low values. It can be the value of an actual item in the distribution. On the other hand, it fails to reflect the full range of values, it is unsuitable for further statistical analysis and arranging the data in order of size can be tedious.

4 THE RANGE

Definition

The *range* is the difference between the highest observation and the lowest observation.

4.1 The main properties of the range as a measure of dispersion are as follows.

(a) It is easy to find and to understand.

(b) It is easily affected by one or two extreme values.

(c) It gives no indication of spread between the extremes.

(d) It is not suitable for further statistical analysis.

Activity 4

Calculate the mean and the range of each of the following sets of data.

(a) x_1	=	4	8	7	3	5	16	24	5
(b) x_2	=	10	7	9	11	11	8	9	7

What do your calculations show about the dispersion of the data sets?

---

5 QUARTILES AND OTHER QUANTILES

Quartiles

5.1 Quartiles are one means of identifying the range within which most of the values in the population occur. The lower quartile is the value below which 25% of the population fall and the upper quartile is the value above which 25% of the population fall. If there were 11 data items the lower quartile would be the third item and the upper quartile the ninth item. It follows that 50% of the total population fall between the lower and the upper quartiles. The quartiles and the median divide the population into four groups of equal size.

Deciles and percentiles

5.2 In a similar way, a population could be divided into ten equal groups, and this time the value of each dividing point is referred to as a *decile*.

When a population is divided into 100 parts, the value of each dividing point is referred to as a *percentile*. For example, in a population of 200 values, the percentiles would be the second, fourth, sixth, eighth and so on, up to the 198th item, in rising order of values.

Quantiles

Definition

Quartiles, deciles and percentiles, and any other similar dividing points for analysing a frequency distribution, are referred to collectively as *quantiles*.

5.3 The purpose of quantiles is to analyse the dispersion of data values. All quantiles can be found easily from an ogive.

The inter-quartile range

5.4 The lower and upper quartiles can be used to calculate a measure of dispersion called the inter-quartile range.

Definition

The *inter-quartile range* is the difference between the values of the upper and lower quartiles and hence shows the range of values of the middle half of the population.

The smaller the inter-quartile range, the less dispersed the population. Because values at the ends of the distribution are not taken into account, the inter-quartile range is not affected by extreme values.

5.5 For example, if the lower and upper quartiles of a frequency distribution were 6 and 11, the inter-quartile range would be 11 – 6 = 5. This shows that the range of values of the middle half of the population is 5 units.

EXAMPLE: QUARTILES

The hours of overtime worked in a particular quarter by the 60 employees of ABC Ltd are shown below. The company has decided to give a bonus of £15 to the 10% of the workforce who worked the most overtime, a bonus of £5 to the 20% of the workforce who worked the least overtime and a £10 bonus to all other employees.

Hours		*Frequency*
More than	*Not more than*	
0	10	3
10	20	6
20	30	11
30	40	15
40	50	12
50	60	7
60	70	6
		60

Required

Calculate the range of overtime hours worked by those employees receiving a £10 bonus.

Solution

Hours	*Cumulative frequency*
>0 ≤ 10	3
>10 ≤ 20	9
>20 ≤ 30	20
>30 ≤ 40	35
>40 ≤ 50	47
>50 ≤ 60	54
>60 ≤ 70	60

The 9th decile is at 60 – (10% of 60) = 54

The 2nd decile is at 20% of 60 = 12

NOTES

EXAMPLE *continued*

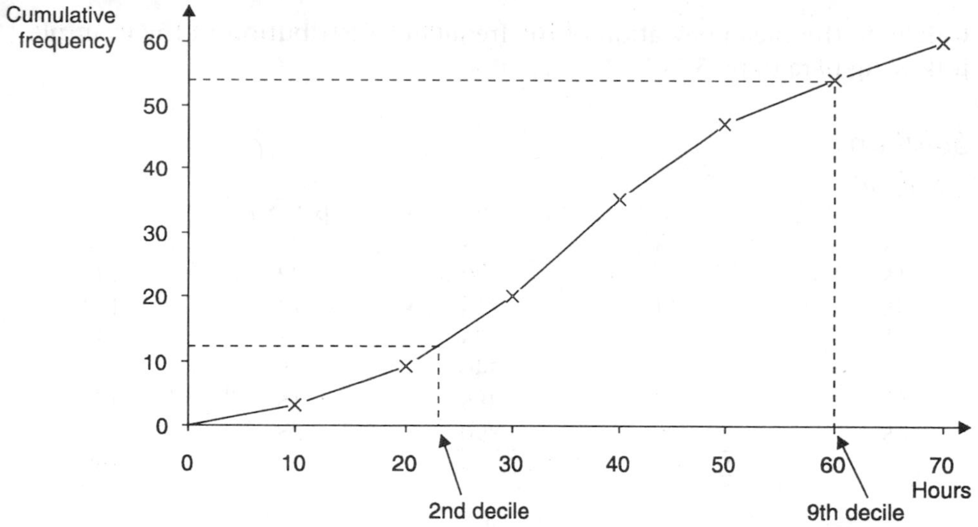

From the ogive the range of hours is approximately 23 to 60.

Activity 5

Find the values of the upper and lower quartiles of the frequency distribution detailed in the example following Paragraph 3.4 of this chapter.

6 THE MEAN DEVIATION

6.1 Because it only uses the middle 50% of the population, the inter-quartile range is a useful measure of dispersion if there are extreme values in the distribution. If there are no extreme values which could potentially distort a measure of dispersion, however, it seems unreasonable to exclude 50% of the data. The mean deviation, which we will look at in this section, and the standard deviation (the topic of Section 7) are therefore often more useful measures.

Definition

The *mean deviation* is a measure of the *average* amount by which the values in a distribution differ from the arithmetic mean.

6.2 Mean deviation = $\dfrac{\Sigma f\,|x-\bar{x}|}{n}$

6.3 (a) $|x - \bar{x}|$ is the difference between each value (x) in the distribution and the arithmetic mean $\bar{x}$ of the distribution. When calculating the mean deviation for grouped data the deviations should be measured to the midpoint of each class: that is, x is the midpoint of the class interval. The vertical bars mean that all differences are taken as positive since the total of all of the differences, if this is not done, will always equal zero. Thus if $x = 3$ and $\bar{x} = 5$, then $x - \bar{x} = -2$ but $|x - \bar{x}| = 2$.

(b) $f\,|x - \bar{x}|$ is the value in (a) above, multiplied by the frequency for the class.

(c) $\Sigma f\,|x - \bar{x}|$ is the sum of the results of all the calculations in (b) above.

(d) n (which equals Σf) is the number of items in the distribution.

EXAMPLE: THE MEAN DEVIATION

Calculate the mean deviation of the frequency distribution in the example following paragraph 5.5.

Solution

Midpoint x	f	fx	$\|x - \overline{x}\|$	$f\|x - \overline{x}\|$
5	3	15	32	96
15	6	90	22	132
25	11	275	12	132
35	15	525	2	30
45	12	540	8	96
55	7	385	18	126
65	6	390	28	168
	$\Sigma f = 60$	$\Sigma fx = 2{,}220$		780

$$\overline{x} = \frac{\Sigma fx}{\Sigma f} = \frac{2{,}220}{60} = 37$$

$$\text{Mean deviation} = \frac{780}{60} = 13 \text{ hours}$$

Thus the mean is 37 hours and the mean deviation is 13 hours.

Activity 6

Calculate the mean deviation of the following frequency distribution.

Value	*Frequency of occurrence*
5	4
15	6
25	8
35	20
45	6
55	6
	50

The usefulness of the mean deviation

6.4 The mean deviation is a measure of dispersion which shows by how much, on average, each item in the distribution differs in value from the arithmetic mean of the distribution.

Unlike quartiles, it uses all values in the distribution to measure the dispersion, but it is not greatly affected by a few extreme values because an average is taken.

The mean deviation is not, however, suitable for further statistical analysis.

NOTES

7 THE STANDARD DEVIATION

Definitions

The *variance* is the average of the squared mean deviation for each value in a distribution.

The *standard deviation* is the square root of the variance.

7.1 Instead of taking the absolute value of the difference between the value and the mean to avoid the total of the differences summing to zero as we did with the mean deviation, we can square the differences. If we do this, we get the most important measure of dispersion in statistics, the standard deviation. It is denoted by σ, the lower case Greek letter sigma.

7.2

Difference between value and mean	$x - \bar{x}$
Square of the difference	$(x - \bar{x})^2$
Sum of the squares of the difference	$\Sigma(x - \bar{x})^2$
Average of the sum (= variance = σ^2)	$\dfrac{\Sigma(x - \bar{x})^2}{n}$

7.3 The units of the variance are the square of those in the original data because we squared the differences. We therefore need to take the square root to get back to the units of the original data.

Square root of the variance = standard deviation = $\sqrt{\dfrac{\Sigma(x-\bar{x})^2}{n}}$

The same process can be applied to determine the standard deviation of data in a frequency distribution.

Square of the difference between value and mean	$(x - \bar{x})^2$
Sum of the squares of the difference	$\Sigma f(x - \bar{x})^2$
Average of the sum (= variance)	$\dfrac{\Sigma f(x - \bar{x})^2}{\Sigma f}$

Square root = standard deviation $= \sqrt{\dfrac{\Sigma f(x-\bar{x})^2}{\Sigma f}}$

This formula can prove time consuming to use. An alternative formula for the standard deviation is shown as follows.

Standard deviation = $\sqrt{\dfrac{\Sigma fx^2}{\Sigma f} - \bar{x}^2}$

Note that these formulae are appropriate if all the details are known of the whole population.

NOTES

EXAMPLE: THE VARIANCE AND THE STANDARD DEVIATION

Calculate the variance and the standard deviation of the frequency distribution in the example following paragraph 5.5.

Solution

Using the alternative formula for the standard deviation, the calculation is as follows.

Midpoint x	f	x^2	fx^2
5	3	25	75
15	6	225	1,350
25	11	625	6,875
35	15	1,225	18,375
45	12	2,025	24,300
55	7	3,025	21,175
65	6	4,225	25,350
	60		97,500

Mean = (from the example following paragraph 6.3) = 37

$$\text{Variance} = \frac{\Sigma fx^2}{\Sigma f} - \bar{x}^2 = \frac{97{,}500}{60} - (37)^2 = 256 \text{ hours}$$

$$\text{Standard deviation} = \sqrt{256} = 16 \text{ hours}$$

Activity 7

Calculate the variance and the standard deviation of the frequency distribution in Activity 6.

The main properties of the standard deviation

7.4 The standard deviation's main properties are as follows.

(a) It is based on all the values in the distribution and so is more comprehensive than dispersion measures based on quantiles, such as the quartile deviation.

(b) It is suitable for further statistical analysis.

(c) It is more difficult to understand than some other measures of dispersion.

The importance of the standard deviation lies in its suitability for further statistical analysis.

8 THE COEFFICIENT OF VARIATION

Definition

The *coefficient of variation* compares the dispersion of two distributions.

8.1 It is sometimes useful to be able to compare the spreads of two distributions.

This comparison can be done using the coefficient of variation.

$$\text{Coefficient of variation} = \frac{\text{Standard deviation}}{\text{mean}}$$

The coefficient of variation is sometimes known as the coefficient of relative dispersion.

8.2 The bigger the coefficient of variation, the wider the dispersion. For example, suppose that two sets of data, A and B, have the following means and standard deviations.

	A	*B*
Mean	120	125
Standard deviation	50	51
Coefficient of variation	0.417	0.408

Although B has a higher standard deviation in absolute terms (51 compared to 50) its relative dispersion is a bit less than A's since the coefficient of variation is a bit smaller.

Activity 8

Calculate the coefficient of variation of the distribution in Activities 6 and 7.

9 SKEWNESS

Definition

Skewness is the asymmetry of a frequency distribution curve.

9.1 As well as being able to calculate the average and spread of a frequency distribution, you should be aware of the skewness of a distribution. A frequency distribution must be either symmetrical or asymmetrical; in other words, skewed.

9.2 A symmetrical frequency distribution is one which can be divided into two halves which are mirror images of each other. The arithmetic mean, the median and the mode will all have the same value, M.

NOTES

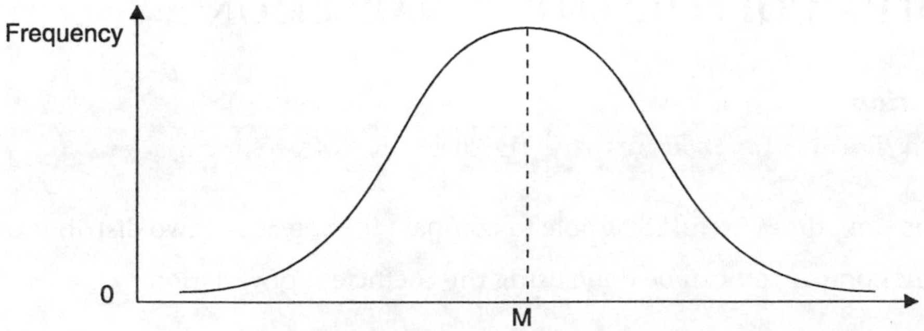

Figure 5.1 Symmetrical frequency distribution

9.3 A positively skewed distribution's graph will lean towards the left hand side, with a tail stretching out to the right. The mean, the median and the mode will have different values.

In a positively skewed distribution, the mode will have a lower value than the median and the mean will have a higher value than the median. The value of the mean is, in fact, higher than a great deal of the distribution.

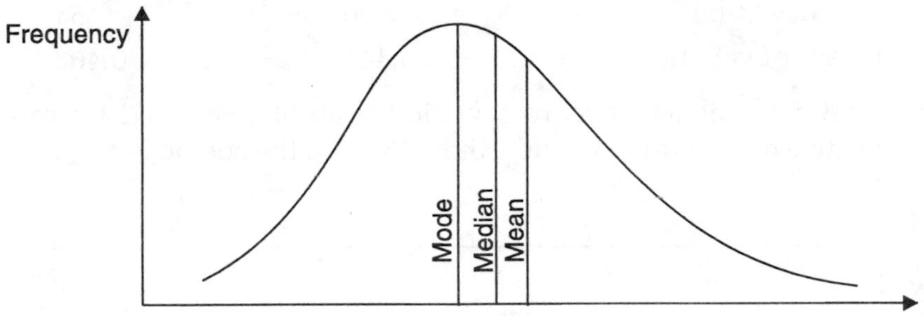

Figure 5.2 Positively skewed distribution graph

9.4 A negatively skewed distribution's graph will lean towards the right-hand side, with a tail stretching out to the left. Once again, the mean, median and mode will have different values.

In a negatively skewed distribution, the mode will have a higher value than the median and the mean will have a lower value than the median. The value of the mean is lower than a great deal of the distribution.

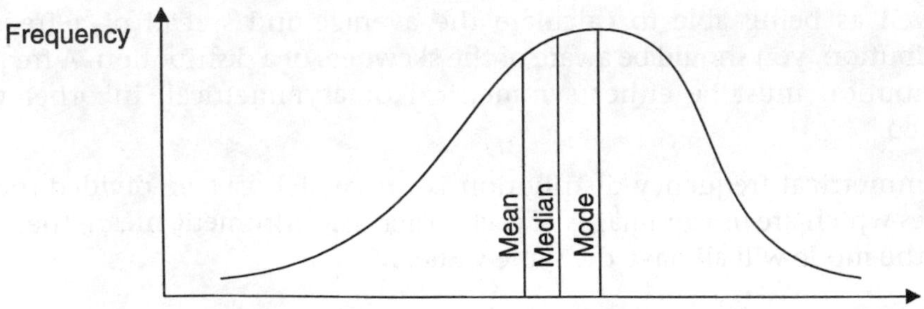

Figure 5.3 Negatively skewed distribution graph

It is a criticism of the mean as an average that for very skewed distributions its value may not be representative of the majority of the items in the distribution since it is affected by extreme values.

Chapter roundup

- This chapter has looked at the three main types of average and at measures of dispersion.
- The arithmetic mean is the best known type of average and is widely understood. It is used for further statistical analysis.
- The mode is the most frequently occurring value.
- The median is the value of the middle member of an array.
- The arithmetic mean, mode and median of a grouped frequency distribution can only be estimated approximately.
- You should now be able to calculate any of the three averages for a basic set of values, an ungrouped frequency distribution and a grouped frequency distribution.
- Measures of dispersion give some idea of the spread of variables about the average.
- The range is the difference between the highest and lowest observations.
- The quartiles and the median divide the population into four groups of equal size.
- Quartiles, deciles and percentiles are referred to collectively as quantiles.
- The inter-quartile range is the difference between the upper and lower quartiles.
- The mean deviation is a measure of the average amount by which the values in a distribution differ from the arithmetic mean.
- The standard deviation, which is the square root of the variance, is the most important measure of dispersion used in statistics. Make sure you understand how to calculate the standard deviation of a set of data.
- The spreads of two distributions can be compared using the coefficient of variation.
- Skewness is the asymmetry of a frequency distribution curve.

Quick quiz

1 State a formula for the arithmetic mean of a frequency distribution.

2 Define the mode.

3 Explain how to estimate the mode from a histogram of a distribution.

4 Define the median.

5 How is the median of a grouped frequency distribution estimated?

6 What are quantiles?

7 When calculating the mean deviation for grouped data, to where should the deviations be measured?

8 Why are the differences between the value and the mean squared in the formula for the standard deviation?

9 Give a formula for the variance of data in a frequency distribution.

10 Define the coefficient of variation of a distribution.

11 Distinguish between positive skewness and negative skewness.

Answers to activities

1 Mean = $\dfrac{\text{Sum of values of items}}{\text{Number of items}}$

Sum of first 10 units = 5 × 10 = 50 kg

Sum of second 10 units = 7 × 10 = 70 kg

Sum of third 20 units = 20 × X = 20X

Sum of all 40 units = 50 + 70 + 20X = 120 + 20X

$$\therefore \text{ Arithmetic mean} = 8 = \frac{120 + 20X}{40}$$

$$\therefore \quad 8 \times 40 = 120 + 20X$$

$$320 - 120 = 20X$$

$$10 = X$$

2 The mid-point of the range 'under £60' is assumed to be £55 and that of the range over £110 to be £115, since all other class intervals are £10. This is obviously an approximation which might result in a loss of accuracy; nevertheless, there is no better alternative assumption to use. Because wages can vary in steps of only 1p, they are virtually a continuous variable and hence the mid-points of the classes are halfway between their end points.

Mid-point of class x £	*Frequency* f	*fx*
55	3	165
65	11	715
75	16	1,200
85	15	1,275
95	10	950
105	8	840
115	6	690
	69	5,835

Arithmetic mean = $\dfrac{£5{,}835}{69}$ = £84.57

3 The times can be arranged as follows.

11	15	17	17	17	18	20	20	21
21	23	24	24	24	27	29	30	37

The median = 21 mins. (We could have found the average of the 10th and 11th items if we had wanted to.)

4 (a) $\bar{x}_1 = \dfrac{72}{8} = 9$

The figures have a mean of 9 and a range of 24 – 3 = 21.

(b) $\bar{x}_2 = \dfrac{72}{8} = 9$

The figures have a mean of 9 and a range of 11 – 7 = 4.

The set of data x_1 is more widely dispersed than the set of data x_2.

NOTES

5

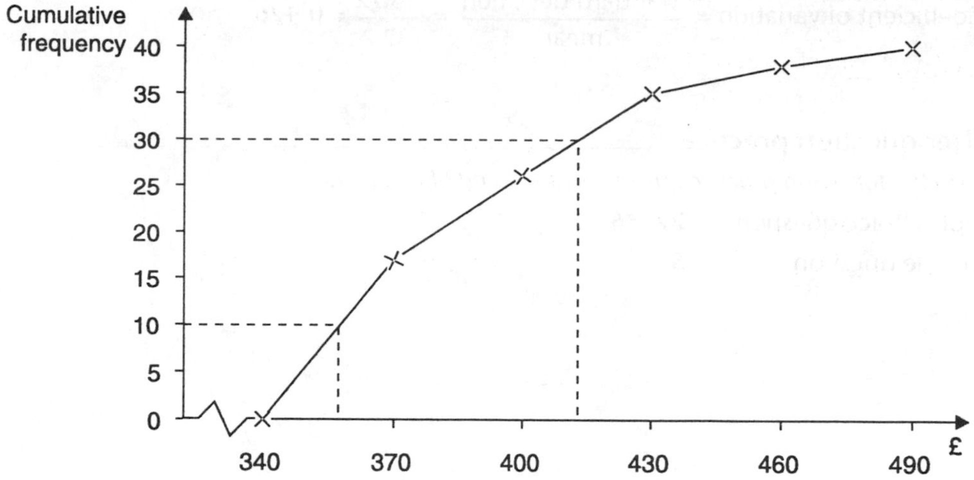

The upper quartile is the $\frac{3}{4} \times 40$ = 30th value.

The lower quartile is the $\frac{1}{4} \times 40$ = 10th value.

Reading off from the ogive these values are at approximately £358 and £412 respectively.

6

x	f	fx	$\lvert x - \bar{x} \rvert$	$f\lvert x - \bar{x} \rvert$
5	4	20	27.2	108.8
15	6	90	17.2	103.2
25	8	200	7.2	57.6
35	20	700	2.8	56.0
45	6	270	12.8	76.8
55	6	330	22.8	136.8
	50	1,610		539.2

Arithmetic mean $\bar{x} = \frac{1,610}{50} = 32.2$

Mean deviation = $\frac{539.2}{50}$ = 10.784, say 10.8.

7

x	f	x^2	fx^2
5	4	25	100
15	6	225	1,350
25	8	625	5,000
35	20	1,225	24,500
45	6	2,025	12,150
55	6	3,025	18,150
	50		61,250

$\bar{x}$ = 32.2 (from Activity 6)

Variance = $\frac{61,250}{50} - (32.2)^2 = 188.16$

Standard deviation = $\sqrt{188.16} = 13.72$

NOTES

8 Coefficient of variation = $\frac{\text{standard deviation}}{\text{mean}} = \frac{13.72}{32.2} = 0.426$

Further question practice

Now try the following practice questions at the end of this text.

Multiple choice questions **27–36**

Exam style question **5**

Chapter 6

PROBABILITY

Introduction

We are now going to move away from the collection, presentation and analysis of data and look at a new topic area, probability. This chapter will demonstrate how vital the role of probability is in business operations and planning and will explain the various techniques for assessing probability. In Chapter 7 we will build upon the basics learnt in this chapter and look at probability distributions. Chapter 8 will expand on one of the probability distributions introduced in Chapter 7, the normal distribution.

Your objectives

After completing this chapter you should:

(a) understand the concept of probability;

(b) know the difference between and be able to calculate permutations and combinations;

(c) be able to apply the laws of probability;

(d) be able to use Venn diagrams;

(e) understand and be able to use expected values;

(f) understand the difference between prior and posterior probabilities.

1 UNCERTAINTY

1.1 Mrs Cracked is responsible for product development at Lovely Lips Ltd, a cosmetics company. She has recently been working hard to perfect 'Perky Pink', a copy of the lipstick that Luscious, the number one pop star of the moment, is rumoured to be going to wear on her forthcoming world tour. She is naturally very upset to read in the music press that Luscious may be cancelling her world tour.

1.2 Although she reckons that this rumour may only have a 40% chance of being true, it presents her with a difficult choice. Sales of Perky Pink are estimated to be 10,000 units, each earning a profit of £1. This projection was, however, based on the assumption of Luscious going on her world tour. If this is not the case, Mrs Cracked reckons sales might be as low as 1,000 units. She is therefore forced to consider abandoning the project now, although £3,000 has already been invested in it.

1.3 To make matters worse, the marketing director then rings to let her know that Lovely Lips Ltd's arch competitor, Kissable and Co, may be planning to launch a similar colour lipstick which would sell for less and would cut Lovely Lips Ltd's sales to 6,000 units. Admittedly the marketing director estimates that the chance of Kissable and Co launching their product is only 50–50 but the possibility must still be taken into account.

1.4 Mrs Cracked and Lovely Lips Ltd therefore have two alternatives: to abandon Perky Pink altogether, or to go ahead and market the lipstick regardless of whether the tour goes ahead or not and take the risk that Kissable and Co will bring out its own product.

1.5 Such a scenario is typical of situations facing countless organisations everyday. Ideally the business community would know with certainty what was going to happen. The real world is, however, not normally so helpful! The future is uncertain. People running organisations must therefore be able to tackle and take account of this uncertainty. They must understand what '50–50' means, what 'a 40% chance' means. They must be able to evaluate choices by quantifying the 'expected' or 'most likely' future results and, in addition, be able to make some attempt to quantify the possible variations.

1.6 There are a number of ways of analysing uncertainty. Underlying all of these methods is, however, one concept: probability. An understanding of the concept of probability is vital if you are to take account of uncertainty.

2 THE CONCEPT OF PROBABILITY

2.1 'The likelihood of rain this afternoon is fifty percent' warns the weather report from your radio alarm clock. 'There's no chance of you catching that bus' grunts the helpful soul as you puff up the hill. The headline on your newspaper screams 'Odds of Rainbow Party winning the election rise to one in four'.

2.2 'Likelihood' and 'chance' are expressions used in our everyday lives to denote a level of uncertainty. Probability, a word which often strikes fear into the hearts of students, is simply the mathematical term used when we need to imply a degree of uncertainty.

Definition

Probability is a measure of likelihood and can be stated as a percentage, a ratio, or more usually as a number between 0 and 1.

NOTES

2.3 Zero probability corresponds to impossibility, whereas a probability of 1 corresponds to certainty. A 50% chance of something happening is a probability of ½. A chance of 1 in 4 is equivalent to a probability of ¼ and we express 'there's no chance of catching the bus' as P(catching the bus) = 0.

2.4 In statistics, probabilities are more commonly expressed as proportions than as percentages: for example, if there are six possible different outcomes in a certain situation, the probabilities might be expressed as follows.

Possible outcome	*Probability as a percentage*	*Probability as a proportion*
A	15.0%	0.150
B	20.0%	0.200
C	32.5%	0.325
D	7.5%	0.075
E	12.5%	0.125
F	12.5%	0.125
	100.0%	1.000

2.5 It is useful to consider how probability can be quantified. A businessman might estimate that if the selling price of a product is raised by 20p, there would be a 90% probability that demand would fall by 30%, but how would he have reached his estimate of 90% probability?

2.6 There are several ways of assessing probabilities.

(a) They may be measurable with mathematical certainty.

(i) If a coin is tossed, there is a 0.5 probability that it will come down heads, and a 0.5 probability that it will come down tails.

(ii) If a die is thrown, there is a one-sixth probability that a 6 will turn up.

(b) They may be measurable from an analysis of past experience. For example, suppose that an analysis of the last 300 working days shows that on 180 days there were no machine breakdowns. Given no change in the average reliability of machinery, we would therefore be able to estimate that the probability of no machine breakdowns during a day is 180/300 = 0.6 (so the probability of at least one breakdown during the day must be 0.4).

(c) Probabilities can be estimated from research or surveys. For example, a new product might be test-marketed in selected trial areas, and from the results of the test it might be estimated that there is a 70% chance that demand would be sufficient to earn a satisfactory profit for the company if the product were sold nationally.

2.7 A final introductory point about probability is that it is a measure of the likelihood of an event happening in the long run, or over a large number of times. If we toss a coin eight times, we cannot predict that it will necessarily come down heads four times and tails four times. The coin may come down heads eight times, or not once in the eight throws; heads may occur any number of times between zero and eight. We can say, however, that in the long run heads will occur about 50% of the time if a coin is tossed a sufficiently large number of times.

3 PERMUTATIONS AND COMBINATIONS

3.1 The theory of permutations and combinations is an important tool in probability theory.

Definition

A *combination* is a set of items, selected from a larger collection of items, regardless of the order in which they are selected.

3.2 We refer to the number of possible combinations of x items from n items. For example, suppose that five people apply for two vacancies as junior administrators in Combo Ltd and these people are called A, B, C, D and E. The different possible combinations of people to fill the two posts from the five applicants would be AB, AC, AD, AE, BC, BD, BE, CD, CE and DE.

Definition

A *permutation* is a set of items, selected from a larger group of items, in which the order of selection or arrangement is significant.

3.3 We refer to the number of possible permutations of x items from n items. In the previous example, suppose that the two vacancies were for the post of senior administrator and junior administrator. The order of selection would be important and the possible permutations would be as follows.

Senior	*Junior*	*Senior*	*Junior*	*Senior*	*Junior*	*Senior*	*Junior*
A	B	B	C	C	D	D	E
A	C	B	D	C	E	E	A
A	D	B	E	D	A	E	B
A	E	C	A	D	B	E	C
B	A	C	B	D	C	E	D

Whereas there were 10 combinations of two from five, there are 20 permutations of two from five.

The formula for the number of permutations

3.4 There is a formula to calculate the number of permutations of x items which are possible from a set of n items. The number is denoted by the term ^nP_x and the formula is

$$^nP_x = \frac{n!}{(n-x)!}$$

The notation here is as follows.

n! is the factorial of n ($1 \times 2 \times 3 \times 4 \times 5 \times \ldots \times n$), eg $3! = 1 \times 2 \times 3$

(n – x)! is the factorial of the difference between n and x, eg $(5-3)! = 2! = 1 \times 2$

EXAMPLE: PERMUTATIONS

(a) In the previous example of five candidates for two different jobs, as described in Paragraph 3.3, the number of different permutations would be

$$^5P_2 = \frac{5!}{(5-2)!} = \frac{5\times4\times3\times2\times1}{3\times2\times1} = 5\times4 = 20$$

(b) 0! is defined to equal 1.

For example, suppose that an investment manager must rank three projects, A, B and C, in order of profitability. How many possible ways are there of ordering them 1st, 2nd and 3rd?

$$^3P_3 = \frac{3!}{0!} = 3\times2\times1 = 6$$

(The permutations are ABC, ACB, BCA, BAC, CBA and CAB.)

The formula for the number of combinations

3.5 There is also a formula to calculate the number of combinations of x items which are possible from a set of n items. This formula is

$$^nC_x = \frac{n!}{(n-x)!x!}$$

(The notation ^nC_x means 'the number of different combinations of x items from a set of n items'.)

EXAMPLE: COMBINATIONS

(a) In the example in Paragraph 3.2 of five candidates applying for two jobs of equal status, the number of possible combinations of two applicants would be

$$^5C_2 = \frac{5!}{3!2!} = \frac{5\times4\times3\times2\times1}{(3\times2\times1)(2\times1)} = \frac{5\times4}{2\times1} = 10$$

(b) The number of ways of choosing a work team of four people from a total number of only four people available would be

$$^4C_4 = \frac{4!}{0!4!} = 1$$

NOTES

EXAMPLE: COMBINATIONS OF ONE OR TWO ITEMS

A hardware storekeeper sells paint which he mixes himself in pairs to get the right colours. If we assume that by mixing two of the basic paints he always gets a colour different to any of the other mixtures and different to any of the basic colours, how many different shades can he obtain by stocking n basic paints? (Note. Any one basic paint itself counts as one shade.)

Solution

The total number of mixtures (combinations) of two paints will be:

$$^{n}C_2 = \frac{n!}{(n-2)!2!} = \frac{n \times (n-1)}{2 \times 1} = \frac{n^2 - n}{2}$$

If we add to this the number of paints stocked, n, (which are themselves different shades) we get a total of

$$\frac{n^2 - n}{2} + n$$

Activity 1

A class of 15 students is about to sit a statistics examination. They will subsequently be listed in descending order by reference to the marks scored. Assume that there are no tied positions with two or more students having the same mark.

Required

Calculate the following.

(a) The number of different possible orderings for the whole class

(b) The number of different possible results for the top three places

(c) The number of different possible ways of having three people taking the top three places (irrespective of order)

4 THE LAWS OF PROBABILITY

4.1 It is the year 2020 and examiners are extinct. A mighty but completely fair computer churns out examinations that are equally likely to be easy or difficult. There is no link between the number of questions on each paper, which is arrived at on a fair basis by the computer, and the standard of the paper. You are about to take five examinations.

Simple probability

4.2 It is vital that the first examination is easy as it covers a subject which you have tried, but unfortunately failed, to understand. What is the probability that it will be an easy examination?

4.3 Obviously (let us hope), the probability of an easy paper is ½ (or 50% or 0.5). This reveals a very important principle (which holds if each result is equally likely).

NOTES

Probability of achieving the desired result

$$= \frac{\text{Number of ways of achieving desired result}}{\text{Total number of possible outcomes}}$$

Let us apply the principle to our example.

Total number of possible outcomes = 'easy' or 'difficult' = 2

Total number of ways of achieving the desired result (which is 'easy') = 1

The probability of an easy examination, or P(easy examination) = ½

EXAMPLE: SIMPLE PROBABILITY

Suppose that a coin is tossed in the air. What is the probability that it will come down heads?

Solution

$$\text{P(heads)} = \frac{\text{Number of ways of achieving desired result (heads)}}{\text{Total number of possible outcomes (heads or tails)}}$$

= ½ or 50% or 0.5.

Complementary outcomes

4.4 You are desperate to pass more of the examinations than your sworn enemy but, unlike you, he is more likely to pass the first examination if it is difficult. (He is very strange!!) What is the probability of the first examination being more suited to your enemy's requirements?

4.5 We know that the probability of certainty is 1. The certainty in this scenario is that the examination will be easy or difficult.

P(easy or difficult examination)	=	1
From Paragraph 4.3, P(easy examination)	=	½
P(not easy examination)	=	P(difficult examination)
	=	1 – P(easy examination)
	=	1 – ½
	=	½

4.6 In general, $P(\overline{X}) = 1 - P(X)$, where $\overline{X}$ is 'not X'.

EXAMPLE: COMPLEMENTARY OUTCOMES

If there is a 25% chance of the Rainbow Party winning the next general election, use the law of complementary outcomes to calculate the probability of the Rainbow Party *not* winning the next election.

Solution

P(winning)	=	25% = ¼
P(not winning)	=	1 – P(winning) = 1 – ¼ = ¾

NOTES

The simple addition or OR law

4.7 The time pressure in the second examination is enormous. The computer will produce a paper which will have between five and nine questions. You know that, easy or difficult, the examination must have six questions at the most for you to have any hope of passing it.

What is the probability of the computer producing an examination with six or fewer questions? In other words, what is the probability of an examination with five *or* six questions?

4.8 Don't panic. Let us start by using the basic principle.

$$P(5 \text{ questions}) = \frac{\text{Total number of ways of achieving a five-question examination}}{\text{Total number of possible outcomes } (= 5,6,7,8 \text{ or } 9 \text{ questions})}$$

$$= \frac{1}{5}$$

Likewise $P(6 \text{ questions}) = \frac{1}{5}$

Either five questions or six questions would be acceptable, so the probability of you passing the examination must be greater than if just five questions or just six questions (but not both) were acceptable. We therefore add the two probabilities together so that the probability of passing the examination has increased.

4.9 So $P(5 \text{ or } 6 \text{ questions}) = P(5 \text{ questions}) + P(6 \text{ questions})$

$$= \frac{1}{5} + \frac{1}{5} = \frac{2}{5}$$

In general, the simple addition or OR law is:

$P(X \text{ or } Y \text{ or } Z) = P(X) + P(Y) + P(Z)$

where X, Y and Z are *mutually exclusive outcomes*, which means that the occurrence of one of the outcomes excludes the possibility of any of the others happening. In the example the outcomes are mutually exclusive because it is impossible to have five questions and six questions in the same examination.

Venn diagram representation

4.10 You may find it useful to consider a Venn diagram representation of the simple addition/OR law.

4.11 In terms of a Venn diagram, mutually exclusive outcomes are presented as follows.

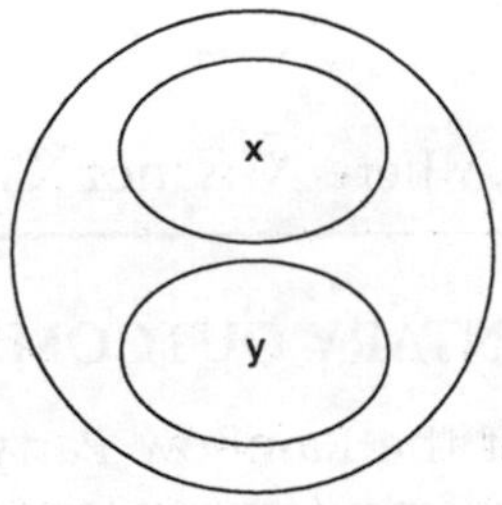

Figure 6.1 A Venn diagram of the simple addition/OR law.

4.12 If outcomes are mutually exclusive, the probability that one of them will occur (and, by definition, it is not possible for more than one of them to occur) is the sum of their individual probabilities. In terms of a Venn diagram this is represented by the fact that the probability of the union (one outcome or the other outcome or both outcomes) of two non-overlapping outcomes is the sum of their individual probabilities. Thus if X and Y are mutually exclusive outcomes, we have $P(X \text{ or } Y) = P(X) + P(Y)$.

This extends immediately to any number of outcomes.

NOTES

EXAMPLE: MUTUALLY EXCLUSIVE OUTCOMES

The delivery of an item of raw material from a supplier may take up to six weeks from the time the order is placed. The probabilities of various delivery times are as follows.

Delivery time	*Probability*
≤1 week	0.10
>1 week <2 weeks	0.25
>2 weeks <3 weeks	0.20
>3 weeks <4 weeks	0.20
>4 weeks <5 weeks	0.15
>5 weeks <6 weeks	0.10
	1.00

What is the probability that a delivery will take the following times?

(a) Two weeks or less

(b) More than three weeks

Solution

(a) $P(\leq 1 \text{ or } >1 \leq 2 \text{ weeks}) = P(\leq 1 \text{ week}) + P(>1 \leq 2 \text{ weeks})$
$= 0.10 + 0.25$
$= 0.35$

(b) $P(>3 \leq 6 \text{ weeks}) = P(>3 \leq 4 \text{ weeks}) + P(>4 \leq 5 \text{ weeks}) + P(>5 \leq 6 \text{ weeks})$
$= 0.20 + 0.15 + 0.10$
$= 0.45$

The simple multiplication or AND law

4.13 You still have three examinations to sit: astrophysics, geography of the moon and computer art. Stupidly, you forgot to revise for the astrophysics examination, which will have between 15 and 20 questions. You think that you may scrape through this paper if it is easy and if there are only 15 questions.

What is the probability that the paper the computer produces will exactly match your needs? Do not forget that there is no link between the standard of the examination and the number of questions.

4.14 The best way to approach this question is diagrammatically, showing all the possible outcomes.

	Number of questions					
	15	*16*	*17*	*18*	*19*	*20*
Type of paper						
Easy (E)	E and 15*	E and 16	E and 17	E and 18	E and 19	E and 20
Difficult (D)	D and 15	D and 16	D and 17	D and 18	D and 19	D and 20

The diagram shows us that, of the twelve possible outcomes, there is only one 'desired result' (which is asterisked). We can therefore calculate the probability as follows.

P(easy paper *and* 15 questions) = $\frac{1}{12}$

NOTES

4.15 The answer can be found more easily as follows.

P(easy paper and 15 questions) = P(easy paper) × P(15 questions) = $\frac{1}{2} \times \frac{1}{6} = \frac{1}{12}$

4.16 In general, the simple multiplication or AND law is:

P(X and Y) = P(X) P(Y)

where X and Y are *independent* events: whether it is an easy or difficult paper has no effect on the number of questions.

EXAMPLE: INDEPENDENT EVENTS

A die is thrown and a coin is tossed simultaneously. What is the probability of throwing a 5 and getting heads on the coin?

Solution

The probability of throwing a 5 on a die is $\frac{1}{6}$.

The probability of a tossed coin coming up heads is $\frac{1}{2}$.

The probability of throwing a 5 and getting heads on a coin is $\frac{1}{2} \times \frac{1}{6} = \frac{1}{12}$.

The general rule of addition

4.17 The three examinations you still have to sit are placed face down in a line in front of you at the final examination sitting. There is an easy astrophysics paper, a difficult geography of the moon paper and a difficult computer art paper. Without turning over any of the papers you are told to choose one of them. What is the probability that the first paper that you select is difficult or is the geography of the moon paper?

4.18 Let us think about this carefully.

There are two difficult papers, so P(difficult) = $\frac{2}{3}$.

There is one geography of the moon paper, so P(geography of the moon) = $\frac{1}{3}$.

4.19 If we use the OR law and add the two probabilities then we will have double-counted the difficult geography of the moon paper. It is included in the set of difficult papers and in the set of geography of the moon papers. In other words, we are *not* faced with mutually exclusive outcomes because the occurrence of a geography of the moon paper does not exclude the possibility of the occurrence of a difficult paper. We therefore need to take account of this double counting.

P(difficult paper or geography of the moon paper) = P(difficult paper) + P(geography of the moon paper) – P(difficult paper and geography of the moon paper).

Using the AND law, P(difficult paper or geography of the moon paper)

$= \frac{2}{3} + \frac{1}{3} - (\frac{1}{3}) = \frac{2}{3}$

NOTES

4.20 In general, the general rule of addition is:

P(X or Y) = P(X) + P(Y) – P(X and Y)

where the word 'or' is used in an inclusive sense: either X or Y or both. X and Y are therefore *not* mutually exclusive: it is *not* impossible to have an examination which is difficult *and* about the geography of the moon.

Venn diagram representation

4.21 Suppose we want to make a representation of the general addition law. We have the possibility that X and Y will both occur at the same time. If we were to add together the probability of the outcomes in X (difficult papers) with the probability of the outcomes in Y (geography of the moon paper) we shall have included twice over the probabilities of the outcomes common to both X and Y (difficult geography of the moon papers).

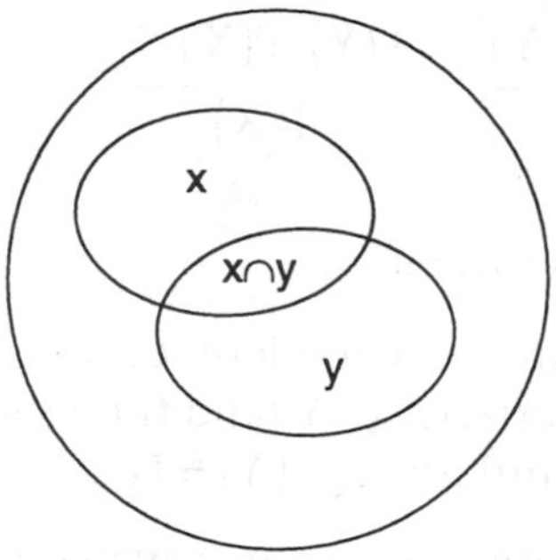

Figure 6.2 A Venn diagram of the general addition law

4.22 The probability of the simultaneous occurrence of an outcome in X and Y must therefore be subtracted out.

This gives $P(X \cup Y) = P(X) + P(Y) - P(X \cap Y)$

Note. For union ($\cup$) read 'or', that is an outcome in X or Y or both.

For intersection ($\cap$) read 'and', that is an outcome in X and Y.

Activity 2

If one card is drawn from a normal pack of 52 playing cards, what is the probability of getting an ace or a spade?

The general rule of multiplication

4.23 Computer art is your last examination. Understandably you are very tired and you are uncertain whether you will be able to stay awake. You believe that there is a 70% chance of your falling asleep if it becomes too hot and stuffy in the examination hall. It is well known that the air conditioning system serving the examination hall was installed in the 1990s and is therefore extremely unreliable. There is a 1 in 4 chance of it breaking down during the examination, thereby causing the temperature in the hall to rise. What is the likelihood that you will drop off?

4.24 The scenario in Paragraph 4.23 has led us to face what is known as conditional probability. We can rephrase the information provided as 'the probability that you will fall asleep, given that it is too hot and stuffy, is equal to 70%' and we can write this as follows.

P(fall asleep | too hot and stuffy) = 70%

NOTES

4.25 Whether you fall asleep is conditional upon whether the hall becomes too hot and stuffy. The events are not, therefore, independent and so we cannot use the simple multiplication law. So:
P(it becomes too hot and stuffy and you fall asleep)
= P(too hot and stuffy) × P(fall asleep | too hot and stuffy)
= 25% × 70% = 0.25 × 0.7 = 0.175 = 17.5%

4.26 In general, if X and Y are two outcomes, then the probability that X and Y will occur is:

$$P(X \text{ and } Y) = P(X) \times P(Y \mid X)$$
$$= P(Y) \times P(X \mid Y)$$

where X and Y are *dependent* events.

4.27 We can rearrange the rule above as follows.

$$P(Y \mid X) = \frac{P(X \text{ and } Y)}{P(X)} = \frac{P(Y)\ P(X \mid Y)}{P(X)}$$

This is called Bayes's theorem.

4.28 When X and Y are independent events, then P(Y | X) = P(Y) since, by definition, the occurrence of Y (and therefore P(Y)) does not depend upon the occurrence of X. Similarly P(X | Y) = P(X).

4.29 For example, suppose that a company plans to sell 12 new products next year, seven electrical products and five non-electrical products. Of the total of 12 products, two electrical and three non-electrical products are expected to make a profit.

If X is the event that the product is electrical and Y is the event that the product is profitable, then P(Y | X) is the probability that the product, given that it is electrical, is also profitable.

$$\text{This is } \frac{P(X \text{ and } Y)}{P(X)} = \frac{2/12}{7/12} = \frac{2}{7} = 0.286$$

EXAMPLE: CONDITIONAL PROBABILITIES

The estimated probability that the labour force in a factory will improve its productivity over both of the next two years is 0.6. It is also thought that there is a 0.8 probability that productivity will improve in the first year.

Given that productivity does rise in the first year, what is the probability that productivity will also rise in the second year?

Solution

Let outcome X = an increase in productivity in Year 1

Let outcome Y = an increase in productivity in Year 2

$$P(Y \mid X) = \frac{P(X \text{ and} Y)}{P(X)}$$

$$= \frac{0.6}{0.8}$$

$$= 0.75$$

NOTES

Venn diagram representation

4.30 The general rule of multiplication can also be built up using Venn diagrams.

4.31 Suppose we are looking at the probability of event X, given that another event Y has occurred (P(X | Y)).

We know that event Y has occurred and given this fact, we want to know the probability of occurrence of event X. Because event Y has occurred, the only outcomes that can have occurred are those in event Y. Hence the only way X can occur is if the outcome is in both X and Y, that is an outcome in $X \cap Y$.

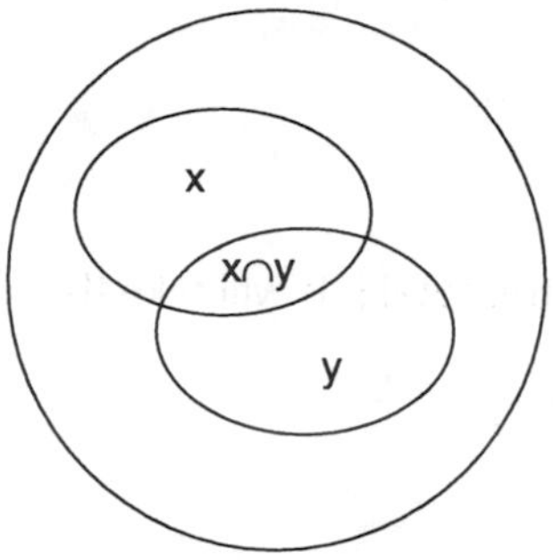

Figure 6.3 Venn diagram of the general rule of multiplication

The chance of this happening is the chance of an $X \cap Y$ outcome as a proportion of all the possible Y outcomes which might have occurred. Hence the conditional probability of X given Y is $P(X \mid Y) = P(X \cap Y) \div P(Y)$.

Since $P(X \cap Y)$ is P(X and Y) we can rearrange this to P(X and Y) = P(Y) P(X | Y).

See paragraph 4.22 for a definition of $\cap$.

Activity 3

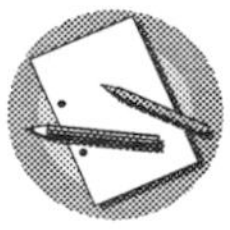

The independent probabilities that the three sections of a management accounting department will encounter one computer error in a week are respectively 0.1, 0.2 and 0.3. There is never more than one computer error encountered by any one section in a week. Calculate the probability that there will be the following number of errors encountered by the management accounting department next week.

(a) At least one computer error

(b) One and only one computer error

Activity 4

A glass bottle manufacturer has three inspection points: one for size, the second for colour and the third for flaws such as cracks and bubbles in the glass. The probability that each inspection point will incorrectly accept or reject a bottle is 0.02.

Required

Calculate the following probabilities.

(a) A perfect bottle will be passed through all inspection points.

(b) A bottle faulty in colour and with a crack will be passed through all inspection points.

(c) A bottle faulty in size only will be passed through all inspection points.

NOTES

Activity 5

Two accountants work together to prepare some costings for inclusion in a report to senior management. Both start work on the same day, and each has a different set of tasks to perform. The possible times required by each person to do his part of the job are as follows.

Accountant X		*Accountant Y*	
Time Days	*Probability*	*Time Days*	*Probability*
6	0.2	6	0.1
8	0.5	8	0.4
10	0.3	10	0.5

What is the probability that the total job will take the following number of days?

(a) 6 days

(b) 8 days

(c) 10 days

5 VENN DIAGRAMS AND PROBABILITY

5.1 It is possible to use Venn diagrams to solve probability problems. For example if there are two outcomes they can be depicted by two overlapping circles, one for each outcome. The known probabilities can be filled in, then the unknown probabilities can be derived from the fact that all the probabilities on the diagram must add up to 1.

NOTES

EXAMPLE: VENN DIAGRAMS

Two outcomes are denoted by M and N. $\overline{M}$ (or M') denotes 'not M' and $\overline{N}$ denotes 'not N'. The following probabilities are given.

P(M) = 0.50 P(M and N) = 0.15 P($\overline{M}$ and $\overline{N}$) = 0.10

Required

Calculate P(N).

Solution

We can draw a Venn diagram with a circle for each outcome, M and N.

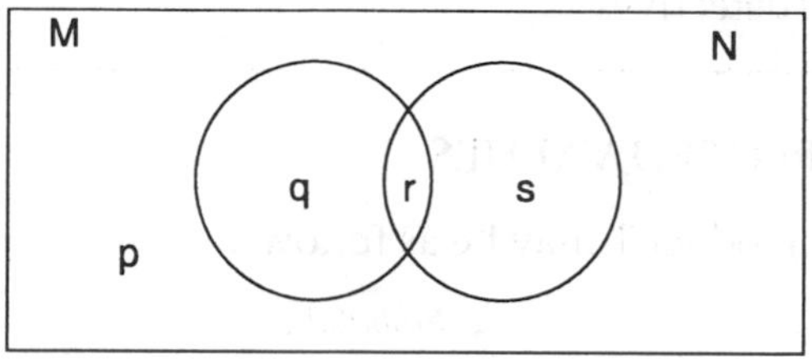

The given probabilities are as follows.

P(M)	=	q + r	= 0.50
P(M and N)	=	r	= 0.15
P($\overline{M}$ and $\overline{N}$)	=	p	= 0.10

We want to know P(N), which is equal to r + s. We therefore need to deduce s.

$$p + (q + r) + s = 1.00$$
$$0.10 + 0.50 + s = 1.00$$
$$s = 1.00 - 0.10 - 0.50 = 0.40$$
$$P(N) = r + s = 0.15 + 0.40$$
$$= 0.55$$

Activity 6

A food company is introducing a new flavour to its range of yoghurts and stops 120 customers at random in a supermarket and asks their opinions about three new flavours, strawberry (S), raspberry (R) and vanilla (V). It discovers the following.

Number who like S	49
Number who like V	25
Number who like R	67
Number who like S and R	12
Number who like S and V	15
Number who like R and V	13
Number who like all three	7

Determine the following probabilities.

(a) A customer who likes exactly one flavour

(b) A customer who likes none of the flavours

NOTES

6 EXPECTED VALUES

Definition

An *expected* value (or EV) is a weighted average value, based on probabilities.

6.1 If the probability of an outcome of an event is p, then the expected number of times that this outcome will occur in n events (the expected value) is equal to $n \times p$.

6.2 For example, suppose that the probability that a transistor is defective is 0.02. How many defectives would we expect to find in a batch of 4,000 transistors?

EV = $4{,}000 \times 0.02$

= 80 defectives

EXAMPLE: EXPECTED VALUES

The daily sales of Product T may be as follows.

Units	*Probability*
1,000	0.2
2,000	0.3
3,000	0.4
4,000	0.1
	1.0

Required

Calculate the expected daily sales.

Solution

The EV of daily sales may be calculated by multiplying each possible outcome (volume of daily sales) by the probability that this outcome will occur.

Units	*Probability*		*Expected value Units*
1,000	0.2		200
2,000	0.3		600
3,000	0.4		1,200
4,000	0.1		400
		EV of daily sales	2,400

In the long run the expected value should be approximately the actual average, if the event occurs many times over. In the example above, we do not expect sales on any one day to equal 2,400 units, but in the long run, over a large number of days, average sales should equal 2,400 units a day.

Expected values and single events

6.3 The point made in the example above is an important one. An expected value can be calculated when the event will only occur once or twice, but it will not be a true long-run average of what will actually happen, because there is no long run.

NOTES

6.4 Suppose, for example, that a businessman is trying to decide whether to invest in a project. He estimates that there are three possible outcomes.

Outcome	*Profit/(loss)*	*Probability*
	£	
Success	10,000	0.2
Moderate success	2,000	0.7
Failure	(4,000)	0.1

The expected value of profit may be calculated as follows.

Profit/(loss)	*Probability*	*Expected value*
£		£
10,000	0.2	2,000
2,000	0.7	1,400
(4,000)	0.1	(400)
	Expected value of profit	3,000

6.5 In this example, the project is a one-off event, and, as far as we are aware, it will not be repeated. The actual profit or loss will be £10,000, £2,000 or £(4,000), and the average value of £3,000 will not actually happen. There is no long-run average of a single event.

6.6 Nevertheless, the expected value can be used to help the manager decide whether or not to invest in the project. All other things being equal a project with a positive EV (an expected value which is a profit) should be accepted, and a project with a negative EV (an expected value which is a loss) should be rejected.

6.7 Provided that we understand the limitations of using expected values for single events, they can offer a helpful guide for management decisions, and suggest to managers whether any particular decision is worth the risk of taking (subject, of course, to reasonable accuracy in the estimates of the probabilities themselves).

Activity 7

A company manufactures and sells product D. The selling price of the product is £6 per unit, and estimates of demand and variable costs of sales are as follows.

Probability	*Demand*	*Probability*	*Variable cost per unit*
Units		£	
0.3	5,000	0.1	3.00
0.6	6,000	0.3	3.50
0.1	8,000	0.5	4.00
		0.1	4.50

The unit variable costs do not depend on the volume of sales.

Fixed costs will be £10,000.

Required

Calculate the expected profit.

6.8 The expected value is summarised in equation form as follows.

$$E(x) = \Sigma x P(x)$$

This is read as 'the expected value of x is equal to the sum of the products of each value of x and the corresponding probability of that value of x occurring'.

NOTES

The expected value of a probability

6.9 You might be required to calculate a weighted average probability of an event occurring: an EV of a probability. Consider the following example.

EXAMPLE: THE EXPECTED VALUE OF PROBABILITY

A salesman has three small areas to cover, areas A, B and C. He never sells more than one item per day, and the probabilities of making a sale when he visits each area are as follows.

Area	*Probability*
A	30%
B	25%
C	10%

He visits only one area each day. He visits Area A as often as he visits Area B, but he only visits Area C half as often as he visits Area A.

Required

(a) Calculate the probability that on any day he will visit Area C.

(b) Calculate the probability that he will make a sale on any one day.

(c) Calculate the probability that if he does make a sale, it will be in Area A.

Solution

(a) The probabilities of visiting each area are obtained from the ratios in which he visits them.

Area	*Ratio*	*Probability*
A	2	0.4
B	2	0.4
C	1	0.2
	5	1.0

The probability that he will visit Area C is 0.2.

(b) The probability of making a sale on any one day is found as follows.

Area	*Probability of a sale*	*Probability of visiting area*	*EV of probability of a sale*
	x	p	px
A	0.30	0.4	0.12
B	0.25	0.4	0.10
C	0.10	0.2	0.02
			0.24

The probability of making a sale is 0.24 or 24%.

(c) The probability of making a sale is 0.24 and the probability that the sale will be in Area A rather than B or C can be established as follows.

$$\frac{\text{EV of probability of sale in A}}{\text{EV of probability of sale in A, B or C}} = \frac{0.12}{0.24} = 0.5.$$

One half of all sales will be made in Area A.

7 PRIOR AND POSTERIOR PROBABILITIES

7.1 Consider a situation in which we are considering the sex and hair colour of people in a given group or population consisting of 70% men and 30% women. We have established the probabilities of hair colourings as follows.

	Men	*Women*
Brown	0.60	0.35
Blonde	0.35	0.55
Red	0.05	0.10

These probabilities of sex and hair colouring might be referred to as prior probabilities, to distinguish them from posterior probabilities.

Posterior probabilities consider the situation in reverse or retrospect, so that we can ask the question: 'Given that a person taken at random from the population is brown haired, what is the probability that the person is male (or female)?'

7.2 Posterior probabilities can be established by drawing a probability tree as follows.

Figure 6.4 A probability tree

The probability of being a man, given that a person is brown haired is

$$\frac{\text{Probability of being a man and brown haired}}{\text{Probability of being a man or woman and brown haired}} = \frac{0.42}{0.42 + 0.105}$$

$$= \frac{0.42}{0.525} = 0.80$$

EXAMPLE: POSTERIOR PROBABILITIES

As another example of the same type of computation, suppose that two machines produce the same product. The older machine produces 35% of the total output but eight units in every 100 are defective. The newer machine produces 65% of the total output but two units in every 100 are defective.

Determine the probability that a defective unit picked at random was produced by the older machine.

Solution

We want to establish the posterior probability that, given a defective unit, it was produced by the older machine.

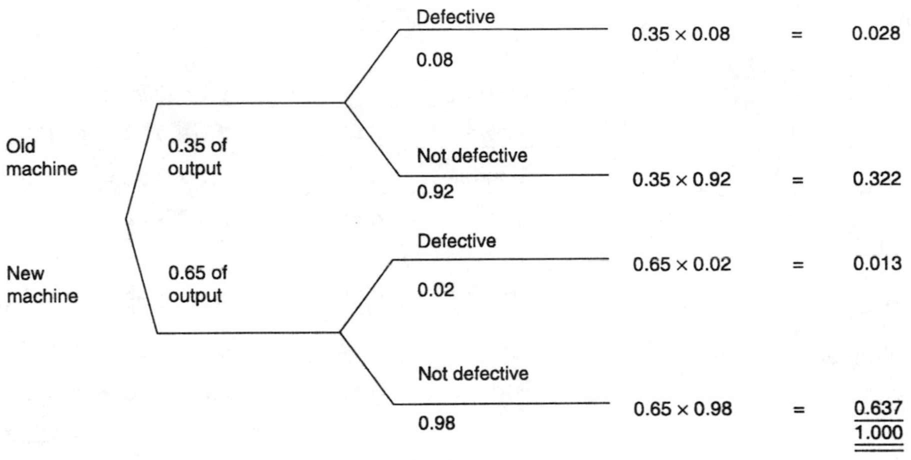

The probability of a defective unit being from the older machine is

$$\frac{0.028}{(0.028+0.013)} = 0.683$$

We could alternatively have used Bayes's theorem (see Paragraph 4.27), as follows.

Let X be a unit's being defective.

Let Y be a unit's having come from the older machine.

$P(Y) = 0.35$

$P(X \mid Y) = 0.08$

$P(X) = (0.35 \times 0.08) + (0.65 \times 0.02) = 0.041$

$$\text{Then } P(Y \mid X) = \frac{P(Y)\,P(X|Y)}{P(X)} = \frac{0.35 \times 0.08}{0.041} = 0.683$$

NOTES

Chapter roundup

- In this chapter we introduced the concept of uncertainty in the business environment and explained that a knowledge of probability is vital if uncertainty is to be analysed.
- We introduced a number of terms and rules, which we have summarised below, and which you must be able to explain and use as appropriate.
- A combination is a set of items selected from a larger collection of items, regardless of the order in which they are selected.
- A permutation is a set of items selected from a larger group of items, in which the order of selection or arrangement is significant.
- Mutually exclusive outcomes are outcomes where the occurrence of one of the outcomes excludes the possibility of any of the others happening.
- Independent events are events where the occurrence of one event in no way affects the outcome of the other events.
- Dependent or conditional events are events where the occurrence of one event depends on the occurrence of the others.
- The addition laws for two events, X and Y, are as follows.

  P(X or Y) = P(X) + P(Y) when X and Y are mutually exclusive outcomes.

  P(X or Y) = P(X) + P(Y) – P(X and Y) when X and Y are independent events.

  The multiplication laws for two events, X and Y, are as follows.

  P(X and Y) = 0 when X and Y are mutually exclusive outcomes.

  P(X and Y) = P(X) P(Y) when X and Y are independent events.

  P(X and Y) = P(X) P(Y | X)

  = P(Y) P(X | Y) when X and Y are dependent/conditional events.
- Bayes's theorem is used to calculate the conditional probability of an outcome.
- An expected value (EV) is a weighted average, based on probabilities.
- Ensure that you can differentiate between prior and posterior probabilities.
- This chapter has introduced some important topics that underpin later chapters. Make sure you are happy with all the concepts before moving on.

Quick quiz

1 What is the difference between a combination of items and a permutation of items?

2 State the formula for the number of combinations of x items from a set of n items.

3 Define mutually exclusive outcomes, independent events and dependent events.

4 What is the formula for the conditional probability of Y given X?

5 How would you calculate the expected value of a probability distribution?

NOTES

Answers to activities

1 (a) The number of different possible orderings of the whole class is

$$^{15}P_{15} = \frac{15!}{(15-15)!} = \frac{15!}{0!} = 15!$$

(b) The number of different possible results for the top three places is given by the number of permutations of three out of 15.

$$^{15}P_{3} = \frac{15!}{(15-3)!} = \frac{15!}{12!} = 15 \times 14 \times 13 = 2{,}730$$

(c) The number of ways of having three people taking the top three places is given by the number of combinations of three out of 15.

$$^{15}C_{3} = \frac{15!}{(15-3)!\,3!} = \frac{15\times14\times13}{3\times2\times1} = 455$$

2 $P(\text{ace}) = \frac{4}{52}$

$P\ (\text{spade}) = \frac{13}{52}$

$P(\text{ace of spades}) = \frac{1}{52}$

$\therefore P(\text{ace or spades}) = \frac{4}{52} + \frac{13}{52} - \frac{1}{52} = \frac{16}{52} = \frac{4}{13}$

3 (a) The probability of at least one computer error is 1 minus the probability of no error. The probability of no error is $0.9 \times 0.8 \times 0.7 = 0.504$.

(Since the probability of an error is 0.1, 0.2 and 0.3 in each section, the probability of no error in each section must be 0.9, 0.8 and 0.7 respectively.)

The probability of at least one error is $1 - 0.504 = 0.496$.

(b) Y = yes, N = no

		Section 1	*Section 2*	*Section 3*
(i)	Error?	Y	N	N
(ii)	Error?	N	Y	N
(iii)	Error?	N	N	Y

			Probabilities
(i)	$0.1 \times 0.8 \times 0.7$	=	0.056
(ii)	$0.9 \times 0.2 \times 0.7$	=	0.126
(iii)	$0.9 \times 0.8 \times 0.3$	=	0.216
		Total	0.398

The probability of only one error only is 0.398.

4 The probability of incorrect testing is 0.02 at each stage, and so the probability of correct testing is 0.98.

(a) A perfect bottle has a 98% probability of passing each stage, and so its probability of passing all three stages is $0.98 \times 0.98 \times 0.98 = 0.941192$.

(b) A bottle faulty in colour and with a crack must pass three stages.

Size: probability 0.98

Colour: probability 0.02

Flaws: probability 0.02

Probability of passing $= 0.98 \times 0.02 \times 0.02 = 0.000392$

(c) A bottle faulty in size only must pass three stages.

Size: probability 0.02

Colour: probability 0.98

Flaws: probability 0.98

Probability of passing $= 0.02 \times 0.98 \times 0.98 = 0.019208$

5

X Days		*Y* Days				
P(6	and	6)	=	0.2×0.1	=	0.02
P(6	and	8)	=	$0.2 \times 0.4 = 0.08$		
P(8	and	8)	=	$0.5 \times 0.4 = 0.20$	=	0.33
P(8	and	6)	=	$0.5 \times 0.1 = 0.05$		
P(10)			=	P(A = 10) + P(B = 10) – P (A and B = 10)		
				$0.3 + 0.5 - (0.3 \times 0.5)$	=	0.65
						1.00

(a) The probability of 6 days is 2%

(b) The probability of 8 days is 33%

(c) The probability of 10 days is 65%

6

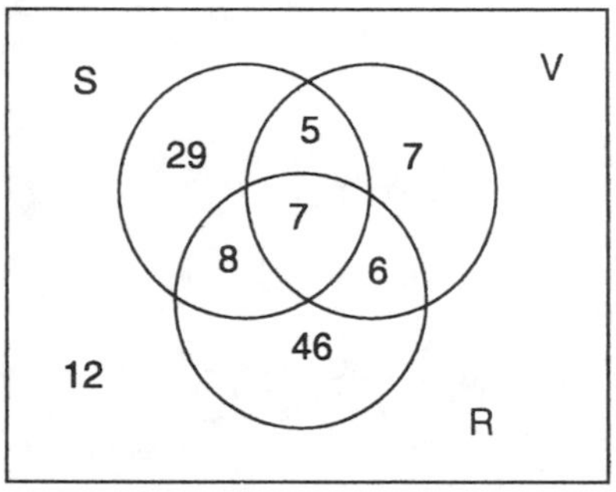

The figures are found by entering the 7 who like all three flavours first, then finding the numbers who like any two as balancing figures (for example, S, R not V = 12 – 7 = 5), then finding the number who like only one, and finally the number who like none.

(a) $\text{P(likes exactly one flavour)} = \dfrac{29+7+46}{120} = 0.683$

(b) $\text{P(likes no flavour)} = \dfrac{(120-(29+5+7+8+7+6+46))}{120} = 0.1$

7 The EV of demand is as follows.

Demand *Units*	*Probability*		*Expected value* *Units*
5,000	0.3		1,500
6,000	0.6		3,600
8,000	0.1		800
		EV of demand	5,900

The EV of the variable cost per unit is as follows.

Variable costs £	*Probability*		*Expected value* £
3.00	0.1		0.30
3.50	0.3		1.05
4.00	0.5		2.00
4.50	0.1		0.45
		EV of unit variable costs	3.80

		£
Sales	5,900 units × £6.00	35,400
Less variable costs	5,900 units × £3.80	22,420
Contribution		12,980
Less fixed costs		(10,000)
Expected profit		2,980

NOTES

Further question practice

Now try the following practice questions at the end of this text.

Multiple choice questions	**37–44**
Exam style question	**6**

Chapter 7

PROBABILITY DISTRIBUTIONS

Introduction

In Chapter 6 we looked at the calculation and interpretation of probability and uncertainty. This chapter begins by examining probability distributions in general. The importance of probability distributions is that they extend the areas to which probability can be applied and they provide a method of arriving at the probability of an event without having to go through all of the probability rules examined in the previous chapter. We will then turn our attention to three probability distributions and the ways in which they can be used in practice.

The normal distribution, one of the probability distributions examined in this chapter, is the basis for the topics looked at in Chapter 8.

Your objectives

After completing this chapter you should:

(a) understand the difference between a frequency distribution and a probability distribution;

(b) know when and how to use the binomial distribution;

(c) know when and how to use the Poisson distribution;

(d) know the circumstances in which the normal distribution applies;

(e) understand the significance of the standard deviation to normal distributions;

(f) be able to use normal distribution tables;

(g) be able to apply the continuity correction.

NOTES

1 PROBABILITY DISTRIBUTIONS

1.1 A frequency distribution gives an analysis of the number of times each particular value occurs in a set of items. A probability distribution simply replaces actual numbers (frequencies) with proportions of the total. For example, in a statistics test, the marks out of 10 awarded to 50 students might be as follows.

Marks out of 10	*Number of students (frequency distribution)*	*Proportion or probability (probability distribution)*
0	0	0.00
1	0	0.00
2	1	0.02
3	2	0.04
4	4	0.08
5	10	0.20
6	15	0.30
7	10	0.20
8	6	0.12
9	2	0.04
10	0	0.00
	50	1.00

Definition

A *probability distribution* analyses the proportion of times each value occurs in a set of items.

1.2 A graph of the probability distribution would be the same as the graph of the frequency distribution, but with the vertical axis marked in proportions rather than in numbers. In our example, this would be as follows.

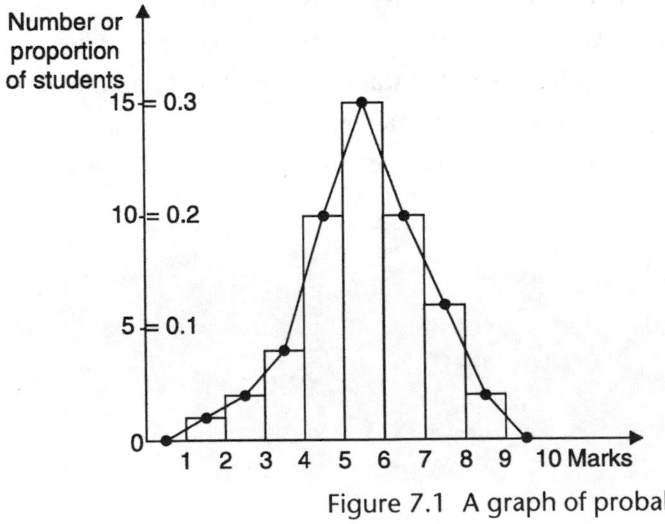

Figure 7.1 A graph of probability distribution

1.3 The area under the curve in the frequency distribution represents the total number of students whose marks have been recorded, 50 people. The area under the curve in a probability distribution is 100%, or 1 (the total of all the probabilities).

1.4 In this chapter, we shall look at three types of distribution commonly found in business applications.

(a) The binomial distribution

(b) The Poisson distribution

(c) The normal distribution

1.5 The binomial and Poisson distributions describe the behaviour of *attributes* (success or failure, good or bad, black or white and so on) while the normal distribution describes the behaviour of variables. The binomial and Poisson are *discrete* distributions whereas the normal distribution is *continuous*.

2 THE BINOMIAL DISTRIBUTION

Definition

The *binomial distribution* can be derived from a situation which involves the repetition of an event which has only two possible outcomes such as success or failure, win or lose, late or not late and so on. Each repetition (or trial) must be independent. For example, whether a coin comes down heads or tails on a second toss is entirely independent of whether it was heads or tails on a first toss.

In n independent trials of an event (tossing a coin, rolling a die), each of which has the same probability of success, p, and the same probability of failure, q = 1 – p, a binomial distribution will indicate the probability that one of the results (either p or q depending on the situation in question) will occur a certain number of times within the total of n.

EXAMPLE: A BINOMIAL DISTRIBUTION

Suppose, for example, that a coin is tossed twice. The probability of the coin coming down as heads is 0.5 on each throw, and the probability of tails is also 0.5. In two throws, the possible results will be as follows.

First toss		*Second toss*		*Probability*
P (heads	and	heads)	0.5×0.5	0.25
P (heads	and	tails)	0.5×0.5	0.25
P (tails	and	heads)	0.5×0.5	0.25
P (tails	and	tails)	0.5×0.5	0.25
				1.00

The probabilities are a binomial distribution for the toss of a coin twice.

EXAMPLE: ANOTHER BINOMIAL DISTRIBUTION

If a coin is tossed three times, the possible outcomes are as follows.

	First toss	*Second toss*	*Third toss*	*Probability*
3 heads	H	H	H	*0.125
2 heads	H	T	H	
	H	H	T	**0.375
	T	H	H	
1 head	H	T	T	
	T	H	T	**0.375
	T	T	H	
0 heads	T	T	T	*0.125
				1.000

* $(0.5 \times 0.5 \times 0.5)$
** $3 \times (0.5 \times 0.5 \times 0.5)$
The right-hand column gives the binomial distribution for three tosses of the coin.

NOTES

2.1 If an experiment is performed n times then the probability of x successes is given by

$$P(x) = \frac{n!}{x!(n-x)!} p^x q^{n-x}$$

where p = the probability of success in a single trial
q = the probability of failure in a single trial
q = 1 – p

The first part of the expression, $\frac{n!}{x!(n-x)!}$ is the formula for the number of combinations ^nC_x.
The formula could therefore be re-written as $P(x) = {}^nC_x\, p^x (1-p)^{n-x}$

EXAMPLE: TOSSING A COIN

A coin is tossed five times. What are the various results which might occur (that is, x heads and (5 – x) tails) and what is the probability of each result?

Solution

Let P(x) = the probability that x heads occurs.

The probability of heads is 0.5 (= p) and the probability of tails is 0.5 (= q = 1 – p).

No of heads	*No of tails*			*Probability*
5	0	$P(0) = \frac{5!}{5!0!} (0.5)^5 (0.5)^0$	=	0.03125
4	1	$P(1) = \frac{5!}{4!1!} (0.5)^4 (0.5)^1$	=	0.15625
3	2	$P(2) = \frac{5!}{3!2!} (0.5)^3 (0.5)^2$	=	0.31250
2	3	$P(3) = \frac{5!}{2!3!} (0.5)^2 (0.5)^3$	=	0.31250
1	4	$P(4) = \frac{5!}{1!4!} (0.5)^1 (0.5)^4$	=	0.15625
0	5	$P(5) = \frac{5!}{0!5!} (0.5)^0 (0.5)^5$	=	0.03125
				1.00000

NOTES

EXAMPLE: PROBABILITIES OTHER THAN 0.5

A company is planning to sell a new product in four areas, North, South, East and West. The probability that the product will be successful in an area is 0.3. Success in one area will be independent of success or failure in the other areas.

Required

Calculate the probability of success in no area, one area, two areas, three areas or four areas.

Solution

The probabilities are p = 0.3 and q = 0.7. The number of areas, four, gives us our value for n.

Number of successes				*Probability*
P(0)	=	$\frac{4!}{0!4!}(0.3)^0(0.7)^4$	=	0.2401
P(1)	=	$\frac{4!}{1!3!}(0.3)^1(0.7)^3$	=	0.4116
P(2)	=	$\frac{4!}{2!2!}(0.3)^2(0.7)^2$	=	0.2646
P(3)	=	$\frac{4!}{3!1!}(0.3)^3(0.7)^1$	=	0.0756
P(4)	=	$\frac{4!}{4!0!}(0.3)^4(0.7)^0$	=	0.0081
				1.0000

Activity 1

The demand for an item of raw material is usually less than 10 units per month, but there is a 10% probability that demand in one month will be 10 units or more.

Calculate the following probabilities for a six-month period.

(a) Demand will equal or exceed 10 units in two of the six months.

(b) Demand will equal or exceed 10 units in three of the six months.

(c) Demand will equal or exceed 10 units in at least two months.

NOTES

The mean and the standard deviation of a binomial distribution

2.2 The arithmetic mean of a binomial distribution is np. (This is the same as the expected value, or EV.)

The standard deviation of a binomial distribution = $\sqrt{npq} = \sqrt{np(1-p)}$

The variance of a binomial distribution is therefore npq = np (1–p)

Although the mean and standard deviation can be calculated using normal techniques, these formulae are considerably more convenient. The next paragraph shows that the two methods produce the same result.

2.3 Consider the example of three tosses of a coin (see example following Paragraph 2.1). If x is the number of heads and f is the probability of the result occurring, the mean and the standard deviation could be calculated as follows.

No. of heads	*Probability* *f*	*fx*	*fx²*
0	0.125	0.000	0.000
1	0.375	0.375	0.375
2	0.375	0.750	1.500
3	0.125	0.375	1.125
	1.000	1.500	3.000

$\bar{x} = \frac{\Sigma fx}{\Sigma f} = \frac{1.5}{1} = 1.5$. This is also the *expected value* of the number of heads.

$s = \sqrt{[3.000/1 - 1.5^2]} = \sqrt{0.75} = 0.866$

The mean is 1.5 heads in the three tosses of a coin, with a standard deviation of 0.866 heads.

2.4 The same results could have been obtained more quickly using the formulae as follows.

Mean = np = 3 × 0.5 = 1.5

Standard deviation = $\sqrt{npq} = \sqrt{3 \times 0.5 \times 0.5} = \sqrt{0.75} = 0.866$.

The binomial distribution and quality inspection schemes

2.5 Binomial distributions are quite commonly found, since they usefully describe any situation in which we are considering the likelihood of something either happening or else not happening. Binomial distributions are therefore often applied to quality control sampling for defectives and the next example is of this nature.

EXAMPLE: QUALITY INSPECTION SCHEME

The quality control department of Woof Ltd checks 12 squeaky bones from each batch of 500 produced. The batch of bones is rejected if more than three defective bones are found. In fact, 10% of all bones are defective.

Required

Calculate the probability that a batch of bones will be rejected.

Solution

A batch will be rejected if 4, 5, 6, 7, 8, 9, 10, 11 or 12 bones in the sample are defective.

One method of calculating the rejection probability is to find the probability of those numbers of defective bones and add the probabilities together.

A quicker method is to find the probabilities of 0, 1, 2 or 3 defectives, add them together and deduct the total probability from 1.

We are dealing with a binomial distribution with n = 12 and p = 0.10

$$P(3\text{ defectives}) = \frac{12!}{3!9!}(0.1)^3(0.9)^9 = 0.085$$

$$P(2\text{ defectives}) = \frac{12!}{2!10!}(0.1)^2(0.9)^{10} = 0.230$$

$$P(1\text{ defective}) = \frac{12!}{1!11!}(0.1)^1(0.9)^{11} = 0.377$$

$$P(0\text{ defectives}) = \frac{12!}{0!12!}(0.1)^0(0.9)^{12} = 0.282$$

$$\underline{\underline{0.974}}$$

Hence P(3 or fewer defectives) = P(0) + P(1) + P(2) + P(3) = 0.974

So P(batch rejected) = P(more than 3 defectives) = 1 – 0.974 = 0.026

We can expect just 2.6% of the batches of squeaky bones to be rejected by this sampling scheme.

Activity 2

A product is tested in batches of 15 as it comes off a production line. It is estimated that 10% of the product is defective. Determine the probability that in a batch:

(a) none are defective;

(b) one is defective;

(c) more than two are defective.

NOTES

3 THE POISSON DISTRIBUTION

Definition

The *Poisson distribution* is used in the following situations.

(a) Where events occur *randomly* (that is, they are independent of each other) within an interval, for example defects in a length of rope, or cars arriving at a junction in an hour

(b) As an approximation to the binomial distribution, when n is large (say 50 or more) and p is small (say 0.1 or less). These conditions are, however, only a guide

Like the binomial distribution the Poisson distribution is *discrete*: when we estimate the probability P(x), the probability of an event happening no times at all, once, twice, or whatever, x must be a whole number.

3.1 There is a formula which can be used to calculate P(x).

$$P(x) = \frac{m^x}{x!} e^{-m}$$

where	P(x)	is the probability of an event occurring x times
	m	is the expected, or average number of times an event occurs per unit of time (or space)
	e	is a special constant whose value is approximately 2.71828. This is universally available via your scientific calculator.
	x	= 0, 1, 2, 3, ...

The mean of a Poisson distribution is obviously m and the standard deviation is $\sqrt{m}$.

3.2 When a Poisson distribution is used to approximate a binomial distribution, m equals np, which is the mean of a binomial distribution.

Applications of the Poisson distribution

3.3 The examples and activity that follow illustrate applications of the Poisson distribution. Remember, however, that the Poisson distribution only applies when *events occur randomly*.

EXAMPLE: THE OCCURRENCE OF RANDOM EVENTS

The mean number of calls received on a telephone per hour is 1.6.

Required

Calculate the following probabilities.

(a) Exactly two calls will be received in an hour

(b) More than two calls will be received in an hour

(c) Exactly five calls will be received in a three-hour period

Solution

(a) $P(2) = \frac{1.6^2}{2!} e^{-1.6} = 0.2584$

(b) $P(>2) = 1 - (P(0) + P(1) + P(2))$

$= 1 - (0.2019 + 0.3230 + 0.2584)$

NOTES

EXAMPLE *continued*

$= 1 - 0.7833$

$= 0.2167$

(c) P(5 in 3 hours)

If the mean per hour is 1.6, the mean per three hours is $3 \times 1.6 = 4.8$.

Therefore P (5 in 3 hours) =

$$\frac{4.8^5}{5!}e^{-4.8} = \frac{2{,}548.0397}{120} \times \frac{1}{121.5104}$$

$= 0.1747$

EXAMPLE: THE POISSON DISTRIBUTION AS A APPROXIMATION TO THE BINOMIAL DISTRIBUTION

Transistors are packed in boxes of 1,000. On average 0.1% will be defective.

Required

Calculate the proportion of boxes which will contain the following number of defectives.

(a) 0 defectives

(b) 1 defective

(c) 2 defectives

(d) 3 or more defectives

Solution

The binomial distribution applies, with $n = 1{,}000$ and $np = 1{,}000 \times 0.001 = 1$.

Since n is large and p is small, the Poisson distribution will be used as an approximation to the binomial distribution. Any error will be small, and a lot of computational work will be saved.

(a) $P(0) = \frac{m^0}{0!}e^{-m} = \frac{1^0}{0!}e^{-1} = e^{-1} = 0.3679$

(b) $P(1) = \frac{1^1}{1!}e^{-1} = e^{-1} = 0.3679$

(c) $P(2) = \frac{1^2}{2!}e^{-1} = \frac{1}{2}(0.36788) = 0.1839$

(d) P(3 or more) $= 1 - P(0) - P(1) - P(2)$

$= 1 - 0.3679 - 0.3679 - 0.1839$

$= 0.0803$

Activity 3

The mean number of invoices received by a company on any one day is 2.6. What is the probability that seven invoices will be received over a two-day period?

Acceptance sampling and the Poisson distribution

3.4 Acceptance sampling is a statistical method of deciding whether or not to accept a batch of items received from an outside supplier. It is most appropriate for low cost components bought and used in large quantities, such as transistors, because n will be very large and the probability of defectives should be very small.

EXAMPLE: ACCEPTANCE SAMPLING

Hitech Electronics buy transistors in huge quantities from Jap Components. From past experience they know that in an average batch of 100,000 transistors approximately 0.1% are defective. They wish to design a quality control procedure so that a batch with a higher percentage of defectives will be rejected and returned to Jap Components.

Suppose that a reasonable sample to test is 1,000 or 1%. The mean number of defectives in a sample of this size is $m = 1{,}000 \times 0.001 = 1$.

For $m = 1$, we have the following.

	Probabilities	*Cumulative probabilities*
P(0)	0.3679	0.3679
P(1)	0.3679	0.7358
P(2)	0.1839	0.9197
P(3)	0.0613	0.9810

From the cumulative probabilities it can be seen that the probability of finding three or fewer defectives is 0.9810 or 98.1%. Consequently the probability of finding four or more defectives is 1.9%. Hitech might well decide to adopt the rule, 'test 1,000 transistors and reject the delivery if four or more defectives are found'. This would, of course, mean rejecting 1.9% of deliveries which are satisfactory.

Now let us consider what would happen if a sub-standard batch with, say, 0.8% defectives was received. In this case $m = 1{,}000 \times 0.008 = 8$.

For $m = 8$, $e^{-m} = 0.0003354$ and we have the following probabilities.

	Probabilities	*Cumulative probabilities*
P(0)	0.0003	0.0003
P(1)	0.0027	0.0030
P(2)	0.0107	0.0137
P(3)	0.0286	0.0423

From the above figures it can be seen that there is only a 0.04 or 4% chance that a batch with 0.8% defectives will give three or fewer defectives in a sample of 1,000. In other words, only 4% of batches with this level of defectives will be accepted when they should have been returned to Jap Components.

Activity 4

Sunnyday Travel Tours organise holiday excursions. One of their regular excursions is to Malta, but the number of places on each Malta excursion is restricted to 100 tourist class passengers and 50 luxury class passengers.

Because of cancellations after bookings are made, the tour company accepts up to 104 tourist class holiday bookings for the 100 places, but will not overbook luxury class places. If there are any vacancies in luxury class places, the spare berths can be filled with tourist class customers, if more than 100 places are booked and are not subsequently cancelled.

Over the past few years, the mean number of vacant luxury class places has been 2. The numbers of tourist class customers per excursion who did not subsequently cancel their bookings have followed the following distribution.

Numbers booked and not subsequently cancelled	*Probability*
100 or more	0.25
101 or more	0.15
102 or more	0.09
103 or more	0.06
104	0.01

Required

(a) Using the Poisson distribution, and ignoring the effect of excess tourist class passengers taking luxury class places, calculate the probability that on any excursion there will be the following number of vacant luxury class places.

(i) No vacant luxury class places

(ii) At least two vacant luxury class places

(b) Assuming a Poisson distribution for the number of vacant luxury class places, calculate the probability that all the tourist class customers who book and do not subsequently cancel can be fitted into a berth on the tour, using available vacant luxury class places.

4 THE NORMAL DISTRIBUTION

Definition

The *normal distribution* is an important probability distribution of continuous variables that occurs frequently in practice. In other words, in calculating P(x), x can be any value, and does not have to be a whole number.

4.1 Examples of continuous variables include the following.

(a) The heights of people. The height of a person need not be an exact number of centimetres, but can be anything within a range of possible figures.

(b) The temperature of a room. It need not be an exact number or degrees, but can fall anywhere within a range of possible values.

4.2 The normal distribution can also apply to discrete variables which can take many possible values. For example, the volume of sales, in units, of a product might be any whole number in the range 100–5,000 units. There are so many possibilities within this range that the variable is for all practical purposes continuous.

NOTES

4.3 The normal distribution can be drawn as a graph, and it forms a bell-shaped curve.

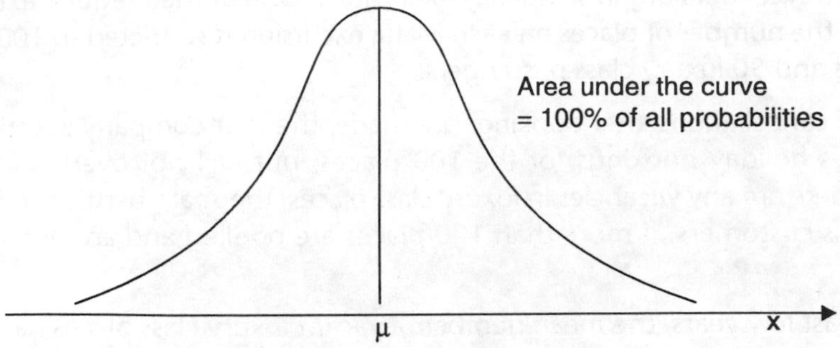

Figure 7.2 Normal distribution

4.4 The normal curve is symmetrical. The left hand side of the area under the curve to the left of μ is the mirror image of the right hand side.

μ is the mean, or average of the distribution.

Because it is a probability distribution, the area under the curve totals exactly 1.

4.5 The normal distribution is important because in the practical application of statistics, it has been found that many probability distributions are close enough to a normal distribution to be treated as one without any significant loss of accuracy.

The standard deviation and the normal distribution

4.6 For any normal distribution, the dispersion around the mean of the frequency of occurrences can be measured exactly in terms of the standard deviation.

4.7 The entire frequency curve represents all the possible outcomes and their frequencies of occurrence and the normal curve is symmetrical; therefore 50% of outcomes have a value greater than the mean value, and 50% of outcomes have a value less than the mean value.

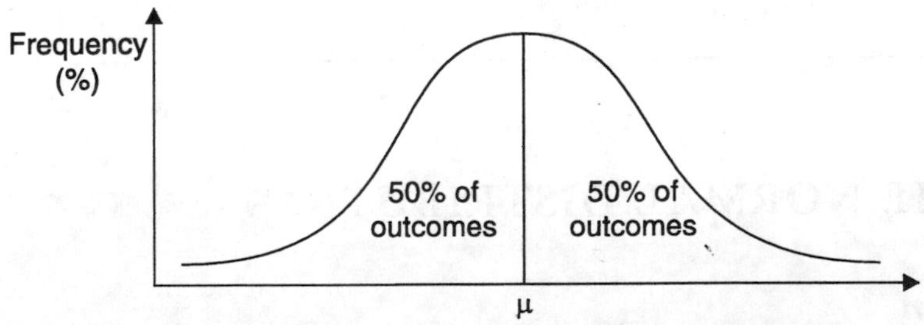

Figure 7.3 A frequency curve

4.8 About 68% of frequencies have a value within one standard deviation either side of the mean.

Thus if a normal distribution has a mean of 80 and a standard deviation of 3, 68% of the total outcomes would occur within the range ± one standard deviation from the mean, that is, within the range 77–83.

Since the curve is symmetrical, 34% of the values must fall in the range 77–80 and 34% in the range 80–83.

NOTES

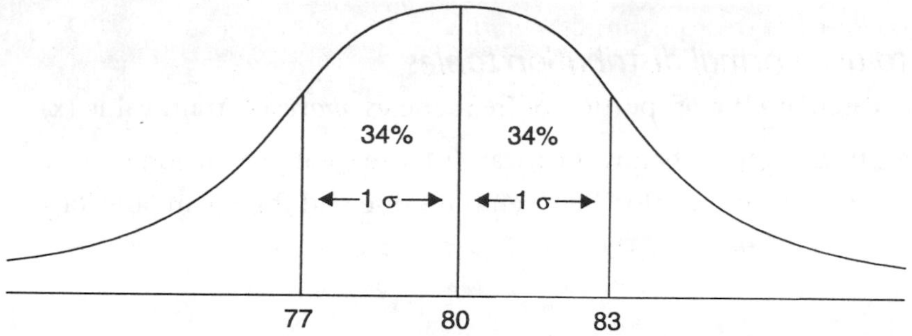

Figure 7.4 Normal distribution curve

4.9 95% of the frequencies in a normal distribution occur in the range ±1.96 standard deviations from the mean.

In our example, when $\mu = 80$, and $\sigma = 3$, 95% of the frequencies in the distribution would occur in the range

$80 \pm 1.96\ (3)$

$= 80 \pm 5.88$ (the range 74.12 to 85.88)

47.5% of outcomes would be in the range 74.12 to 80 and 47.5% would be in the range 80 to 85.88.

4.10 99% of the frequencies occur in the range ±2.58 standard deviations from the mean.

In our example, 99% of frequencies in a normal distribution with $\mu = 80$ and $\sigma = 3$ would lie in the range

$80 \pm 2.58\ (3)$

$= 80 \pm 7.74$

$= 72.26$ to 87.74.

Activity 5

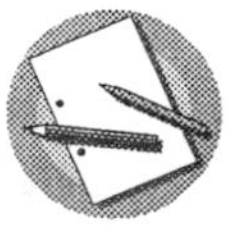

A normal distribution for daily output (in units) of workers in a factory has a mean of 50 and a standard deviation of 10. Within what range from 50 upwards would 47½ % of the frequencies fall?

Normal distribution tables

4.11 Although there is an infinite number of normal distributions, depending on values of the mean μ and the standard deviation σ, the relative dispersion of frequencies around the mean, measured as proportions of the total population, is exactly the same for all normal distributions. In other words, whatever the normal distribution, 47.5% (for example) of outcomes will always be in the range between the mean and 1.96 standard deviations below the mean.

4.12 A normal distribution table, shown at the beginning of this text, gives the proportion of the total between the mean and a point above or below the mean for any multiple of the standard deviation.

4.13 Distances above or below the mean are expressed in numbers of standard deviations z.

$$z = \frac{x - \mu}{\sigma}$$

where z = the number of standard deviations above or below the mean
x = the value of the variable under consideration
μ = the mean
σ = the standard deviation

NOTES

How to use normal distribution tables

4.14 To calculate the proportion of frequencies *above* a certain value (x):

(a) if the value is below the mean (μ), the total proportion is:
0.5 plus proportion between the value and the mean (area (a));

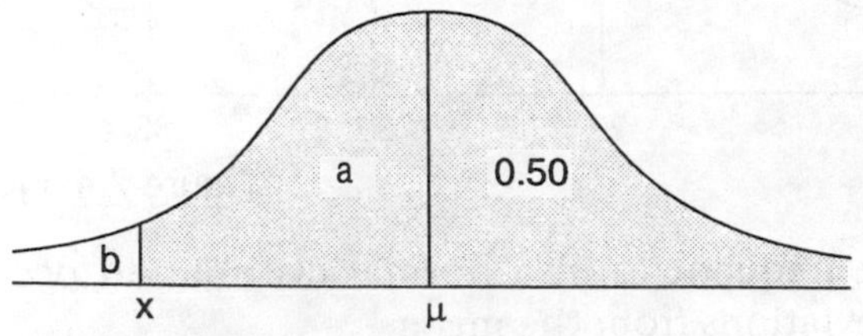

(b) if the value is above the mean, the proportion (b) is 0.5 – proportion between the value and the mean (area (a)).

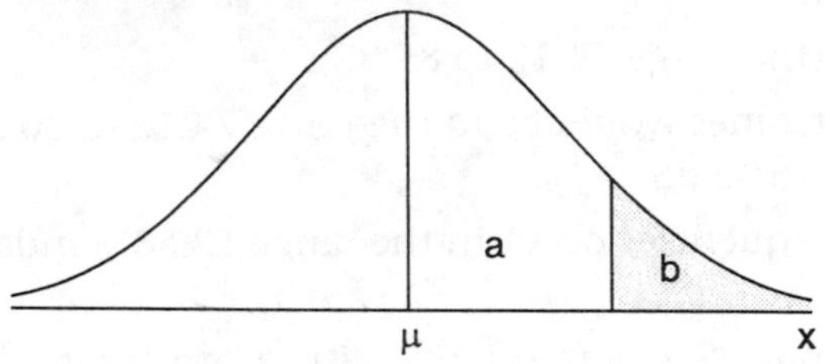

To calculate the proportion of frequencies below a certain value:

(c) if the value is below the mean, the proportion (b) is 0.5 – proportion between the value and the mean (area (a));

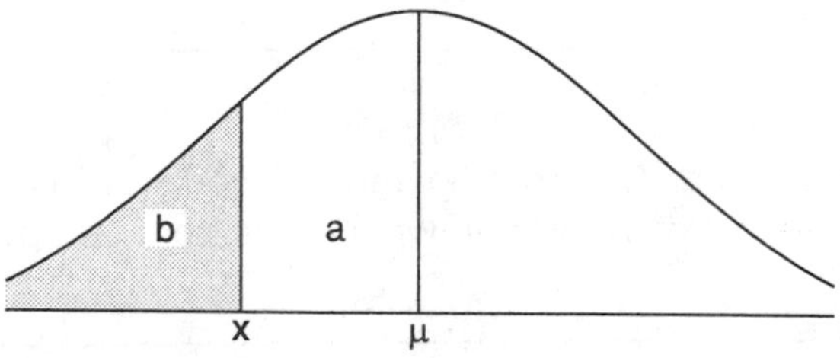

(d) if the value is above the mean, the proportion required is 0.5 plus the proportion between the value and the mean (area (a)).

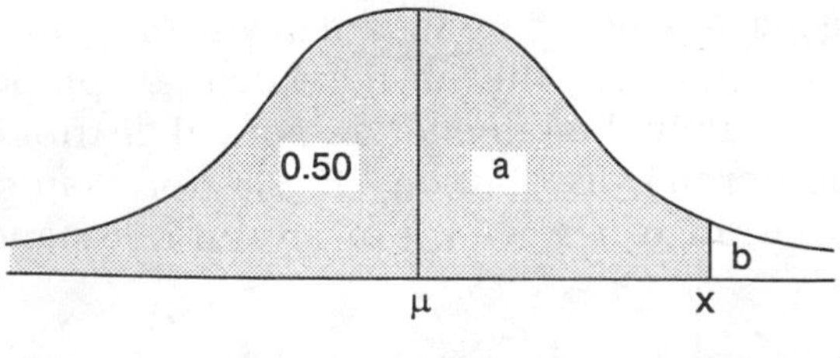

EXAMPLE: THE NORMAL DISTRIBUTION

A frequency distribution is normal, with a mean of 100 and a standard deviation of 10.

What proportion of the total frequencies will be:

(a) above 80;

(b) above 90;

(c) above 100;

(d) above 115;

(e) below 85;

(f) below 110;

(g) in the range 80 – 110;

(h) in the range 90 – 95?

Solution

(a) 80 is $\frac{100-80}{10}$ = 2 standard deviations below the mean. From the tables, where z = 2 the proportion is 0.4772.

The proportion of frequencies above 80 is 0.5 + 0.4772 = 0.9772.

(b) 90 is $\frac{100-90}{10}$ = 1 standard deviation below the mean. From the tables, when z = 1, the proportion is 0.3413.

The proportion of frequencies above 90 is 0.5 + 0.3413 = 0.8413.

(c) 100 is the mean. The proportion above this is 0.5.

(d) 115 is $\frac{115-100}{10}$ = 1.5 standard deviations above the mean. From the tables, where z = 1.5, the proportion is 0.4332.

The proportion of frequencies above 115 is therefore 0.5 – 0.4332 = 0.0668.

(e) 85 is 1.5 standard deviations below the mean. The proportion of frequencies below 85 is therefore the same as the proportion above 115, 0.0668.

(f) 110 is (110 – 100)/10 = 1 standard deviation *above* the mean. From the tables, where z = 1, the proportion is 0.3413. The proportion of frequencies *below* 110 is therefore 0.5 + 0.3413 = 0.8413.

(g) The range 80 to 110 may be divided into two parts:

(i) 80 to 100 (the mean);

(ii) 100 to 110.

The proportion in the range 80 to 100 is (2 standard deviations) 0.4772

The proportion in the range 100 to 110 is (1 standard deviation) 0.3413

The proportion in the total range 80 to 110 is 0.4772 + 0.3413 = 0.8185.

(h) The range 90 to 95 may be analysed as:

(i) the proportion above 90 and below the mean

(ii) minus the proportion above 95 and below the mean

Proportion above 90 and below the mean (1 standard deviation)	0.3413
Proportion above 95 and below the mean (0.5 standard deviations)	0.1915
Proportion between 90 and 95	0.1498

Using the normal distribution

4.15 Many distributions of variables such as lengths, weights and times follow, at least approximately, normal distributions and hence you may be faced with any number of different scenarios involving this particular probability distribution. The example and exercise which follow are indicative of normal distribution problems.

EXAMPLE: USING THE NORMAL DISTRIBUTION

Your company requires a special type of inelastic rope which is available from only two suppliers. Supplier A's ropes have a mean breaking strength of 1,000 kg with a standard deviation of 100 kg. Supplier B's ropes have a mean breaking strength of 900 kg with a standard deviation of 75kg. The distribution of the breaking strengths of each type of rope is normal. Your company requires that the breaking strength of a rope must be not less than 750 kg.

Required

Decide which rope you should buy and why.

Solution

Supplier A. 750 kg lies 250 kg below the mean which is 250/100 = 2.5 standard deviations below the mean. From tables, the probability of the breaking strength being at least 750 kg is 0.5 + 0.4938 = 0.9938.

Supplier B. 750 kg lies 150 kg below the mean, which is 150/75 = 2 standard deviations below the mean. From tables, the probability of the breaking strength being at least 750 kg is 0.5 + 0.4772 = 0.9772.

If the company is most concerned about the breaking strength not being less than 750 kg (rather than with the mean breaking strength of each supplier's rope) it would be better to purchase supplier A's rope.

Activity 6

The salaries of employees in an industry are normally distributed, with a mean of £14,000 and a standard deviation of £4,000.

(a) What proportion of employees earn less than £12,000?

(b) What proportion of employees earn between £11,000 and £19,000?

The normal distribution and measurement errors

4.16 One particular application of the normal distribution is the assessment of whether errors which have occurred in a process which provides standard measures (weight of jam in jars, volume of juice in bottles, width of individual components) are acceptable. The following example will illustrate the general approach to such problems.

NOTES

EXAMPLE: MEASUREMENT ERRORS

A machine is set to fill bags with 1 kg of flour. A member of the quality control department checks the filled bags for errors. These error recordings are known to have a normal distribution with a mean value of 0 g and a standard deviation of 25 g. The bags of flour are acceptable as long as the error lies between 62.5 g too light and 75 g too heavy.

Required

Calculate the chance that a bag of flour chosen at random is unacceptable.

Solution

The diagram below illustrates the scenario.

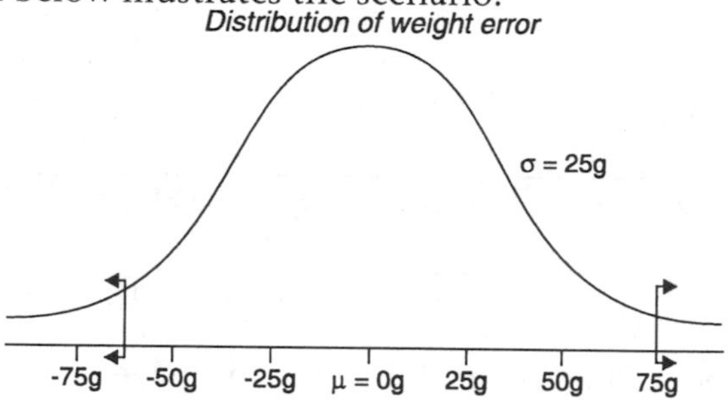

(a) We need to calculate P(error < –62.5 g)

–62.5 g is 2.5 ((62.5 – 0)/25) standard deviations below the mean.

From the tables, when z = 2.5 standard deviations above the mean, the proportion is 0.4938. The proportion of frequencies below z = 2.5 is therefore 0.5 – 0.4938 = 0.0062.

(b) We now need to calculate P(error > 75 g)

From the tables, for 3 standard deviations above the mean, the proportion is 0.49865. The proportion above z = 3 is therefore 0.5 – 0.49865 = 0.00135.

(c) Since the outcomes 'error < –62.5 g' and 'error > 75 g' are mutually exclusive, we can use the additional law:

P(error < –62.5 g or > 75 g) = P(error < –62.5 g) + P(error > 75 g) = 0.0062 + 0.00135 = 0.00755

There is therefore a 0.755% chance that a randomly chosen bag of flour will be unacceptable.

The continuity correction

4.17 When normal distributions are used for discrete variables rather than continuous variables, it is appropriate to use a continuity correction when estimating probabilities. Quite simply, what this means is that if values can only be whole numbers, 0, 1, 2, 3 and so on, then in the normal distribution, the value 0 should be represented by – 0.5 to + 0.5, 1 should be represented by 0.5 to 1.5, 2 by 1.5 to 2.5 and 3 by 2.5 to 3.5 and so on.

4.18 When the range of values of the discrete variable we are interested in is large, the continuity correction can be ignored because it will be insignificant. It ought to be used, however, when the range is small enough to make a difference of 0.5 potentially significant.

4.19 Suppose that we have a normal distribution for the number of players in a football team of 11 who have broken their leg at some time in the past, with a

NOTES

mean of 5.3 and a standard deviation of 1.2. Values are only whole numbers, since we cannot have a fraction of a player. What is the probability that in a particular football team, Mishap United, at least four players will have broken their leg at some time in the past?

4.20 We should apply the continuity correction, as follows.

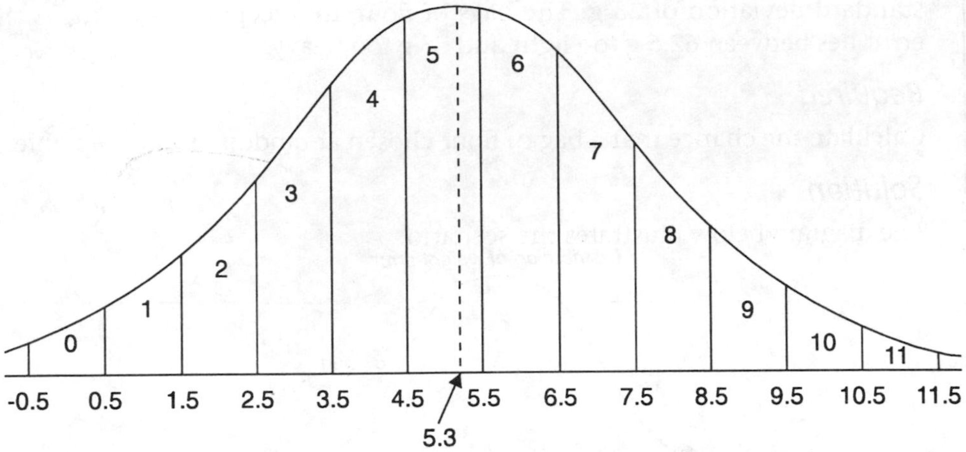

Figure 7.5 The continuity correction

The possible number of players in the team who have suffered a broken leg will range between 0 and 11 and the values 0, 1, 2, 3, 4 and so on, are represented by the ranges shown in the diagram.

The probability of at least four is the probability of exceeding 3.5.

3.5 is $(5.3 - 3.5)/1.2 = 1.5$ standard deviations below the mean.

From the table, when $z = 1.5$, $P = 0.4332$, and so the probability of four or more players having broken a leg is $0.5 + 0.4332 = 0.9332$.

The normal distribution and the binomial distribution

4.21 When n in a binomial distribution gets large, then so long as p is reasonably close to 0.5 (say 0.3–0.7) a binomial distribution approximates closely to a normal distribution. This can save a lot of work.

EXAMPLE: THE NORMAL DISTRIBUTION AS AN APPROXIMATION TO THE BINOMIAL DISTRIBUTION

The probability that a company secretary will make a mistake filling in a Companies House form is 0.3.

Required

Calculate the probability that fewer than 570 forms out of 2,000 will be in error.

Solution

Using a binomial distribution, we could make calculations as follows.

$$P(0) = \frac{2{,}000!}{0!\,2{,}000!}(0.7)^{2{,}000}(0.3)^0$$

$$P(1) = \frac{2{,}000!}{1!\,1{,}999!}(0.7)^{1{,}999}(0.3)^1$$

P(2) = ...

This would be a laborious process.

EXAMPLE *continued*

Instead, we can assume that the binomial distribution approximates closely to a normal distribution, with:

(a) a mean of np = 2,000 × 0.3 = 600

(b) a standard deviation of $\sqrt{npq} = \sqrt{2{,}000 \times 0.3 \times 0.7} = 20.49$.

We need a cut-off point for 'fewer than 570'. We will be as accurate as we can, and use 569.5. This gives z = (569.5 – 600)/20.49 = –1.49, or about 1.5 standard deviations below the mean. We want the area to the left of this, which is the same as the area to the right of z = 1.5 standard deviations above the mean.

Normal distribution tables give us the required probability:
0.5 – 0.4332 = 0.0668.

Activity 7

An analysis of a college's student register shows that 62% of all students are female. A group of 200 of the students is randomly selected. Using a suitable normal distribution as an approximation, determine the probability that the number of male students is more than 86.

Chapter roundup

- We have covered three of the most important probability distributions in this chapter. It is not always easy to recognise when a binomial, a Poisson or a normal distribution applies. The following guidelines might help.
- *The binomial distribution*

  There are two possible conditions (good/bad, black/white, male/female, acceptable/not acceptable and so on).

  Outcomes have discrete values (0, 1, 2, 3) and not continuous values (1.257)

  A probability p is given for the likelihood that an item will have one of the conditions, so that the probability of an item having the other condition is 1 – p. (1 – p) is sometimes referred to as q so that p + q = 1.

  The arithmetic mean of a binomial distribution is np and the standard deviation is √npq.
- *The Poisson distribution*

  This is similar to a binomial distribution (it is discrete), but is concerned with events occurring at random in an interval, or with rare events (small p). It can be used as an approximation to the binomial when n is large and p is small.
- *The normal distribution*

  This is the most commonly applied probability distribution. It applies to variables with a continuous range of possible values (continuous variables), such as distance and time. It provides a good approximation for a binomial distribution with large n and p fairly close to 0.5.

NOTES

Quick quiz

1 What is the formula for the binomial distribution?

2 What are the formulae for the mean and standard deviation of a binomial distribution?

3 When is the Poisson distribution a good approximation to the binomial distribution?

4 What is the formula for the Poisson distribution?

5 What is the value of e to use in the Poisson formula?

6 What is the value of the standard deviation of a Poisson distribution?

7 When is the normal distribution a good approximation to the binomial distribution?

8 Explain when the continuity correction should be used with the normal distribution.

Answers to activities

1 (a) Let the probability of demand equalling or exceeding 10 units be p, and the probability of demand being less than 10 units be q.

$p = 0.1, q = 0.9$

$$P(2) = \frac{6!}{2!4!}(0.1)^2(0.9)^4 = 0.0984$$

(b) $$P(3) = \frac{6!}{3!3!}(0.1)^3(0.9)^3 = 0.01458$$

(c) $P(\geq 2) = 1 - [P(0) + P(1)]$

$$P(0) = \frac{6!}{0!6!}(0.1)^0(0.9)^6 = 0.5314$$

$$P(1) = \frac{6!}{1!5!}(0.1)^1(0.9)^5 = 0.3543$$

$P(\geq 2) = 1 - 0.5314 - 0.3543 = 0.1143$

2 $n = 15, p = 0.1$

(a) $$P(0) = \frac{15!}{0!15!} 0.1^0\, 0.9^{15} = 0.21$$

(b) $$P(1) = \frac{15!}{1!14!} 0.1^1\, 0.9^{14} = 0.34$$

(c) $P(> 2) = 1 - P(0,1,2)$

$$P(2) = \frac{15!}{2!13!} 0.1^2\, 0.9^{13} = 0.27$$

$\therefore P(>2) = 1 - (0.21 + 0.34 + 0.27) = 0.18$

3 Mean per two days $= 2.6 \times 2 = 5.2$

$$P(7 \text{ over 2 days}) = \frac{5.2^7}{7!}e^{-5.2} = 0.1125$$

4 (a) We have $m = 2$.

$P(0) = \frac{2^0}{0!}e^{-2}$	$= e^{-2}$	$= \frac{1}{2.71828^2}$	=	0.1353
$P(1) = \frac{2^1}{1!}e^{-2}$	$= 2e^{-2}$		=	0.2707
			=	0.4060
P(2 or more)		= balancing figure		0.5940
				1.0000

NOTES

(i) The probability of no vacant luxury class places is 0.1353.

(ii) The probability of at least two vacant places is 0.5940.

(b) We want to know the probability that the tour company will not end up with more customers than places because of overbooking. There will be too many customers when the following combinations occur.

Luxury class places		*Tourist class places*
50	+	101 or more
49	+	102 or more
48	+	103 or more
47	+	104

Luxury class places

Probability of	50 places and 0 vacancies	=	P(0) = 0.1353
	49 places	=	P(1) = 0.2707
	48 places	=	$P(2) = \frac{2^2}{2!}e^{-2} = 0.2707$
	47 places	=	$P(3) = \frac{2^3}{3!}e^{-2} = 0.1804$

The probability distribution of tourist class numbers is given in the problem.

The probability of having too many customers is

$(0.1353 \times 0.15) + (0.2707 \times 0.09) + (0.2707 \times 0.06) + (0.1804 \times 0.01) = 0.0627$

The probability of being able to offer every customer a place is 1 – 0.0627 = 0.9373.

5 Between 50 and 50 + (1.96 × 10) = 69.6. Thus 47.5 % of workers would have daily outputs of between 50 and 69.6 units.

6 (a) £12,000 is (12,000 – 14,000)/4,000 = 0.50 standard deviations below the mean.

From tables, the proportion of the normal distribution more than 0.50 standard deviations below the mean is 0.5 – 0.1915 = 0.3085

(b) £11,000 is (11,000 – 14,000)/4,000 = 0.75 standard deviations below the mean.

£19,000 is (19,000 – 14,000)/4,000 = 1.25 standard deviations above the mean.

The proportion with earnings between £11,000 and £14,000 is 0.2734

The proportion with earnings between £14,000 and £19,000 is 0.3944

The required proportion is 0.2734 + 0.3944 = 0.6678

7 p = (100 – 62)% = 38% = 0.38

Mean = n × p = 200 × 0.38 = 76

Standard deviation = $\sqrt{n \times p \times q}$ $= \sqrt{200 \times 0.38 \times 0.62}$

= 6.86

P(more than 86) = P(more than 86.5)

86.5 is (86.5 – 76)/6.86 = 1.53 standard deviations above the mean.

P(number of males > 86) = 0.5 – 0.4370 = 0.0630

Further question practice

Now try the following practice questions at the end of this text.

Multiple choice questions **45–54**

Chapter 8

ESTIMATION AND HYPOTHESIS TESTING

Introduction

We often need to rely on samples to get information about whole populations. In this chapter we will look at ways to squeeze as much information as we can out of a sample. Our methods are based on the concept of a sampling distribution, which shows the results we could have got from all possible samples, not just the sample we actually took. The standard deviation of a sampling distribution is its standard error, and we can use this to set limits (confidence limits) on how uncertain we are about our estimate of a population mean or proportion. We can use the same approach to test a theory (a hypothesis) which we might have about a population, such as a theory that the mean weight per brick of a large batch of bricks is 4 kg.

Finally, we will look at a different type of test, called the chi-squared test, which can answer questions like: is whether or not a person drives connected with whether or not they have a credit card? (contingency tables); and does the distribution of wages in the population follow a normal distribution? (distribution fitting).

Your objectives

After completing this chapter you should:

(a) understand the concept of a sampling distribution;

(b) be able to compute standard errors and confidence limits;

(c) know the steps in hypothesis testing;

(d) be able to test hypotheses concerning means and proportions;

(e) be able to test hypotheses using large and small samples;

(f) be able to use the chi-squared test.

1 POPULATIONS AND SAMPLES

1.1 We take a sample in order to estimate something about the population as a whole. For example, we might ask 1,000 people in Britain how much they earn, and work out the average for those 1,000 people. This would give us an idea of the average earnings of everyone in Britain. The sample average is likely to be close to the population average but not exactly the same.

1.2 This chapter is mainly concerned with the accuracy of the estimates of the *mean* of a population which are provided by the analysis of the *mean* of a sample. The theory we will be looking at only holds if:

(a) the samples are taken at random;

(b) the samples are fairly large (over 30).

1.3 Small samples need a slightly different treatment, which is discussed in the section below on the t distribution.

1.4 It is helpful to distinguish between the mean and standard deviation of a sample, and the mean and standard deviation of the population which the sample comes from. We shall therefore use the following symbols.

$\bar{x}$ is the mean of a sample

μ (mu) is the mean of the population

s is the standard deviation of a sample

σ (sigma) is the standard deviation of the population

1.5 Suppose that we wish to estimate the mean of a population, say the average weight of an item of product made in a factory. A sample of, say, 100 units of the product might be taken, and the mean weight per unit of the sample might be, say, 5.8 kg.

Another sample of 100 units might then be taken and the mean weight might be, say, 6.3 kg.

A large number of samples might be taken and the mean of each sample calculated. These means will not all be the same and they can be plotted as a frequency distribution. This distribution is called a 'sampling distribution of the mean'.

Definition

A sampling distribution of the mean is a frequency distribution of the mean of a large number of samples.

In our example, a frequency distribution of the mean weight per unit in each of 250 samples (of 100 units per sample) might be as follows.

Mean weight per unit $\bar{x}$			
at least	*less than*	*Mid-point of class interval*	*Frequency (No of samples)*
kg	kg	kg	
5.45	5.55	5.5	3
5.55	5.65	5.6	7
5.65	5.75	5.7	16
5.75	5.85	5.8	30
5.85	5.95	5.9	44
5.95	6.05	6.0	50
6.05	6.15	6.1	44
6.15	6.25	6.2	30
6.25	6.35	6.3	16
6.35	6.45	6.4	7
6.45	6.55	6.5	3
			250 samples

The mean weight per unit of 100 units in a sample might thus range from 5.45 to 6.55 kg. The true mean of the population, that is, the true mean weight of all units produced, presumably lies somewhere within this range. In this chapter we will see how to work out how close a sample mean is likely to be to the population mean.

2 THE STANDARD ERROR AND CONFIDENCE LIMITS

2.1 A sampling distribution of the mean has the following important properties.

(a) It is very close to being normally distributed. This is true even if the distribution of the population from which the samples are drawn is nowhere near normal. The larger the sample the more closely will the sampling distribution approximate to a normal distribution.

(b) The mean of the sampling distribution is the same as the population mean.

(c) The sampling distribution has a standard deviation which is called the *standard error of the mean (se).*

Definition

The *standard error of the mean* is the standard deviation of a sampling distribution of the mean.

2.2 In our example, the 250 samples give an estimate of the population mean. This distribution of sample means would be (approximately) normally distributed, with a mean of about 6 kg (weight per unit of product).

This mean of 6 kg would be the same as the population mean, μ.

The standard deviation of the sampling distribution (which could be calculated as 0.2 kg: workings not shown) is the standard error (se).

It can be shown that the standard error of the mean is

$$se = \sigma/\sqrt{n}$$

where n is the size of each sample and σ is the standard deviation of the population.

Estimating the standard error

2.3 The standard error is given by $\sigma/\sqrt{n}$, but σ is the standard deviation of the whole population and is normally not known. To overcome this problem the standard deviation of a sample is taken as the best estimate of the standard deviation of the whole population, so that $se = s/\sqrt{n}$, where s is the standard deviation of a sample.

For reasons which are outside the scope of this Study Guide, if we need to calculate s we will use a formula for s which is slightly different from that used to find the standard deviation of a population when we have data on every member.

The formula is $s = \sqrt{\Sigma(x-\bar{x})^2/(n-1)}$

Activity 1

A sample of 50 items has a sample standard deviation of 2.7. Find the standard error of the mean.

The central limit theorem

Definition

The *central limit theorem* is the name given to the statistical rule that if the sample size is large (> 30) then, even if the distribution of the parent population is unknown, the sampling distribution of sample means is normally distributed.

2.4 We can use this fact to get extra information from our sample results. Thus in the above example with a standard error of 0.2 kg, someone might have taken a sample with a mean of 5.7 kg. Since nearly all of a normal distribution lies within three standard deviations of the mean, the person could be practically certain that the population mean is in the range $5.7 \pm (3 \times 0.2) = 5.7 \pm 0.6 = 5.1 - 6.3$ kg.

Confidence limits

2.5 From our knowledge of the properties of a normal distribution, together with the rule that sample means are normally distributed around the true population mean with a standard deviation equal to the standard error, we can predict (using normal distribution tables) that:

(a) 68% of all sample means will be within one standard error of the population mean;

(b) 95% of all sample means will be within 1.96 standard errors of the population mean;

(c) 99% of all sample means will be within 2.58 standard errors of the population mean.

By looking at it the other way we can see that:

(a) with 68% probability, the population mean lies within the range: sample mean ± one standard error;

(b) with 95% probability, the population mean lies within the range: sample mean ± 1.96 standard errors;

(c) with 99% probability, the population mean lies within the range: sample mean ± 2.58 standard errors.

These degrees of certainty are known as *confidence levels*, and the ends of the ranges around the sample mean are called *confidence limits*. The ranges are called *confidence intervals*.

EXAMPLE: CONFIDENCE INTERVALS

From a random sample of 576 of a company's 20,000 employees, it was found that the average number of days each person was absent from work due to illness was eight days a year, with a standard deviation of 3.6 days.

What are the confidence limits for the average number of days absence a year through sickness per employee for the company as a whole:

(a) at the 95% level of confidence;

(b) at the 99% level of confidence?

EXAMPLE *continued*

Solution

We must first calculate the standard error.

se = $3.6/\sqrt{576} = 0.15$.

(a) At the 95% level of confidence, the true average number of days absence a year is in the range $8 \pm (1.96 \times 0.15)$

$= 8 \pm 0.294$

$=$ 7.706 to 8.294 days, say 7.7 to 8.3 days.

(b) At the 99% level of confidence, the true average number of days absence a year is in the range $8 \pm (2.58 \times 0.15)$

$= 8 \pm 0.387$

$=$ 7.613 to 8.387 days, say 7.6 to 8.4 days.

2.6 Why is it necessary to calculate confidence limits? If the sample mean in the example above was eight days would it not be sufficient to use eight days as a *point estimate* of the population mean?

2.7 In practice, a sample mean might indeed be used as a 'point estimate' of the population mean. However, we could not be sure how reliable the estimate might be, without first considering the size of the standard error. The sample mean might be above or below the true population mean, but we can say with 95% confidence that the sample mean is no more than 1.96 standard errors above or below the true population mean.

If the confidence limits cover a wide range of values, a point estimate of the population mean from the sample would not be reliable. On the other hand, if the confidence limits cover a narrow range of values, a point estimate of the population mean, using the sample mean, would be reliable.

Activity 2

The cost of assembling an item of equipment has been estimated by obtaining a sample of 144 jobs. The average cost of assembly derived from the sample was £4,000, with a standard deviation of £1,500.

Estimate confidence limits for the true average cost of assembly. Use the 95% level of confidence.

The standard error of a proportion

2.8 The arithmetic mean is a very important statistic, and sampling is often concerned with estimating the mean of a population. Many surveys, however, attempt to estimate a proportion rather than a mean. Examples include surveys concerned with:

(a) attitudes or opinions about an issue;

(b) the percentage of times an event occurs (for example, the proportion of faulty items out of the total number of items produced in a manufacturing department).

2.9 Suppose, for example, that we wished to know what proportion of an electorate intends to vote for the Jacobin party at the forthcoming general election. Several samples might be obtained, and the proportion of Jacobin voters in a sample might vary, say, from 37% to 45%. The proportion of Jacobin voters in each sample could be arranged into a sampling distribution which:

(a) is normally distributed;

(b) has a mean equal to the proportion of pro-Jacobin voters in the population;

(c) has a standard deviation equal to the standard error of a proportion.

The formula for the standard error of a proportion is $\sqrt{\frac{\pi(1-\pi)}{n}}$

where π is the proportion in the population
n is the size of the sample.

We use the sample proportion p as an estimate of the population proportion, π, when this is unavailable. Just as we use μ for a population mean, we can use π for a population proportion (but we must not confuse this with the constant π = 3.14159).

EXAMPLE: A CONFIDENCE INTERVAL FOR A PROPORTION

In a random sample of 500 out of 100,000 employees, 320 were members of a trade union. Estimate the proportion of trade union members in the entire organisation at the 95% confidence level.

Solution

The sample proportion is 320/500 = 0.64.

$$\text{Standard error} = \sqrt{\frac{0.64 \times (1-0.64)}{500}} = \sqrt{\frac{0.64 \times 0.36}{500}} = 0.0215$$

An estimate of the population proportion at the 95% confidence level is the sample proportion ± 1.96 standard errors.

The population proportion is 0.64 ± (1.96 × 0.0215) = 0.64 ± 0.04. The percentage of employees who are trade union members is between 60% and 68% at the 95% level of confidence.

Activity 3

A researcher wishes to know the proportion of people who regularly travel by train. Of a sample of 400 people, 285 said they did so. Estimate the population proportion with 99% confidence.

3 THE PRINCIPLES OF HYPOTHESIS TESTING

Definition

Hypothesis testing is the process of establishing the significance of the results of sample data for beliefs (hypotheses) about the population.

3.1 The procedure for hypothesis testing is as follows.

(a) We establish a hypothesis, for example that the mean value of all of a company's invoices is £200. This is the *null hypothesis* (H_0). We also state an *alternative hypothesis* (H_1). For example that the mean value is not £200.

(b) We test the hypothesis. Are the sample results near enough what we would expect to get if the null hypothesis were true? To test the null hypothesis, we must select a significance level. This is the chance we take of wrongly rejecting the null hypothesis.

(c) Having tested the hypothesis, we draw a conclusion.

NOTES

EXAMPLE: HYPOTHESIS TESTING (1)

A company's management accountant has estimated that the average cost of providing a certain service to a customer is £40.

A sample has been taken, consisting of 150 service provisions, and the mean cost for the sample was £45 with a standard deviation of £10.

Is the sample consistent with the estimate of an average cost of £40?

Solution

To apply a hypothesis test, we begin by stating an initial view, called the null hypothesis, that the average cost per unit of service is £40. The alternative hypothesis will be that it is not £40.

Next, we select a significance level, which indicates how severely we are testing the null hypothesis. Here, we will use 5%, which is a common choice. The lower the significance level, the lower the probability of wrongly rejecting the null hypothesis, but the higher the probability of wrongly accepting it.

Our choice of 5% means that we shall assume that the sample mean (£45) is consistent with our estimated population mean (£40) provided that the sample mean is within what would be a 100% – 5% = 95% confidence interval around a sample mean equal to the mean given by the null hypothesis.

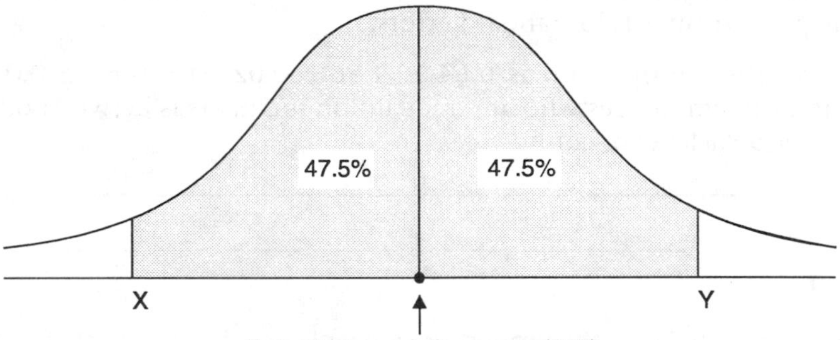

You may prefer to think of this in terms of the diagram above. If the sample mean of £45 is within the range from X to Y, we will conclude that our null hypothesis is acceptable.

X and Y are each 1.96 standard errors from the mean. From our sample, we can calculate the standard error as $10/\sqrt{150} = 0.816$.

We can now test the hypothesis. The sample mean is £5 higher than our hypothesised population mean, and this is 5/0.816 = 6.1 standard errors above the mean.

At the 5% level of significance we would expect the sample mean to be within 1.96 standard errors of the hypothesised mean. It is not, and so at this level of significance, we reject the null hypothesis.

Conclusion

The average cost per unit of service is not £40, and the management accountant is wrong.

Note that if we had got a sample mean within 1.96 standard errors of the hypothesised mean, this would not have proved that the null hypothesis was true. It would only have shown that we did not have enough evidence to reject the null hypothesis.

NOTES

Activity 4

It is thought that the mean number of times a person uses a credit card in a year is 180, neither more nor less. To test this hypothesis, a sample of 55 people is taken. The sample mean is 192 uses and the sample standard deviation is 50 uses. What conclusion should be reached at 5% significance?

EXAMPLE: HYPOTHESIS TESTING (2)

In a manufacturing operation, the standard level of scrapped units is 8% of input.

During one week, 18,400 units were input to the operation of which 1,580 were scrapped.

Does the level of rejects appear to exceed the expected level? Test at the 5% level of significance.

Solution

Let H_0 be that the true level of rejects is 8% or 0.08.

Let H_1 be that the level of rejects is greater than 8%.

The actual level of rejects is $\frac{1,580}{18,400} = 0.08587$

We now need to select a significance level. This has already be stated in the question. We must therefore establish a limit for the number of units scrapped, so as to ensure that there is only a 5% probability of the number of rejects in the sample exceeding the limit, if the average rejection rate for the population is in fact 8%. This may be shown in a diagram as follows.

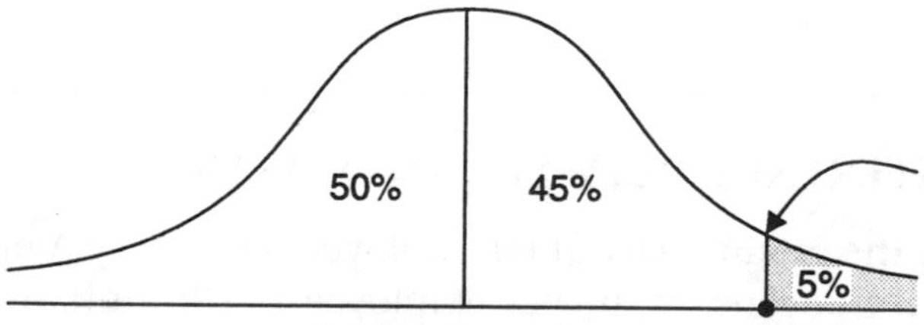

The decision rule limit (as shown in the diagram) must be such that there is only a 5% probability of the actual scrapped units in the sample being a greater amount. This means that 95% of the frequency distribution must lie to the left hand side of the limit. From normal distribution tables, 0.05 of the distribution lies more than 1.65 standard errors above the mean.

The standard error of the proportion, calculated from the proportion in the null hypothesis, is $\sqrt{[pq/n]} = \sqrt{[0.08 \times 0.92/18,400]} = 0.002$.

Next we have to test the null hypothesis. The actual level of rejects is 0.00587 above the expected level. This represents 0.00587/0.002 = 2.935 standard errors.

At the 5% level of significance, we would expect the sample proportion to be not more than 1.65 standard errors above the hypothesised mean. It is not since it is 2.935 standard errors above the hypothesised mean. We therefore reject the null hypothesis and conclude that the level of rejects is higher than 8% (at the 5% level of significance).

NOTES

One-tail tests and two-tail tests

3.2 There are two different types of significance test, known as one-tail (one-sided) or two-tail (two-sided) tests.

3.3 The first example above (the cost of a service) was of a two-tail test, because the alternative hypothesis was of the form '... *does not equal* ...'. In the diagram we wanted 5% of the area in both tails taken together, hence our limits of ±1.96 standard errors. For 1% significance, we would have used ±2.58 standard errors.

The second example (scrapped units) was of a one-tail test, because the alternative hypothesis was of the form '... *is greater than* ...'. Where the alternative hypothesis is of the form '... is less than ...' we also have a one-tail test. In the diagram, we wanted 5% of the area in one tail only, hence our use of 1.65 (2.33 for 1% significance).

Activity 5

It is thought that the mean net weight of bags of sugar produced by a machine is at least 1.03 kg. A sample of 230 bags had a mean net weight of 1.02 kg, with a standard deviation of weights of 0.02 kg. Test the hypothesis that the population mean is at least 1.03 kg at the 1% significance level.

4 DIFFERENCES BETWEEN MEANS

4.1 We may compare the means of two different samples. In such a comparison, we might want to learn whether the mean of one population equals that of the other, or whether there appears to be a difference between them. Hypothesis tests can be made in such cases.

EXAMPLE: THE DIFFERENCE BETWEEN TWO MEANS

Sample I is a sample of the productivity of 60 employees at Factory A on day 1, which shows that the mean output per employee is 106 units with a standard deviation of 8.067 units. Sample II is a sample of 50 employees at Factory A on day 2 which shows a mean output per employee of 103 units with a standard deviation of 6.0605 units.

Is it probable that there has been a change in the productivity at Factory A between day 1 and day 2?

Solution

The standard error of the difference between the two sample means would be calculated as follows.

Sample I	Standard deviation	s_1	$= 8.067$
	Estimate of population variance	σ_1^2	$= 8.067^2 = 65.08$
Sample II	Standard deviation	s_2	$= 6.0605$
	Estimate of population variance	σ_2^2	$= 6.0605^2 = 36.73$

EXAMPLE *continued*

The standard error of the difference between two means is given by the formula

$$\sqrt{\frac{\sigma_1^2}{n_1}+\frac{\sigma_2^2}{n_2}}$$

where σ_1^2 is the population variance estimated from the first sample
n_1 is the size of the first sample
σ_2^2 is the population variance estimated from the second sample
n_2 is the size of the second sample.

Standard error of the difference between the means $= \sqrt{\frac{65.08}{60}+\frac{36.73}{50}}$

$= \sqrt{(1.0847+0.7346)}$

$= 1.35$

The mean output per employee on day 1 was 106 units and on day 2 it was 103 units. The difference between the means was 3. A difference of 3 is 3/1.35 = 2.22 standard errors.

The null hypothesis is that there is no difference between the two population means. The alternative hypothesis is that there is a difference.

We will test the null hypothesis with a two-tail test at the 5% level of significance. The null hypothesis would be accepted if the actual difference between the sample means did not exceed 1.96 standard errors. However, because the difference is 2.22 standard errors, the null hypothesis would be rejected at the 5% level of significance, and management would assume that average productivity on day 2 was different from that on day 1, because 2.22 standard errors is over 1.96. (The null hypothesis would not be rejected, however, at the 1% level of significance because the difference between the sample means is not more than 2.58 standard errors.)

Activity 6

The analysis of average annual sales per customer for two sales areas for 19X6 based on random samples was as follows.

	Midland	*South*
Sample size	100	100
Sample mean	£93.30	£57.70
Sample variance	5,398.60	791.10

Test the hypothesis that there is no difference in the average annual sales per customer between the two areas. Use the 1% significance level.

NOTES

5 DIFFERENCES BETWEEN PROPORTIONS

5.1 We can test whether the proportions in two populations are the same, on the basis of two samples.

EXAMPLE: THE DIFFERENCE BETWEEN TWO PROPORTIONS

In a test of the hypothesis that the proportion of homes with central heating is not more than the proportion of homes with two or more televisions, 60% of a sample of 90 homes were found to have central heating and 55% of a sample of 80 homes were found to have two or more televisions. What conclusion should be reached at the 5% significance level?

Solution

Let p_1 be the sample proportion of homes with central heating (0.6) and let p_2 be the sample proportion of homes with two or more televisions (0.55).

$H_0 : \pi_1 = \pi_2$ (the null hypothesis is that the two population proportions are equal)

$H_1 : \pi_1 > \pi_2$ (the alternative hypothesis is that the proportion of homes with central heating exceeds the proportion of homes with two or more televisions)

This is a one-tail test, with a critical level (at 5% significance) of 1.65.
The standard error of the difference between two sample proportions is:

$$\sqrt{p(1-p)\left(\frac{1}{n_1}+\frac{1}{n_2}\right)}$$

where $p = \dfrac{p_1 n_1 + p_2 n_2}{n_1 + n_2}$

n_1 is the size of the first sample
p_1 is the proportion in the first sample
n_2 is the size of the second sample
p_2 is the proportion in the second sample
$p = (0.6 \times 90 + 0.55 \times 80)/(90 + 80) = 0.576$

$$\text{Standard error} = \sqrt{0.576(1-.576)\left(\frac{1}{90}+\frac{1}{80}\right)} = 0.0759$$

$(0.6 - 0.55)/0.0759 = 0.66$

0.66 is less than 1.65, so the null hypothesis may be accepted.

6 SMALL SAMPLES AND THE *t* DISTRIBUTION

6.1 The sampling and hypothesis testing theory described so far only holds good for fairly large samples ($n > 30$). For small samples, the Central Limit Theorem (see Paragraph 2.4) is not valid. The means of small samples are distributed around the population mean in a manner similar to, but not exactly a normal distribution. The distribution is known as a *t distribution* (sometimes referred to as a 'Student's *t* distribution'.)

NOTES

Definition

A *t distribution* is the distribution of small sample means.

6.2 The techniques for small samples are similar to those for large samples, but the t distribution replaces the normal distribution. In using the *t* distribution, we must assume that the population is approximately normally distributed.

6.3 For small samples, factors such as 1.65 and 1.96 derived from normal distribution tables must be replaced by a factor *t*. *t* varies with the *degrees of freedom*. You do not need to understand what degrees of freedom are to be able apply the t distribution but you may find an intuitive explanation interesting.

Suppose that a sample consisted of just one observation. We could find the average of the observation (its value) but we would be unable to derive any estimates of dispersion. Now suppose that the sample consisted of two observations. We would have one measure of dispersion or difference and hence one degree of freedom. Degrees of freedom can therefore be described as the number of independent pieces of information. So, when estimating dispersion around a single mean, the degrees of freedom will be $n - 1$. The number of degrees of freedom for a sample of size n will therefore be $n - 1$.

6.4 There is a separate *t* distribution for each number of degrees of freedom. *t* distribution tables for selected *t* scores (numbers of standard errors) for various degrees of freedom are given in a table at the start of this text.

6.5 Note that the *t* tables are based on the areas in one tail. The column headed '1 tail: 5%' is therefore used for a one-tail test at 5% significance, or a two-tail test at 10% significance. This is confirmed by the bottom row, where the familiar normal distribution figures (1.65, 1.96, 2.33 and 2.58) are shown.

The rows of the table are for degrees of freedom (df) from 1 upwards.

6.6 For example, in a one-tail test using a sample of 10 items (df = 10 – 1 = 9) at the 5% level of significance H_0 would be rejected if the sample mean was more than 1.83 standard errors from the population mean (1.83 is in the column for 5% in a one-tail test, and the row df = 9).

6.7 Similarly, in a two-tail test using a sample of 16 items (df = 15) at 1% significance, the limit is 2.95 standard errors from the hypothesised mean (2.95 is in the column for 1%, two-tail test). The same factor (2.95) would be used to establish a 99% confidence interval.

NOTES

EXAMPLE: THE *t* DISTRIBUTION

In a quality control check, nine ball point pens were used until they stopped writing. The times taken (in hours) were 220, 250, 240, 290, 200, 300, 230, 210, 220.

Find a 99% confidence interval for the population mean life, given that the sample mean is 240 hours.

Solution

Life x	$x - \bar{x}$	$(x - \bar{x})^2$
220	−20	400
250	+10	100
240	0	0
290	+50	2,500
200	−40	1,600
300	+60	3,600
230	−10	100
210	−30	900
220	−20	400
2,160		9,600

Sample standard deviation = $\sqrt{\Sigma(x-\bar{x})^2/(n-1)}$ (see paragraph 2.3)

$= \sqrt{9{,}600/8} = 34{\cdot}64$

Standard error = $34.64/\sqrt{9} = 11.55$.

The sample size is nine so there are eight degrees of freedom. The value of t for eight degrees of freedom at the 99% confidence level is 3.36 (from the t distribution table, df = 8 and Pr = 1% for two tails).

Population mean $= 240 \pm 3.36 \times 11.55$

$= 240 \pm 38.81$

The mean time to failure is about 240 ± 39 hours at the 99% confidence level, that is, 201 to 279 hours.

Activity 7

The labour cost for making a unit of a new product should be £20. The management accountant has taken a sample of 12 units, and found that the sample had a mean labour cost of £23 per unit, with a standard deviation of £2.089.

Test, at the 5% level of significance, whether the sample indicates that the labour cost per unit exceeds £20.

t Tests and the difference between two means

6.8 We can also use a t test to test the significance of the difference between the means of two small samples. We use a slightly different formula from that described in Section 4 of this chapter, and apply t distribution tables, with $(n_1 + n_2 - 2)$ degrees of freedom, where n_1 and n_2 are the two sample sizes. We must also make the assumption that the two populations are approximately normally distributed with approximately equal standard deviations.

NOTES

EXAMPLE: THE DIFFERENCE BETWEEN TWO MEANS

The following figures were calculated from two series of tests on two batches of the same product, liquid D. Do the figures support the assertion that the mean strengths of the two batches are the same?

	Batch 1	*Batch 2*
Number of tests	6	8
Mean strength (parts per hundred)	4.26	4.35
Sample standard deviation	0.0548	0.0424

Solution

	Batch 1	*Batch 2*
Sample standard deviation	0.0548	0.0424
Sample variance	0.0030	0.0018

$$\text{Pooled estimated } \hat{\sigma} = \sqrt{\frac{(n_1-1)\sigma_1{}^2+(n_2-1)\sigma_2{}^2}{n_1+n_2-2}} = \sqrt{\frac{5\times 0.0030+7\times 0.0018}{6+8-2}}$$

$$= 0.048$$

The standard error of the difference between the two sample means is

$$\hat{\sigma}\sqrt{\frac{1}{n_1}+\frac{1}{n_2}} = 0.048\times\sqrt{\frac{1}{6}+\frac{1}{8}}$$

$$= \quad 0.026$$

The difference between the two sample means is 4.35 – 4.26 = 0.09, which is 0.09/0.026 = 3.46 standard errors.

There are (6 + 8 – 2) = 12 degrees of freedom.

The significance test is a two-tail test, and if we test at the 5% level of significance, the *t* statistic is 2.18.

Since the actual difference between the sample means represents 3.46 standard errors, we reject the null hypothesis, and conclude instead that the mean strengths of the two batches differ.

Activity 8

It is hypothesised that the average amount of cash carried by women is the same as that carried by men, neither more nor less. Samples are taken, with the following results.

	Women	*Men*
Number in sample	10	12
Sample mean	£35	£32
Sample standard deviation	£ 2.40	£ 1.30

What conclusion may be reached at the 5% significance level?

7 NONPARAMETRIC TESTS

7.1 The hypothesis tests we have looked at so far are all *parametric tests*. This means that they make an assumption about the distribution of the population we are sampling from: our tests assume it is approximately normal. With large samples, the assumption can generally be ignored, as its falsity would have very little effect. However, with small samples it becomes very important.

7.2 *Nonparametric tests* (also called *distribution-free tests*) are available, which do not make any such assumption. We will not go into details about such tests here, but you should be aware that they exist.

7.3 Advantages of nonparametric tests

(a) No assumptions about the underlying populations need be made. Thus we are not in danger of making a false assumption that a population is normally distributed.

(b) The mathematical concepts are simpler.

(c) They can be used on very small samples.

7.4 Disadvantages of nonparametric tests

(a) The tests are more prone to error (wrongly accepting H, or wrongly rejecting H) than parametric tests where the assumptions made by the parametric tests are justified. That is, nonparametric tests are less powerful than parametric tests.

(b) The arithmetic often takes a long time.

8 THE CHI-SQUARED TEST

8.1 In sampling and in hypothesis testing of sample results, we often use the normal distribution, and with small samples a *t* distribution is used. Whether a normal distribution is used for large samples, or a *t* distribution for small samples, hypothesis testing concentrates on the *mean* of the population. We could not, for example, use such methods to test whether people's heights were associated with their interest in sport.

8.2 To make such tests, we use the chi-squared distribution. Chi, the Greek letter χ, is pronounced 'ki'. You will often find chi-squared referred to by the Greek letter itself, as χ^2.

Definition

The *chi-squared distribution* is used to test a sample of items in order to decide whether the items in the sample are distributed according to a preconceived or expected distribution pattern.

Contingency tables

8.3 We perform our test of whether the values of two variables are associated by setting up a *contingency table* (so called because it sets out all the possibilities, or contingencies). The table has rows for values of one variable and columns for values of the other.

We have observed values, O, which are the numbers of instances we observed for each cell of the table (for example the number observed at height over 170 cm and interest in sport high).

We need an expected value, E, based on a null hypothesis that the values of the variables are not associated, to go with each observed value.

For each cell,

$$E = \frac{\Sigma O \text{ for the row} \times \Sigma O \text{ for the column}}{\Sigma O \text{ for the whole table}}$$

NOTES

Activity 9

Here is a contingency table, with observed frequencies (numbers of people).

		Height		
		Up to 170 cm	*Over 170 cm*	*Total*
Interest in sport	Low	70	20	90
	High	38	57	95
	Total	108	77	185

(a) For the top left cell (height up to 170 cm, low interest in sport), work out E using the formula given above.

(b) Work out the overall proportion of the 185 people who have low interest in sport, and take that proportion of the 108 people with heights up to 170 cm.

(c) Explain why the formula given above for E is correct.

EXAMPLE: CHI-SQUARED TESTS AND TABLES

An investigation is being carried out into delays in the payment of invoices by the customers of a company. Details of the current debtors are as follows.

	Status as a debtor			
Type of customer	*Slow payer (> 3 months)*	*Average payer (>1 and <3 months)*	*Prompt payer (< 1 month)*	*Total*
Large private companies	8	17	6	31
Small private companies	20	25	22	67
Quoted companies	11	16	9	36
Local authorities	6	8	2	16
	45	66	39	150

Determine whether there is any relationship between the type of customer and its status as a payer. Use the 5% level of significance.

Solution

The problem is to decide whether different types of customer have different payment habits, or whether all customers are much the same in the time they take to pay their debts. The null hypothesis is that there is no association between the type of customer and the customer's payment habits. The alternative hypothesis is that there is such an association.

A contingency table can be drawn up as follows.

		Status as a debtor					
		Slow		*Average*		*Prompt*	
Type of customer	*Total*	*Observed*	*Expected*	*Observed*	*Expected*	*Observed*	*Expected*
Large private companies	31	8	9.3	17	13.6	6	8.1
Small private companies	67	20	20.1	25	29.5	22	17.4
Quoted companies	36	11	10.8	16	15.8	9	9.4
Local authorities	16	6	4.8	8	7.0	2	4.2
	150	45	45.0	66	65.9	39	39.1

For example, the expected frequency for slow paying large private companies is

$$\frac{\text{Row total} \times \text{Column total}}{\text{Table total}} = \frac{31 \times 45}{150} = 9{\cdot}3$$

NOTES

EXAMPLE *continued*

The overall proportion of slow payers is 45/150 = 0.3, so if the null hypothesis is true we would expect $0.3 \times 31 = 9.3$ large private companies to be slow payers.

There are 12 pairs of observed and expected frequencies in this 4×3 table.

A chi-squared statistic χ^2 is calculated by taking the difference between each observed result and the corresponding expected result, squaring the difference, and dividing this square by the expected result. All the figures found are then added up.

$$\chi^2 = \Sigma \frac{(O-E)^2}{E}$$

where O is the observed frequency and E is the expected frequency of each item in the sample.

		O	E	$(O-E)$	$(O-E)^2$	$\frac{(O-E)^2}{E}$
Slow payers						
	Large private companies	8	9.3	–1.3	1.69	0.18
	Small private companies	20	20.1	–0.1	0.01	0.00
	Quoted companies	11	10.8	+0.2	0.04	0.00
	Local authorities	6	4.8	+1.2	1.44	0.30
Average payers						
	Large private companies	17	13.6	+3.4	11.56	0.85
	Small private companies	25	29.5	–4.5	20.25	0.69
	Quoted companies	16	15.8	+0.2	0.04	0.00
	Local authorities	8	7.0	+1.0	1.00	0.14
Prompt payers						
	Large private companies	6	8.1	-2.1	4.41	0.54
	Small private companies	22	17.4	+4.6	21.16	1.22
	Quoted companies	9	9.4	–0.4	0.16	0.02
	Local authorities	2	4.2	–2.2	4.84	1.15
						χ^2 = 5.09

Our next step is to use chi-squared distribution tables. Such a table is shown at the beginning of this Study Guide.

(a) The table has a column for each significance level that we might decide to test at.

(b) There is a row for each number of degrees of freedom, a concept that we encountered earlier in this chapter. Again you do not have to understand what degrees of freedom are but you may find the following interesting.

Consider the contingency table in this example. There are four rows and three columns, giving a total of twelve cells. Each of the row and column totals is fixed and so the individual cells must add up to the relevant totals. In the first row, for example, we have the freedom to put any numbers into two of the three cells but the third is fixed because all three must add up to the fixed total. There are therefore two degrees of freedom. The same can be said of the second and third rows. But all of the values on the fourth row are fixed because of the column totals, so there are 0 degrees of freedom. Totalling these we have 2 + 2 + 2 = 6 degrees of freedom. There is a short cut, however. If you take the number of rows minus one and multiply by the number of columns minus one you get the number of degrees of freedom. For an $m \times n$ table the degrees of freedom are $(m - 1)(n - 1)$.

(c) For each significance level and number of degrees of freedom, the table gives us a critical value. There is no distinction between one-tail and two-tail tests.

Our value for χ^2 is 5.09. We must now determine whether 5.09 is below the critical value in the χ^2 distribution at the 5% level of significance.

EXAMPLE *continued*

The contingency table has four rows and three columns. The degrees of freedom are therefore $(4 - 1)(3 - 1) = 3 \times 2 = 6$.

From the χ^2 table, the critical value at the 5% level of significance when there are six degrees of freedom is 12.6.

The value of χ^2 in our test is 5.09, well below the critical value.

We therefore accept the null hypothesis that there is no difference between the payment patterns of different types of customer.

Activity 10

Here is a contingency table showing the results of tests of the effects of three fertilisers A, B and C on plant growth. Each fertiliser was tried on several different plots of land. Each figure is a number of plots of land.

		Fertiliser			
		A	*B*	*C*	*Total*
Growth	Strong	47	62	22	131
	Weak	25	48	19	92
Total		72	110	41	223

Test at the 1% level for an association between the choice of fertiliser and plant growth.

Yates's correction

8.4 In calculating χ^2 for 2×2 contingency table (when there is only one degree of freedom) you should deduct 0.5 from the absolute value (the value ignoring any minus sign) of (O–E) for each item. This adjustment is called *Yates's correction.*

EXAMPLE: YATES'S CORRECTION

In a market survey carried out on behalf of Waring Titfer Ltd, a hat manufacturer, the following results were obtained.

	Men	*Women*
Never wear hats	82	65
Sometimes wear hats	24	25

The marketing manager wants to know whether the survey reveals any difference between the hat-wearing habits of men and women. Advise him, using the 5% level of significance.

Solution

The null hypothesis is that there is no difference in the hat-wearing habits of men and women.

The contingency table is as follows.

		Men		*Women*	
Attribute	*Total*	*Observed*	*Expected*	*Observed*	*Expected*
Never wear hats	147	82	79.5	65	67.5
Sometimes wear hats	49	24	26.5	25	22.5
	196	106	106.0	90	90.0

NOTES

EXAMPLE *continued*

Because we have a 2 × 2 contingency table, we apply Yates's correction, and calculate, not (O–E), but (|O–E| –0.5). The bars in |O–E| mean that we ignore any minus sign.

Observed	*Expected*	*(O–E)*	*(|O–E| – 0.5)*	*(|O–E| –0.5)²*	$\frac{(\lvert O-E\rvert-0.5)^2}{E}$
82	79.5	+2.5	2	4	0.05
24	26.5	–2.5	2	4	0.15
65	67.5	–2.5	2	4	0.06
25	22.5	+2.5	2	4	0.18
				χ^2 =	0.44

There is only one degree of freedom, since (2 – 1)(2 – 1) = 1

At the 5% level of significance, the critical value in the χ^2 distribution with one degree of freedom is 3.84. Since the value of χ^2 in the test is 0.44 and below the critical value, we accept the null hypothesis that there is no difference between the hat-wearing habits of men and women.

8.5 You may have noticed in the above example that all the values of |O – E| are the same. This is always true for 2 × 2 contingency tables, and can save you time. However, it does *not* work for other sizes of table.

Low expected frequencies

8.6 There is one more correction to bear in mind. χ^2 tests becomes unreliable if any expected frequency E is less than 5. If this happens, you should combine a row or a column with an adjacent row or column to get rid of the low frequency. It does not matter whether you combine rows or columns, but if one alternative would eliminate the problem with less combining of figures than the other, you should choose that first alternative.

For example, the following contingency table has an expected frequency of 4.67 at the top left.

O	*E*	*O*	*E*	*O*	*E*
2	4.67	50	31.08	20	36.25
10	7.77	60	51.80	50	0.43
15	14.56	70	97.12	140	113.32

It could be amended to the following table. A χ^2 test with (3 – 1) (2 – 1) = 2 degrees of freedom could then be performed.

O	*E*	*O*	*E*
52	35.75	20	36.25
70	59.57	50	60.43
85	111.68	140	113.32

Distribution fitting

8.7 Chi-squared tests can also be used to test a hypothesis that some data fit a given distribution. This is called *distribution fitting*, or sometimes *curve fitting*. The value of χ^2 is computed using the same formula as for contingency tables, but the degrees of freedom are computed differently. They are as follows, where n is the number of observed frequencies.

Distribution	*Degrees of freedom*
No specific distribution (just a list of proportions in each class)	n – 1
Poisson with specified mean	n – 2
Binomial, with specified probability and total number	n – 2
Normal, with specified mean and standard deviation	n – 3

EXAMPLE: POISSON DISTRIBUTION

In a traffic survey the numbers of cars passing a given point in 100 five minute periods were as follows.

Number of cars	*Frequency*
0	10
1	25
2	40
3	20
4	3
5 or more	2
	100

The mean number of cars is 1.87 if the final two observations are each taken to be five cars. Test the hypothesis that the number of cars per five minutes follows a Poisson distribution.

Solution

The Poisson probabilities for m = 1.87 are as follows.

P(0) = 0.1541
P(1) = 0.2882
P(2) = 0.2695
P(3) = 0.1680
P(4) = 0.0785

P(5 or more) =1 – [P(0) + P(1) + P(2) + P(3) + P(4)] = 0.0417

Multiply by 100 to obtain the expected frequencies.

No of cars	*Observed frequency*	*Expected frequency*	$\frac{(O-E)^2}{E}$
x	*O*	*E*	
0	10	15.41	1.8993
1	25	28.82	0.5063
2	40	26.95	6.3192
3	20	16.80	0.6095
4	3	7.85	2.9965
5+	2	4.17	1.1292
			χ^2 = 13.4600

At 5% significance level and 6 – 2 = 4 degrees of freedom, the critical value of χ^2 is 9.49.

The value of χ^2 in this case exceeds the critical value and hence the observed frequencies differ significantly from the expected ones. At 5% significance we cannot therefore accept that the traffic flow follows a Poisson distribution.

Activity 11

It is thought that a certain variable fits a normal distribution, with a mean of 0 and standard deviation of 1. Results from 1,000 observations were as follows.

Value	*Proportion of cases*
Below –2	0.04
At least –2 but below –1	0.15
At least –1 but below 0	0.30
At least 0 but below 1	0.35
At least 1 but below 2	0.10
At least 2	0.06

What conclusion should be reached at 1% significance?

Chapter roundup

- If we take many samples (of the same size) from a population, and compute each sample's mean, the resulting list of means is a sampling distribution of the mean. Its standard deviation is the standard error, and its mean is the same as the population mean.
- We can use the standard error to compute confidence intervals, because the sampling distribution is normally distributed. We can also compute confidence intervals for proportions, using the formula for the standard error of a proportion.
- We can test a null hypothesis, of the form that a mean or a proportion equals a certain value, or that two means or two proportions are equal, against an alternative hypothesis. The test may be one-tail or two-tail, depending on the form of the alternative hypothesis.
- A hypothesis test is made by comparing the result from a sample with what we would expect if the null hypothesis were true. If the gap between the reality and the expectation is too wide, we reject the null hypothesis.
- With small samples ($n < 30$), we must use the t distribution with $n - 1$ degrees of freedom instead of the normal distribution.
- Nonparametric tests do not make assumptions about the population, but they are less powerful than parametric tests.
- A chi-squared test can test the hypothesis that two variables are unconnected. Expected frequencies are computed, and are then compared with observed frequencies.
- A chi-squared test can also be used to test whether observed data fit a given distribution. Again, expected frequencies are computed and compared with observed frequencies.

NOTES

Quick quiz

1 What are the conditions for the distribution of sample means to be able to be approximated by a normal distribution?
2 Define the standard error of the mean.
3 What is the formula for the standard error of the mean?
4 What is the formula for the standard error of a proportion?
5 What is a null hypothesis?
6 What is the formula for the standard error of the difference between two sample means?
7 Below what sample size should the t distribution be used rather than the normal distribution?
8 For a sample of size n, how many degrees of freedom should be used when carrying out a t test?
9 What are the advantages and disadvantages of nonparametric tests?
10 What is the formula to calculate the value of χ^2 from some data?
11 How many degrees of freedom should be used in a χ^2 test with an m × n contingency table?
12 Explain Yates's correction.

Answers to activities

1 s = 2.7

se = $2.7/\sqrt{50} = 0.382$

2 The standard error is estimated as $1{,}500\sqrt{144}$ = £125.

At the 95% level of confidence, the population mean is in the range £(4,000 ± (1.96 × 125)) = £(4,000 ± 245), that is, £3,755 to £4,245.

3 The sample proportion is 285/400 = 0.7125.

The standard error is $\sqrt{\dfrac{0.7125\times(1-0.7125)}{400}} = 0.0226$

The 99% confidence interval for the population proportion is

$$0.7125 \pm (2.58 \times 0.0226)$$
$$= 0.7125 \pm 0.0583$$
$$= 0.6542 \text{ to } 0.7708$$

4 H_0 is that $\mu = 180$, and H_1 is that $\mu \neq 180$.

The standard error is $50/\sqrt{55} = 6.74$

The sample mean is 192 – 180 = 12 higher than the hypothesised mean, and is 12/6.74 = 1.78 standard errors above that mean.

As this is within 1.96 standard errors, the null hypothesis (that the population mean is 180 uses) cannot be rejected.

5 H_0: $\mu \geq 1.03$ kg.

H_1: $\mu < 1.03$ kg.

This is a one-tail test. 99% of the frequency distribution must lie to the right hand side of the limit. From tables, 0.01 of the distribution lies more than –2.33 standard errors below the mean. (The minus sign is put in because we will reject H_0 if the sample mean is more than 2.33 standard errors below the hypothesised mean.)

Standard error = $0.02/\sqrt{230} = 0.00132$

$(1.02 - 1.03)/0.00132 = -7.58$.

H_0 should be rejected. There is clear evidence that the population mean weight is below 1.03 kg.

6 The null hypothesis H_0 is that there is no difference between the means of the two areas.

The alternative hypothesis H_1 is that there is a difference.

The standard error of the difference between the two means is

$$\sqrt{\frac{5,398.6}{100}+\frac{791.1}{100}} = 7.87$$

The actual difference between the sample means is 93.3 – 57.7 = 35.6

This is 35.6/7.87 = 4.5 standard errors.

The difference is significant at the 1% level of significance, so the null hypothesis is rejected and it may be concluded that the average annual sales per customer differs between the two areas.

7 The standard error of the mean is $2.089/\sqrt{12} = 0.60$.

The difference between the standard cost of £20 and the actual cost of £23 is £3. This is 3/0.6 = 5 standard errors.

Referring to t distribution tables, at the 5% level of significance (one-tail test, 5%) with 12 – 1 = 11 degrees of freedom, the t statistic is 1.80.

Since the actual difference is well in excess of 1.80, we reject the null hypothesis that the actual average cost does not exceed £20. The actual average cost is greater than £20.

8 $H_0 : \mu_1 = \mu_2$

$H_1 : \mu_1 \neq \mu_2$

This is a two-tail test at 5% significance with 10 + 12 – 2 = 20 degrees of freedom. From tables, 0.475 of the distribution lies between the mean and 2.09 standard errors.

$$\hat{\sigma} = \sqrt{\frac{9 \times 5.76 + 11 \times 1.69}{10 + 12 - 2}} = 1.88$$

$$\text{Standard error} = 1.88 \times \sqrt{\frac{1}{10}+\frac{1}{12}} = 0.80$$

Difference between means = (35 – 32)/0.80 = 3.75 standard errors.

As 3.75 exceeds 2.09, the null hypothesis should be rejected. The conclusion is that the average amounts of cash carried by men and women differ.

9 (a) $\dfrac{\text{Row total} \times \text{Column total}}{\text{Table total}} = \dfrac{90 \times 108}{185} = 52.54$

(b) Proportion with low interest in sport = 90/185 = 0.4865.

$108 \times 0.4865 = 52.54$

NOTES

(c) We have effectively done the same computation in two different ways. The expected values are computed on the basis that height and interest in sport are unconnected, so they should be found by distributing people in any one height class over the interest classes in the same proportion as the population as a whole is distributed over the interest classes.

10 The value of χ^2 is computed as follows.

Growth	*Fertiliser*	*O*	*E*	*(O – E)²/E*
Strong	A	47	42.3	0.52
	B	62	64.6	0.10
	C	22	24.1	0.18
Weak	A	25	29.7	0.74
	B	48	45.4	0.15
	C	19	16.9	0.26
				1.95

The critical value at 1% for (3 – 1)(2 – 1) = 2 degrees of freedom is 9.21.
1.95 is less than 9.21, so there is no evidence of an association between the choice of fertiliser and the strength of plant growth.

11 The expected proportions are derived from normal distribution tables. Thus the expected proportion for the range from 1 to 2 standard deviations below the mean is 0.4772 – 0.3413 = 0.1359 (ie the values 'At least –2 but below –1') from normal distribution tables. Each proportion is then multiplied by 1,000.

O	*E*	*O – E*	*(O – E)²/E*
40	22.8	17.2	12.98
150	135.9	14.1	1.46
300	341.3	–41.3	5.00
350	341.3	8.7	0.22
100	135.9	–35.9	9.48
60	22.8	37.2	60.69
			89.83

The critical level for 6 – 3 = 3 degrees of freedom and 1% significance is 11.3. The hypothesis should therefore be rejected at this level of significance.

Further question practice

Now try the following practice questions at the end of this text.

Multiple choice questions **55–64**

Exam style question **8**

Chapter 9

CORRELATION AND REGRESSION

Introduction

We are now going to turn our attention to the statistical analysis of two-variable data (sales over time, advertising expenditure and sales revenue, output and costs and so on). Measures of correlation and regression can be thought of as the two-variable equivalents of the one-variable measures of location and dispersion: regression locates two-variable data in terms of a mathematical relationship which can be graphed as a curve or a line and correlation describes the nature of the spread of the items about the curve or line. The overall basic aim of correlation and regression is to ascertain the extent to which one variable is related to another.

Your objectives

After completing this chapter you should:

(a) understand the concept of correlation;

(b) be aware of the difference between partial and perfect correlation and positive and negative correlation;

(c) be able to calculate and interpret the correlation coefficient;

(d) be able to calculate and interpret the coefficient of determination;

(e) be able to calculate and interpret Spearman's rank correlation coefficient and know when to use it;

(f) be able to construct a scattergraph and insert a line of best fit;

(g) be able to estimate a line of best fit using linear regression analysis;

(h) understand the meaning of 'least squares';

(i) be able to interpret regression coefficients;

(j) be aware of the degree of reliance that can be placed on estimates.

NOTES

1 CORRELATION

Definition

Correlation means an inter-relationship or correspondence.

1.1 When the value of one variable is related to the value of another, they are said to be correlated.

1.2 Examples of variables which might be correlated are as follows.

(a) A person's height and weight

(b) The distance of a journey and the time it takes to make it

1.3 One way of showing the correlation between two related variables is on a scattergraph or scatter diagram, plotting a number of pairs of data on the graph.

1.4 For example, a scattergraph showing monthly selling costs against the volume of sales for a 12-month period might be as follows.

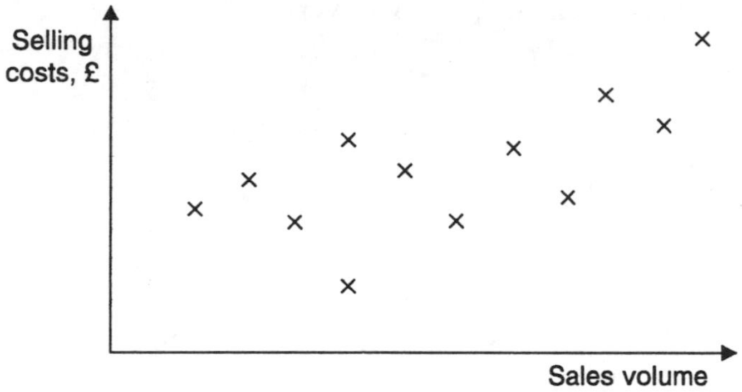

Figure 9.1 A scattergraph

This scattergraph suggests that there is some correlation between selling costs and sales volume, so that as sales volume rises, selling costs tend to rise as well.

Degrees of correlation

1.5 Two variables can be one of the following.

(a) Perfectly correlated

(b) Partly correlated

(c) Uncorrelated

These differing degrees of correlation can be illustrated by scatter diagrams.

1.6 *Perfect correlation*

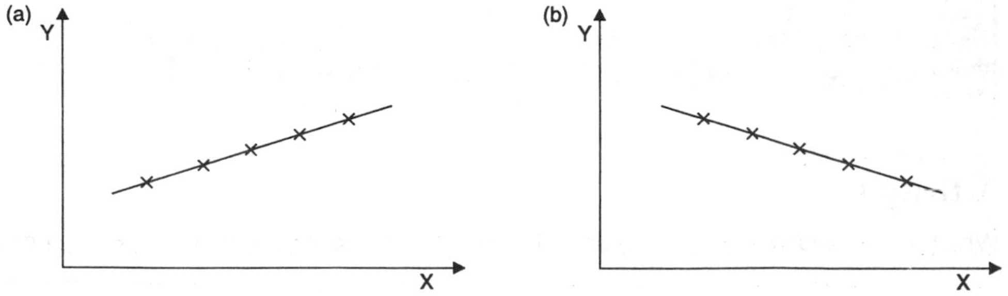

Figure 9.2 Perfect correlation

All the pairs of values lie on a straight line. An exact linear relationship exists between the two variables.

NOTES

1.7 *Partial correlation*

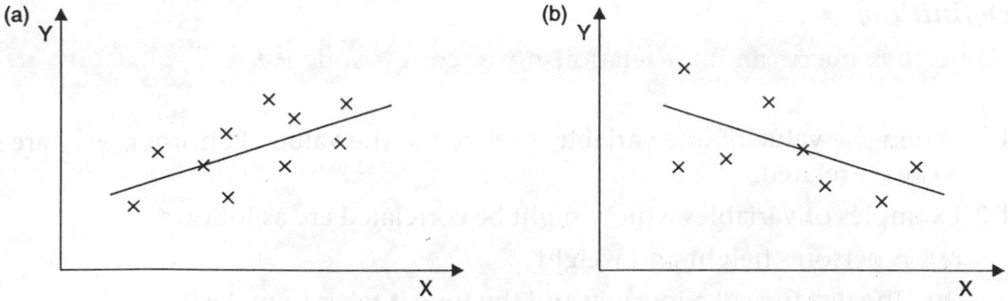

Figure 9.3 Partial correlation

In (a), although there is no exact relationship, low values of X tend to be associated with low values of Y, and high values of X with high values of Y.

In (b), again there is no exact relationship, but low values of X tend to be associated with high values of Y and vice versa.

1.8 *No correlation*

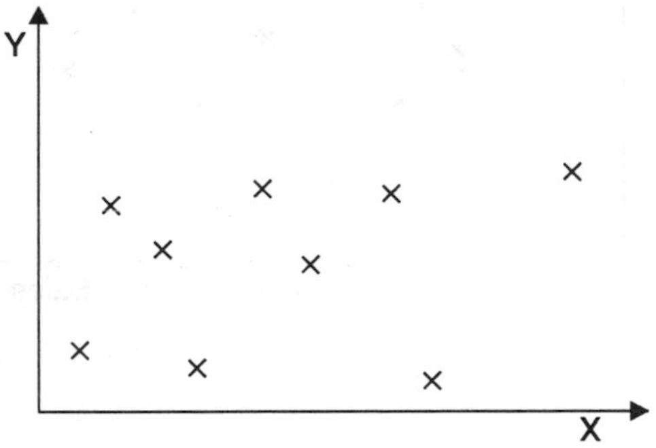

Figure 9.4 No correlation

The values of these two variables are not correlated with each other.

Positive and negative correlation

1.9 Correlation, whether perfect or partial, can be positive or negative.

Definitions

Positive correlation means that low values of one variable are associated with low values of the other, and high values of one variable are associated with high values of the other.

Negative correlation means that low values of one variable are associated with high values of the other, and high values of one variable with low values of the other.

Activity 1

Which of the diagrams in Paragraphs 1.6 and 1.7 demonstrate negative correlation?

NOTES

2 THE PRODUCT MOMENT CORRELATION COEFFICIENT AND THE COEFFICIENT OF DETERMINATION

The correlation coefficient

2.1 The degree of correlation between two variables can be measured, and we can decide, using actual results in the form of pairs of data, whether two variables are perfectly or partially correlated, and if they are partially correlated, whether there is a high or low degree of partial correlation.

2.2 This degree of correlation is measured by the product moment correlation coefficient (the coefficient of correlation), r (also called the Pearsonian correlation coefficient).

Definition

The *coefficient of correlation/product moment correlation coefficient/Pearsonian correlation coefficient* measures the degree of correlation between two variables.

There are several formulae for the correlation coefficient, although each formula will give the same value. These include the following.

2.3 Correlation coefficient, $r = \dfrac{n\Sigma xy - \Sigma x\Sigma y}{\sqrt{\left[n\Sigma x^2 - (\Sigma x)^2\right]\left[n\Sigma y^2 - (\Sigma y)^2\right]}}$

where x and y represent pairs of data for two variables x and y, and n is the number of pairs of data used in the analysis.

This is the formula which will be used in subsequent examples.

2.4 r must always fall between –1 and +1. If you get a value outside this range you have made a mistake.

r = +1 means that the variables are *perfectly positively correlated*
r = –1 means that the variables are *perfectly negatively correlated*
r = 0 means that the variables are *uncorrelated*

EXAMPLE: THE CORRELATION COEFFICENT

The cost of output at a factory is thought to depend on the number of units produced. Data have been collected for the number of units produced each month in the last six months, and the associated costs, as follows.

Month	*Output* '000s *of units*	*Cost* £'000
	x	*y*
1	2	9
2	3	11
3	1	7
4	4	13
5	3	11
6	5	15

Required

Assess whether there is there any correlation between output and cost.

Solution

$$r = \frac{n\Sigma xy - \Sigma x\Sigma y}{\sqrt{\left[n\Sigma x^2 - (\Sigma x)^2\right]\left[n\Sigma y^2 - (\Sigma y)^2\right]}}$$

NOTES

EXAMPLE *continued*

We need to find the values for the following.

(a) Σxy Multiply each value of x by its corresponding y value, so that there are six values for xy. Add up the six values to get the total.

(b) Σx Add up the six values of x to get a total. $(\Sigma x)^2$ will be the square of this total.

(c) Σy Add up the six values of y to get a total. $(\Sigma y)^2$ will be the square of this total.

(d) Σx^2 Find the square of each value of x, so that there are six values for x^2. Add up these values to get a total.

(e) Σy^2 Find the square of each value of y, so that there are six values for y^2. Add up these values to get a total.

Workings

x	y	xy	x^2	y^2
2	9	18	4	81
3	11	33	9	121
1	7	7	1	49
4	13	52	16	169
3	11	33	9	121
5	15	75	25	225
$\Sigma x = 18$	$\Sigma y = 66$	$\Sigma xy = 218$	$\Sigma x^2 = 64$	$\Sigma y^2 = 766$

$(\Sigma x)^2 = 18^2 = 324$ $(\Sigma y)^2 = 66^2 = 4{,}356$

$$n = 6$$

$$r = \frac{(6 \times 218) - (18 \times 66)}{\sqrt{(6 \times 64 - 324) \times (6 \times 766 - 4{,}356)}}$$

$$= \frac{1{,}308 - 1{,}188}{\sqrt{(384 - 324) \times (4{,}596 - 4{,}356)}}$$

$$= \frac{120}{\sqrt{60 \times 240}} = \frac{120}{\sqrt{14{,}400}} = \frac{120}{120} = 1$$

There is perfect positive correlation between the volume of output at the factory and costs.

Correlation in a time series

2.5 Correlation exists in a time series if there is a relationship between the period of time and the recorded value for that period of time. The correlation coefficient is calculated with time as the x variable although it is convenient to use simplified values for x instead of year numbers.

For example, instead of having a series of years 1987 to 1991, we could have values for x from 0 (1987) to 4 (1991).

Note that whatever starting value you use for x (be it 0, 1, 2, ..., 721, ..., 953), the value of r will always be the same.

Activity 2

Sales of product A between 19X7 and 19Y1 were as follows.

Year	*Units sold ('000s)*
19X7	20
19X8	18
19X9	15
19Y0	14
19Y1	11

Required

Determine whether there is a trend in sales. In other words, decide whether there is any correlation between the year and the number of units sold.

The coefficient of determination, r^2

2.6 Unless the correlation coefficient r is exactly or very nearly +1, –1 or 0, its meaning or significance is a little unclear. For example, if the correlation coefficient for two variables is +0.8, this would tell us that the variables are positively correlated, but the correlation is not perfect. It would not really tell us much else. A more meaningful analysis is available from the square of the correlation coefficient, r^2, which is called the coefficient of determination.

Definition

The *coefficient of determination, r^2* (alternatively R^2), measures the proportion of the total variation in the value of one variable that can be explained by variations in the value of the other variable.

2.7 In the activity above, r = –0.992, therefore $r^2 = 0.984$. This means that over 98% of variations in sales can be explained by the passage of time, leaving 0.016 (less than 2%) of variations to be explained by other factors.

2.8 Similarly, if the correlation coefficient between a company's output volume and maintenance costs was 0.9, r^2 would be 0.81, meaning that 81% of variations in maintenance costs could be explained by variations in output volume, leaving only 19% of variations to be explained by other factors (such as the age of the equipment).

2.9 Note, however, that if $r^2 = 0.81$, we would say that 81% of the variations in y can be explained by variations in x. We do not necessarily conclude that 81% of variations in y are caused by the variations in x. We must beware of reading too much significance into our statistical analysis.

Non-linear relationships

2.10 The formulae used above for r and r^2 only work for linear or near linear relationships. All the points on a scatter diagram might lie on a smooth curve as follows.

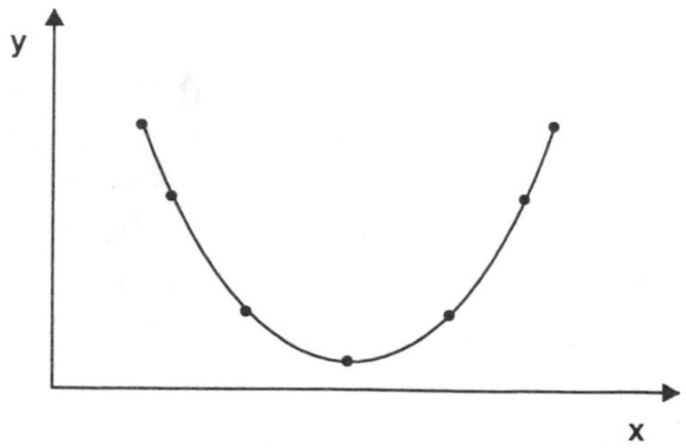

Figure 9.5 Non-linear relationship

If the formula for r were used in a situation such as this, a low value of r would be obtained, suggesting that very little correlation exists, whereas in fact the two sets of variables are perfectly correlated by a non-linear relationship. There are methods of testing correlations of this type, but they are outside the scope of this Study Guide.

Correlation and causation

2.11 If two variables are well correlated, either positively or negatively, this may be due to pure chance or there may be a reason for it. The larger the number of pairs of data collected, the less likely it is that the correlation is due to chance, though that possibility should never be ignored entirely.

2.12 If there is a reason, it may not be causal. For example, monthly net income is well correlated with monthly credit to a person's bank account, for the logical (rather than causal) reason that for most people the one equals the other.

2.13 Even if there is a causal explanation for a correlation, it does not follow that variations in the value of one variable cause variations in the value of the other. For example, sales of ice cream and of sunglasses are well correlated, not because of a direct causal link but because the weather influences both variables.

2.14 Having said this, it is of course possible that where two variables are correlated, there is a direct causal link to be found.

3 SPEARMAN'S RANK CORRELATION COEFFICIENT

3.1 In the examples considered above, the data were given in terms of the values of the relevant variables, such as the number of units. Sometimes however, they are given in terms of order or rank rather than actual values. When this occurs, a correlation coefficient known as *Spearman's rank correlation coefficient*, R, should be calculated using the following formula.

$$\text{Coefficient of rank correlation } R_s = 1 - \left[\frac{6\Sigma d^2}{n(n^2 - 1)}\right]$$

where n = number of pairs of data

d = the difference between the rankings in each set of data.

Definition

Spearman's rank correlation coefficient, R, is used to measure the correlation between the order or rank of two variables.

The coefficient of rank correlation can be interpreted in exactly the same way as the ordinary correlation coefficient. Its value can range from –1 to +1.

NOTES

EXAMPLE: THE RANK CORRELATION COEFFICIENT

The examination placings of seven students were as follows.

Student	*Statistics placing*	*Economics placing*
A	2	1
B	1	3
C	4	7
D	6	5
E	5	6
F	3	2
G	7	4

Required

Judge whether the placings of the students in statistics correlate with their placings in economics.

Solution

Correlation must be measured by Spearman's coefficient because we are given the placings of students, and not their actual marks.

$$R = 1 - \left[\frac{6\Sigma d^2}{n(n^2-1)}\right]$$

where d is the difference between the rank in statistics and the rank in economics for each student.

Student	*Rank statistics*	*Rank economics*	*d*	*d^2*
A	2	1	1	1
B	1	3	2	4
C	4	7	3	9
D	6	5	1	1
E	5	6	1	1
F	3	2	1	1
G	7	4	3	9
			Σd^2 =	26

$$R = 1 - \frac{6 \times 26}{7 \times (49-1)} = 1 - \frac{156}{336} = 0.536$$

The correlation is positive, 0.536, but the correlation is not strong.

Tied ranks

3.2 If in a problem some of the items tie for a particular ranking, these must be given an average place before the coefficient of rank correlation is calculated. Here is an example.

Position of students in examination			*Express as*
A	1 =	average of 1 and 2	1.5
B	1 =		1.5
C	3		3
D	4		4
E	5 =	average of 5, 6 and 7	6
F	5 =		6
G	5 =		6
H	8		8

NOTES

Activity 3

Five artists were placed in order of merit by two different judges as follows.

Artist	*Judge P* *Rank*	*Judge Q* *Rank*
A	1	4 =
B	2 =	1
C	4	3
D	5	2
E	2 =	4 =

Required

Assess how the two sets of rankings are correlated.

4 LINES OF BEST FIT

4.1 The correlation coefficient measures the degree of correlation between two variables, but it does not tell us how to predict values for one variable (y) given values for the other variable (x). To do that, we need to find a line which is a good fit for the points on a scattergraph, and then use that line to find the value of y corresponding to each given value of x.

4.2 We will be looking at two ways of doing this, the scattergraph method and linear regression using the least squares method.

5 THE SCATTERGRAPH METHOD

Definition

The *scattergraph method* is to plot pairs of data for two related variables on a graph, to produce a scattergraph, and then to *use judgement* to draw what seems to be a line of best fit through the data.

5.1 For example, suppose we have the following pairs of data about sales revenue and advertising expenditure.

Period	*Advertising expenditure* £	*Sales revenue* £
1	17,000	180,000
2	33,000	270,000
3	34,000	320,000
4	42,000	350,000
5	19,000	240,000
6	41,000	300,000
7	26,000	320,000
8	27,000	230,000

These pairs of data would be plotted on a scattergraph (the horizontal axis representing the independent variable and the vertical axis the dependent) and a line of best fit might be judged as the one shown below. It was drawn to pass through the middle of the data points, thereby having as many data points below the line as above it.

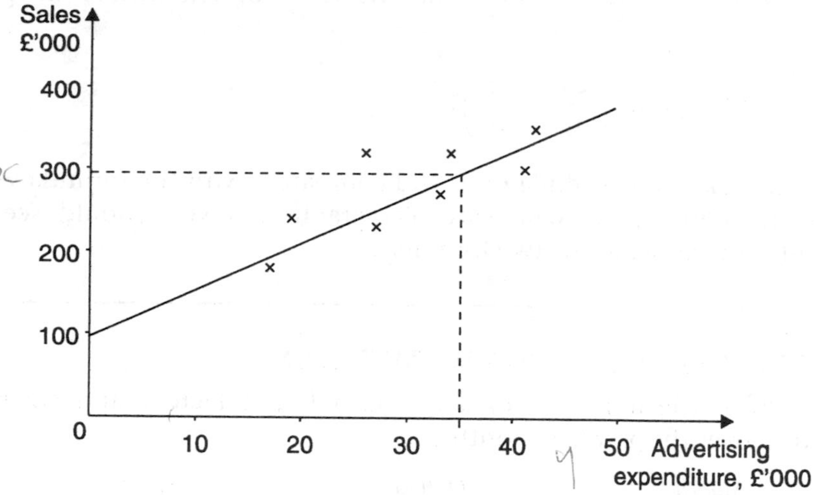

Figure 9.6 The scattergraph method

5.2 Suppose the company to which these data relate wants a forecast sales figure, given a marketing decision to spend £35,000 on advertising. An estimate of sales can be read directly from the scattergraph as shown (£290,000).

6 LINEAR REGRESSION USING THE LEAST SQUARES METHOD

Definition

The *least squares method of linear regression analysis* provides a technique for estimating the equation of a line of best fit.

6.1 The equation of a straight line has the form $y = a + bx$

where x and y are related variables
x is the independent variable
y is the dependent variable
a is the intercept of the line on the vertical axis
and b is the gradient of the line.

6.2 The least squares method provides estimates for the values of a and b using the following formulae.

$$b = \frac{n\Sigma xy - \Sigma x\Sigma y}{n\Sigma x^2 - (\Sigma x)^2}$$

$$a = \frac{\Sigma y}{n} - \frac{b\Sigma x}{n}$$

where n is the number of pairs of data.

6.3 There are some points to note about these formulae.

(a) The line of best fit that is derived represents the *regression of y upon x*.

A different line of best fit could be obtained by interchanging x and y in the formulae. This would then represent the *regression of x upon y* ($x = a + by$) and it would have a slightly different slope. For examination purposes, always use the regression of y upon x, where x is the independent variable,

NOTES

and y is the dependent variable whose value we wish to forecast for given values of x. In a time series, x will represent time.

(b) Since $a = \frac{\Sigma y}{n} - \frac{b\Sigma x}{n}$, it follows that the line of best fit must *always* pass through the point $\left(\frac{\Sigma y}{n}, \frac{\Sigma x}{n}\right)$.

(c) If you look at the formula for b and compare it with the formula we gave for the correlation coefficient (Paragraph 2.3) you should see some similarities between the two formulae.

EXAMPLE: THE LEAST SQUARES METHOD

You are given the following data for output at a factory and costs of production over the past five months.

Month	*Output* *x* *'000 units*	*Costs* *y* *£'000*
1	20	82
2	16	70
3	24	90
4	22	85
5	18	73

There is a high degree of correlation between output and costs, and so it is decided to calculate fixed costs and the variable cost per unit of output using the least squares method.

Required

(a) Calculate an equation to determine the expected level of costs, for any given volume of output.

(b) Prepare a budget for total costs if output is 22,000 units.

(c) Confirm that the degree of correlation between output and costs is high by calculating the correlation coefficient.

Solution

(a) *Workings*

x	*y*	*xy*	x^2	y^2
20	82	1,640	400	6,724
16	70	1,120	256	4,900
24	90	2,160	576	8,100
22	85	1,870	484	7,225
18	73	1,314	324	5,329
$\Sigma x = 100$	$\Sigma y = 400$	$\Sigma xy = 8{,}104$	$\Sigma x^2 = 2{,}040$	$\Sigma y^2 = 32{,}278$

n = 5 (There are five pairs of data for x and y values)

$$b = \frac{n\Sigma xy - \Sigma x\Sigma y}{n\Sigma x^2 - (\Sigma x)^2}$$

$$= \frac{(5 \times 8{,}104) - (100 \times 400)}{(5 \times 2{,}040) - 100^2}$$

EXAMPLE ***continued***

$$= \frac{40{,}520 - 40{,}000}{10{,}200 - 10{,}000} = \frac{520}{200}$$

$$= 2.6$$

$$a = \frac{\Sigma y}{n} - \frac{b\Sigma x}{n}$$

$$= \frac{400}{5} - 2.6 \times \left(\frac{100}{5}\right)$$

$$= 28$$

$$y = 28 + 2.6x$$

where y = total cost, in thousands of pounds
x = output, in thousands of units.

(b) If the output is 22,000 units, we would expect costs to be

$28 + 2.6 \times 22 = 85.2 = £85{,}200.$

(c) $$r = \frac{520}{\sqrt{200 \times (5 \times 32{,}278 - 400^2)}}$$

$$= \frac{520}{\sqrt{200 \times 1{,}390}} = \frac{520}{527.3} = +0.99$$

Activity 4

The expense claims and recorded car mileages on company business, relating to a particular day, of a sample of salesmen of a company are as follows.

Salesman	*Mileage*	*Expenses* £
A	100	60
B	80	48
C	20	20
D	120	55
E	70	38
F	50	38
G	80	44
H	40	30
I	50	40
J	60	50

Required

(a) Plot the data on a scatter diagram.

(b) Determine, by the method of least squares, a linear model to predict expenses, mileage having been given.

(c) Plot the model on your scatter diagram.

(d) Three further salesmen submit expense claims with mileages as follows.

Salesman	*Mileage*	*Expenses £*
K	110	64
L	30	48
M	160	80

Discuss in each case whether or not the claim is reasonable.

Regression lines and time series

6.4 The same technique can be applied to calculate a regression line (a trend line) for a time series. This is particularly useful for purposes of forecasting. As with correlation, years can be numbered from 0 upwards.

Activity 5

Sales of product B over the seven year period from 19X1 to 19X7 were as follows.

Year	*Sales of B '000 units*
19X1	22
19X2	25
19X3	24
19X4	26
19X5	29
19X6	28
19X7	30

There is high correlation between time and the volume of sales.

Required

Calculate the trend line of sales, and forecast sales in 19X8 and 19X9.

The meaning of 'least squares'

6.5 The term 'squares' in 'least squares regression analysis' refers to the squares of the differences between actual values of the dependent variable (y) and predicted values given by the regression line of best fit. These differences are referred to as *residuals* or *residual errors*. 'Least squares' means that the line of best fit that is calculated is the one that minimises the sum of the squares of all the residuals. The differences are measured vertically on a graph, not at an angle to take the shortest route to the regression line.

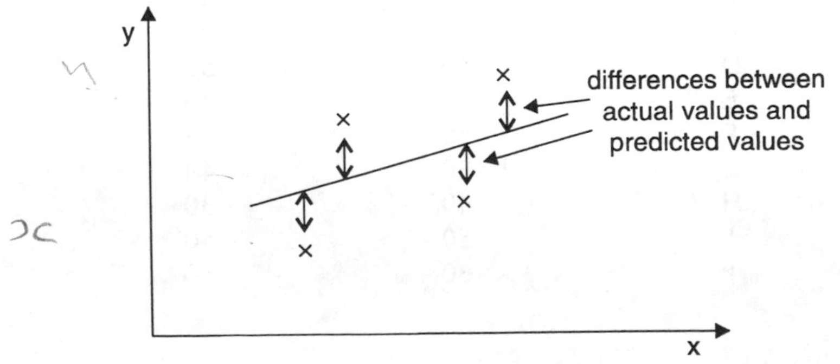

Figure 9.7 Graph showing 'least squares' method

7 INTERPRETATION OF THE REGRESSION COEFFICIENTS

7.1 We said earlier that the least squares method of linear regression analysis provides estimates for a and b and, given values for x and y, you should now be able to determine a and b yourself.

7.2 a and b are known as the coefficients of the regression line y = a + bx but what do they actually mean?

7.3 We explained in Paragraph 6.1 that a is the intercept of the line of best fit on the vertical axis. The scatter diagram from Activity 4 has been reproduced after Paragraph 7.6 but the regression line has been extended so that it meets the y axis. The intercept of this line on the y axis would appear to be approximately 18 or 19; the value of a was calculated as 18.18 using linear regression analysis. This means that when mileage is zero, expenses are £18.00. In other words, there are other costs, unrelated to the distance travelled, of £18 per day. These might include subsistence costs.

7.4 b is the gradient or slope of the line of best fit. The slope of a line is dependent upon the change in y for an increase in x. In diagram (a) below, an increase in the value of x from 5 to 6 produces an increase in y of 10 from 10 to 20. In diagram b, a similar increase in x produces an increase of 5 in y.

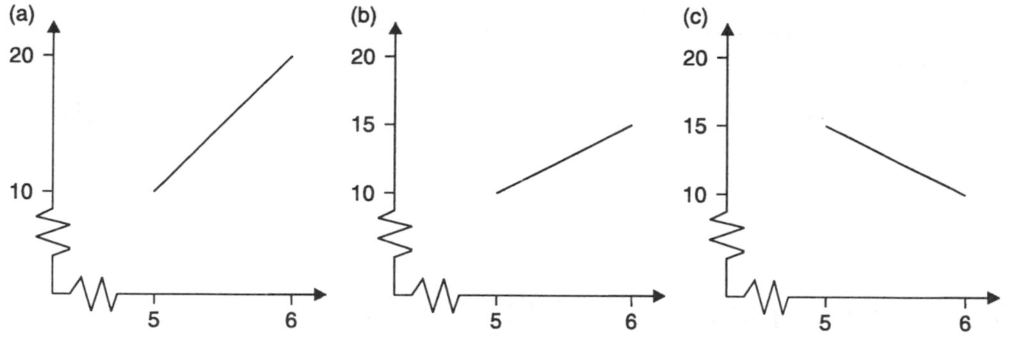

Figure 9.8 Graphs showing different gradients

$$\text{The gradient of the line in a} = \frac{\text{change in y}}{\text{increase in x}} = \frac{20-10}{6-5} = \frac{10}{1} = 10$$

$$\text{The gradient of the line in b} = \frac{\text{change in y}}{\text{increase in x}} = \frac{15-10}{6-5} = 5$$

$$\text{The gradient of the line in c} = \frac{\text{change in y}}{\text{increase in x}} = \frac{10-15}{6-5} = -5$$

In (a) and (b), y *increases* as x *increases* and the gradient is *positive*. In (c), however, y *decreases* as x *increases* and hence the gradient is *negative*.

7.5 In numerical terms the gradient gives the rate of change in y for an increase in x.

7.6 In the scatter diagram below the gradient $= \dfrac{\text{change in y}}{\text{increase in x}} = \dfrac{61-18}{120} = 0.36$

NOTES

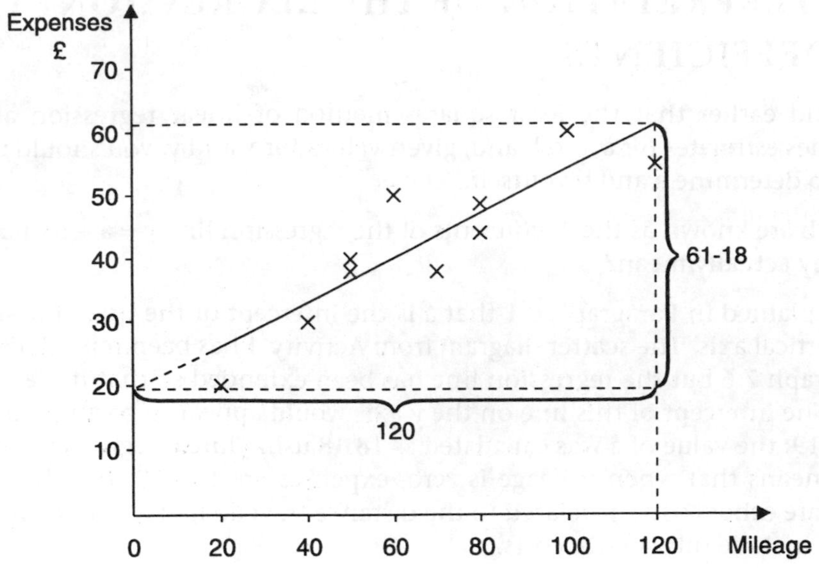

Figure 9.9 Scatter diagram of expenses and mileage

This means that an increase of one mile travelled produces an increase in costs of £0.36. The coefficient 0.36 therefore indicates that there is a variable motoring cost of 36p per mile on average.

Activity 6

Interpret the coefficients of the regression line determined in the example following Paragraph 6.3.

8 RELIABILITY OF ESTIMATES

8.1 The coefficient of determination (r^2) which is computed by squaring the correlation coefficient provides an estimate of the variation in y which is due to the regression (ie changes in the other variable). In Activity 5, r = 0.94 (working shown below) and so $r^2 = 0.884$. This tells us that 88.4% of the variation in sales can be explained by the variation in time. This would suggest that a fairly large degree of reliance can be placed on the estimate for 19X8 and 19X9.

We do not necessarily conclude that 88.4% of variations in y are caused by variations in time. It might be that high sales happened to coincide with a general economic boom, which was the real cause of increase.

$$r = \frac{(7 \times 587) - (21 \times 184)}{\sqrt{[(7 \times 91) - (21 \times 21)] \times [(7 \times 4{,}886) - (184 \times 184)]}}$$

$$= \frac{4{,}109 - 3{,}864}{\sqrt{(637 - 441) \times (34{,}202 - 33{,}856)}}$$

$$= \frac{245}{\sqrt{196 \times 346}} = \frac{245}{260.4}$$

$$= 0.94$$

8.2 If there is a perfect linear relationship between x and y (r = ±1) then we can predict y from any given value of x with great confidence.

8.3 If correlation is high (for example r = 0.9) the actual values will all lie quite close to the regression line and so predictions should not be far out. If correlation is below about 0.7, predictions will only give a very rough guide as to the likely value of y.

8.4 As with any analytical process, the amount of data available is very important. Even if correlation is high, if we have fewer than about 10 pairs of values, we must regard any estimate as being somewhat unreliable.

8.5 When calculating a line of best fit, there will be a range of values for x. In the least squares method example following paragraph 6.3 the line y = 28 + 2.6x was predicted from data with output values ranging from x = 16 to x = 24. Depending on the degree of correlation between x and y, we might safely use the estimated line of best fit to predict values for y, provided that the value of x remains within the range 16 to 24. We would be on less safe ground if we used the formula to predict a value for y when x = 10, or 30, or any other value outside the range 16 – 24, because we would have to assume that the trend line applies outside the range of x values used to establish the line in the first place.

(a) Interpolation means using a line of best fit to predict a value within the two extreme points of the observed range.

(b) Extrapolation means using a line of best fit to predict a value outside the two extreme points.

9 THE ADVANTAGES AND DISADVANTAGES OF REGRESSION ANALYSIS

9.1 The advantages of the least squares method of regression analysis are as follows.

(a) It can be used to estimate a line of best fit using all the data available. It is likely to provide a more reliable estimate than any other technique of producing a straight line of best fit (for example, estimating by eye).

(b) The reliability of the estimated line can be evaluated by calculating the correlation coefficient r.

9.2 The disadvantages of the method are as follows.

(a) It assumes a linear relationship between the two variables, whereas a non-linear relationship may exist.

(b) It assumes that what has happened in the past will provide a reliable guide to the future. For example, if a line is calculated for total costs of production, based on historical data, the estimate could be used to budget for future costs. However, if there has been cost inflation, a productivity agreement with the workforce, a move to new premises, the dismissal of large numbers of office staff and the introduction of new equipment, future costs of production might bear no relation to costs in the past.

(c) The technique assumes that the value of one variable, y, can be predicted or estimated from the value of one other variable, x. In reality, the value of y might depend on several other variables, not just on x.

Chapter roundup

- When the value of one variable is related to the value of another, they are said to be correlated.
- Two variables might be perfectly correlated, partly correlated or uncorrelated. Correlation can be positive or negative.
- The degree of correlation between two variables is measured by the product moment correlation coefficient, r. The nearer r is to +1 or –1, the stronger the relationship.
- The coefficient of determination, r^2, measures the proportion of the total variation in the value of one variable that can be explained by the variation in the value of the other variable.
- Spearman's rank correlation coefficient is used when data is given in terms of order or rank rather than actual values.
- The scattergraph method involves the use of judgement to draw what seems to be a line of best fit through plotted data.
- Linear regression analysis (the least squares method) is one technique for estimating a line of best fit. Ensure that you know how to use the formulae to calculate a and b in y = a + bx.
- Correlation and regression analysis do not indicate cause and effect. Even if r = 1, the correlation could still be spurious, both variables being influenced by a third.

Quick quiz

1 Give some examples of variables which might be correlated.

2 Distinguish between positive and negative correlation.

3 What range of values can the product moment correlation coefficient take?

4 How should the coefficient of determination be interpreted?

5 When should Spearman's rank correlation coefficient be used?

6 What is the scattergraph method for finding a line of best fit?

7 When using the least squares method of linear regression, does it matter which variable is chosen as x?

8 What is a residual?

9 What are the advantages and disadvantages of the least squares method of linear regression?

NOTES

Answers to activities

1 Diagrams in Paragraphs 1.6 (b) and 1.7 (b)

2 *Workings*

Let 19X7 to 19Y1 be years 0 to 4.

x	*y*	*xy*	x^2	y^2
0	20	0	0	400
1	18	18	1	324
2	15	30	4	225
3	14	42	9	196
4	11	44	16	121
$\Sigma x = 10$	$\Sigma y = 78$	$\Sigma xy = 134$	$\Sigma x^2 = 30$	$\Sigma y^2 = 1{,}266$

$(\Sigma x)^2 = 100$ $\quad$ $(\Sigma y)^2 = 6{,}084$

$n = 5$

$$r = \frac{(5\times134)-(10\times78)}{\sqrt{(5\times30-100)\times(5\times1{,}266-6{,}084)}}$$

$$= \frac{670-780}{\sqrt{(150-100)\times(6{,}330-6{,}084)}} = \frac{-110}{\sqrt{50\times246}}$$

$$= \frac{-110}{\sqrt{12{,}300}} = \frac{-110}{110.90537} = -0.992$$

There is partial negative correlation between the year of sale and units sold. The value of r is close to –1, therefore a high degree of correlation exists, although it is not quite perfect correlation. This means that there is a clear downward trend in sales.

3

	Judge P Rank	*Judge Q Rank*	*d*	d^2
A	1.0	4.5	3.5	12.25
B	2.5	1.0	1.5	2.25
C	4.0	3.0	1.0	1.00
D	5.0	2.0	3.0	9.00
E	2.5	4.5	2.0	4.00
				28.50

$$R = 1 - \frac{6\times28.5}{5\times(25-1)} = -0.425$$

There is a slight negative correlation between the rankings.

4 (a)

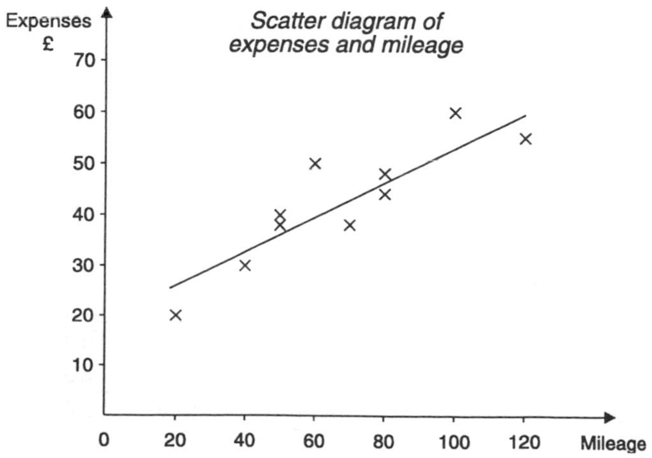

(b) The independent variable, x, is the mileage. The dependent variable, y, is the expenses in pounds.

NOTES

x	y	x^2	xy
100	60	10,000	6,000
80	48	6,400	3,840
20	20	400	400
120	55	14,400	6,600
70	38	4,900	2,660
50	38	2,500	1,900
80	44	6,400	3,520
40	30	1,600	1,200
50	40	2,500	2,000
60	50	3,600	3,000
670	423	52,700	31,120

$$b = \frac{(10 \times 31{,}120) - (670 \times 423)}{10 \times 52{,}700 - 670^2}$$

$$= \frac{311{,}200 - 283{,}410}{527{,}000 - 448{,}900}$$

$$= \frac{27{,}790}{78{,}100}$$

$$= 0.36$$

$$a = \frac{423}{10} - 0.36 \times \frac{670}{10} = 18.18$$

The linear model is y = 18.18 + 0.36x.

(c) The line may be plotted using two points as follows.

x = 20, y = 25.38

x = 120, y = 61.38

The line is plotted on the graph above.

(d) For mileage of 110 miles, the model would predict expenses of 18.18 + (0.36 ×110) = £57.78, so K's claim of £64 is not unreasonably high.

For mileage of 30 miles, the model would predict expenses of 18.18 + (0.36 ×30) = £28.98, so L's claim of £48 is very high and should be investigated.

The model is based on data for mileages from 20 to 120 miles. It should not be used to extrapolate to 160 miles, but if it were to be so used it would predict expenses of 18.18 + (0.36 × 160) = £75.78. On this basis, M's claim for £80 is not unreasonable.

5 Workings

Year	x	y	xy	x^2
19X1	0	22	0	0
19X2	1	25	25	1
19X3	2	24	48	4
19X4	3	26	78	9
19X5	4	29	116	16
19X6	5	28	140	25
19X7	6	30	180	36
	$\Sigma x = 21$	$\Sigma y = 184$	$\Sigma xy = 587$	$\Sigma x^2 = 91$

n = 7

Where y = a + bx

$$b = \frac{(7 \times 587) - (21 \times 184)}{(7 \times 91) - (21 \times 21)}$$

$$= \frac{245}{196}$$

$$= 1.25$$

$$a = \frac{184}{7} - \frac{1.25 \times 21}{7}$$

$$= 22.5357, \text{ say } 22.5$$

$y = 22.5 + 1.25x$ where $x = 0$ in 19X1, $x = 1$ in 19X2 and so on.

Using this trend line, predicted sales in 19X8 (year 7) would be

$22.5 + 1.25 \times 7 = 31.25$ = 31,250 units.

Similarly, for 19X9 (year 8) predicted sales would be

$22.5 + 1.25 \times 8 = 32.50$ = 32,500 units.

6 The coefficient $a = 28$ indicates that when there is no output costs of £28,000 will still be incurred. In other words, fixed costs are £28,000.

The coefficient $b = 2.6$ indicates as output levels increase by one unit, costs increase by £2.60. The variable cost per unit is therefore £2.60.

Further question practice

Now try the following practice questions at the end of this text.

Multiple choice questions	**65–71**
Exam style question	**9**

Chapter 10

TIME SERIES ANALYSIS

Introduction

In Chapter 9 we looked at how the relationship between two variables, and the strength of that relationship, can be assessed. This chapter looks at how the relationship between a variable (such as turnover, customer levels, output) and time can be analysed so as to forecast future values for the variable.

Your objectives

After completing this chapter you should:

(a) know what a time series is;

(b) know what a historigram is;

(c) be able to describe the components of a time series;

(d) be able to find the trend using moving averages;

(e) be able to find seasonal variations using both the additive and multiplicative models;

(f) be able to forecast by extrapolating a trend and adjusting for seasonal variations;

(g) understand the concept of residuals;

(h) be aware of the concept of deseasonalisation.

NOTES

1 THE COMPONENTS OF TIME SERIES

Definition

A *time series* is a series of figures or values recorded over time.

1.1 The following are examples of time series.

(a) Output at a factory each day for the last month

(b) Monthly sales over the last two years

(c) Total annual costs for the last 10 years

(d) The Retail Prices Index each month for the last 10 years

(e) The number of people employed by a company each year for the last 20 years

Definition

A graph of a time series is called a *historigram*. (Note the 'ri'; this is not the same as a histogram.)

1.2 Consider the following time series.

Year	*Sales* *£'000*
19X0	20
19X1	21
19X2	24
19X3	23
19X4	27
19X5	30
19X6	28

The historigram is as follows.

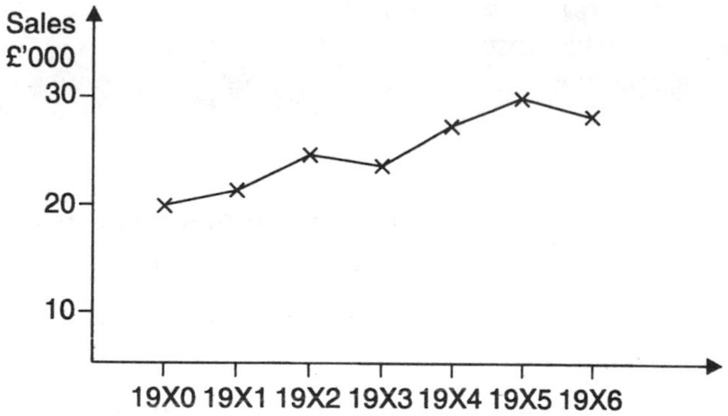

Figure 10.1 An historigram

The horizontal axis is always chosen to represent time, and the vertical axis represents the values of the data recorded.

1.3 There are several features of a time series which it may be necessary to identify.

(a) A trend

(b) Seasonal variations or fluctuations

(c) Cycles, or cyclical variations

(d) Non-recurring, random variations. These may be caused by unforeseen circumstances, such as a change in the government of the country, a war, the collapse of a company, technological change or a fire.

NOTES

The trend

Definition

The *trend* is the underlying long-term movement over time in the values of the data recorded.

1.4 In the following examples of time series, there are three types of trend.

	Output per labour hour Units	*Cost per unit* £	*Number of employees*
19X4	30	1.00	100
19X5	24	1.08	103
19X6	26	1.20	96
19X7	22	1.15	102
19X8	21	1.18	103
19X9	17	1.25	98
	(A)	(B)	(C)

(a) In time series (A) there is a downward trend in the output per labour hour. Output per labour hour did not fall every year, because it went up between 19X5 and 19X6, but the long-term movement is clearly a downward one.

(b) In time series (B) there is an upward trend in the cost per unit. Although unit costs went down in 19X7 from a higher level in 19X6, the basic movement over time is one of rising costs.

(c) In time series (C) there is no clear movement up or down, and the number of employees remained fairly constant around 100. The trend is therefore a static, or level one.

Seasonal variations

Definition

Seasonal variations are short-term fluctuations in recorded values, due to different circumstances which affect results at different times of the year, on different days of the week, at different times of day, or whatever.

1.5 Here are some examples.

(a) Sales of ice cream will be higher in summer than in winter, and sales of overcoats will be higher in autumn than in spring.

(b) Shops might expect higher sales shortly before Christmas, or in their winter and summer sales.

(c) Sales might be higher on Friday and Saturday than on Monday.

(d) The telephone network may be heavily used at certain times of the day (such as mid-morning and mid-afternoon) and much less used at other times (such as in the middle of the night).

1.6 'Seasonal' is a term which may appear to refer to the seasons of the year, but its meaning in time series analysis is somewhat broader, as the examples given above show.

NOTES

EXAMPLE: A TREND PLUS SEASONAL VARIATIONS

The number of customers served by a company of travel agents over the past four years is shown in the following historigram.

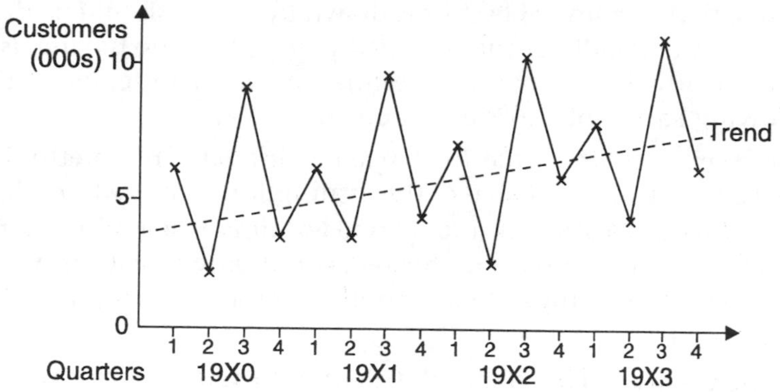

In this example, there would appear to be large seasonal fluctuations in demand, but there is also a basic upward trend.

Activity 1

What seasonal variations would you expect to see in sales of video recorders?

Cyclical variations

1.7 Cyclical variations are medium-term changes in results caused by circumstances which repeat in cycles. In business, cyclical variations are commonly associated with economic cycles, successive booms and slumps in the economy. Economic cycles may last a few years. Cyclical variations are longer term than seasonal variations.

Summarising the components

1.8 In practice a time series could incorporate all four features and, to make reasonably accurate forecasts, the four features often have to be isolated. We can begin the process of isolating each feature by summarising the components of a time series by the following equation

$$Y = T + S + C + R$$

where Y = the actual time series

T = the trend series

S = the seasonal component

C = the cyclical component

R = the residual component

Though you should be aware of the cyclical component, it is unlikely that you will be expected to carry out any calculation connected with isolating it. The mathematical model which we will use, the additive model, therefore excludes any reference to C and is

$$Y = T + S + R$$

We will begin by isolating the trend.

2 FINDING THE TREND

2.1 There are three principal methods of finding a trend.

(a) *Inspection.* As we saw in Chapter 9, the trend line can be drawn by eye on a graph in such a way that it appears to lie evenly between the recorded points, that is, a line of best fit is drawn by eye. It should be drawn to pass through the middle of the recorded points, thereby having as many data points below it as above it. The line on the historigram in the example following Paragraph 1.6 is an example.

(b) *Regression analysis by the least squares method.* This method, which we looked at in Chapter 9, makes the assumption that the trend line, whether up or down, is a straight line. Periods of time (such as quarters for which sales figures are given) are numbered, commonly from 0, and the regression line of the data on those period numbers is found. That line is then taken to be the trend.

(c) *Moving averages.* This method attempts to remove seasonal (or cyclical) variations by a process of averaging and is looked at in detail in the next section.

3 MOVING AVERAGES

Finding the trend by moving averages

Definition

Moving averages are consecutive averages of the results of a fixed number of periods.

3.1 Since a moving average is an average of several time periods, it is related to the mid-point of the overall period.

3.2 Moving averages could cover the sales of a shop over periods of seven days (Monday to the next Sunday for example) or a business's costs over periods of four quarters, or whatever else was appropriate to the circumstances.

EXAMPLE: MOVING AVERAGES

Year	*Sales* *Units*
19X0	390
19X1	380
19X2	460
19X3	450
19X4	470
19X5	440
19X6	500

Required

Take a moving average of the annual sales over a period of three years.

Solution

(a) Average sales in the three year period 19X0 – 19X2 were

$$\left(\frac{390+380+460}{3}\right) = \frac{1,230}{3} = 410$$

NOTES

EXAMPLE *continued*

This average relates to the middle year of the period, 19X1.

(b) Similarly, average sales in the three year period 19X1 – 19X3 were

$$\left(\frac{380+460+450}{3}\right)=\frac{1{,}290}{3}=430$$

This average relates to the middle year of the period, 19X2.

(c) The average sales can also be found for the periods 19X2 – 19X4, 19X3 - 19X5 and 19X4 - 19X6, to give the following.

Year	*Sales*	*Moving total of 3 years' sales*	*Moving average of 3 years' sales (÷ 3)*
19X0	390		
19X1	380	1,230	410
19X2	460	1,290	430
19X3	450	1,380	460
19X4	470	1,360	453
19X5	440	1,410	470
19X6	500		

Note the following points.

(i) The moving average series has five figures relating to the years from 19X1 to 19X5. The original series had seven figures for the years from 19X0 to 19X6.

(ii) There is an upward trend in sales, which is more noticeable from the series of moving averages than from the original series of actual sales each year.

3.3 The above example averaged over a three-year period. Over what period should a moving average be taken? The answer to this question is that the moving average which is most appropriate will depend on the circumstances and the nature of the time series. Note the following points.

(a) A moving average which takes an average of the results in many time periods will represent results over a longer term than a moving average of two or three periods.

(b) On the other hand, with a moving average of results in many time periods, the last figure in the series will be out of date by several periods. In our example, the most recent average related to 19X5. With a moving average of five years' results, the final figure in the series would relate to 19X4.

(c) When there is a known cycle over which seasonal variations occur, such as all the days in the week or all the seasons in the year, the most suitable moving average would be one which covers one full cycle.

Activity 2

Using the following data, what is the three-month moving average for April?

Month	*No of new houses finished*
January	500
February	450
March	700
April	900
May	1,250
June	1,000

Moving averages of an even number of results

3.4 In the previous example, moving averages were taken of the results in an odd number of time periods, and the average then related to the mid-point of the overall period.

3.5 If a moving average were taken of results in an even number of time periods, the basic technique would be the same, but the mid-point of the overall period would not relate to a single period. For example, suppose an average were taken of the following four results.

Spring	120	
Summer	90	average 115
Autumn	180	
Winter	70	

The average would relate to the mid-point of the period, between summer and autumn.

3.6 The trend line average figures need to relate to a particular time period; otherwise, seasonal variations cannot be calculated. To overcome this difficulty, we take a moving average of the moving average. An example will illustrate this technique.

EXAMPLE: MOVING AVERAGES OVER AN EVEN NUMBER OF PERIODS

Calculate a moving average trend line of the following results.

Year	*Quarter*	*Volume of sales '000 units*
19X5	1	600
	2	840
	3	420
	4	720
19X6	1	640
	2	860
	3	420
	4	740
19X7	1	670
	2	900
	3	430
	4	760

Solution

A moving average of four will be used, since the volume of sales would appear to depend on the season of the year, and each year has four quarterly results.

The moving average of four does not relate to any specific period of time; therefore we will take a moving total of pairs of four-quarter totals and divide that moving total by 8 (ie the number of data items which contributed to the total).

EXAMPLE *continued*

Year	*Quarter*	*Actual volume of sales '000 units*	*Moving total of 4 quarters' sales '000 units*	*Moving total of 8 quarters' sales '000 units*	*Mid-point of 2 moving averages Trend line '000 units*
19X5	1	600			
	2	840			
			2,580		
	3	420		5,200	650.00
			2,620		
	4	720		5,260	657.50
			2,640		
19X6	1	640		5,280	660.00
			2,640		
	2	860		5,300	662.50
			2,660		
	3	420		5,350	668.75
			2,690		
	4	740		5,420	677.50
			2,730		
19X7	1	670		5,470	683.75
			2,740		
	2	900		5,500	687.50
			2,760		
	3	430			
	4	760			

The final moving averages are related to specific quarters (from the third quarter of 19X5 to the second quarter of 19X7).

4 FINDING THE SEASONAL VARIATIONS

4.1 Once a trend has been established, by whatever method, we can find the seasonal variations.

4.2 The additive model for time series analysis is Y = T + S + R. We can therefore write Y – T = S + R. In other words, if we deduct the trend series from the actual series, we will be left with the seasonal and residual components of the time series. If we assume that the residual component is relatively small, and hence negligible, the seasonal component can be found as S = Y – T, the de-trended series.

4.3 We will use an example to illustrate the process.

EXAMPLE: THE TREND AND SEASONAL VARIATIONS

Output at a factory appears to vary with the day of the week. Output over the last three weeks has been as follows.

	Week 1 '000 units	*Week 2 '000 units*	*Week 3 '000 units*
Monday	80	82	84
Tuesday	104	110	116
Wednesday	94	97	100
Thursday	120	125	130
Friday	62	64	66

Required

Find the seasonal variation for each of the 15 days, and the average seasonal variation for each day of the week using the moving averages method.

NOTES

EXAMPLE *continued*

Solution

Actual results fluctuate up and down according to the day of the week and so a moving average of five will be used. The difference between the actual result on any one day (Y) and the trend figure for that day (T) will be the seasonal variation (S) for the day.

The seasonal variations for the 15 days are as follows.

		Actual (Y)	*Moving total of five days' output*	*Trend (T)*	*Seasonal variation (Y–T)*
Week 1	Monday	80			
	Tuesday	104			
	Wednesday	94	460	92.0	+2.0
	Thursday	120	462	92.4	+27.6
	Friday	62	468	93.6	–31.6
Week 2	Monday	82	471	94.2	–12.2
	Tuesday	110	476	95.2	+14.8
	Wednesday	97	478	95.6	+1.4
	Thursday	125	480	96.0	+29.0
	Friday	64	486	97.2	–33.2
Week 3	Monday	84	489	97.8	–13.8
	Tuesday	116	494	98.8	+17.2
	Wednesday	100	496	99.2	+0.8
	Thursday	130			
	Friday	66			

	Monday	*Tuesday*	*Wednesday*	*Thursday*	*Friday*
Week 1			+2.0	+27.6	–31.6
Week 2	–12.2	+14.8	+1.4	+29.0	–33.2
Week 3	–13.8	+17.2	+0.8		
Average	–13.0	+16.0	+1.4	+28.3	–32.4

You will notice that the variation between the actual results on any one particular day and the trend line average is not the same from week to week. This is because Y – T contains not only seasonal variations but random variations (residuals). In calculating the averages of the deviations, Y – T, for each day of the week, the residual components are expected to cancel out, or at least to be reduced to a negligible level.

Our estimate of the 'seasonal' or daily variation is almost complete, but there is one more important step to take. Variations around the basic trend line should cancel each other out, and add up to 0. In practice this is rarely the case because of random variation. The average seasonal estimates must therefore be corrected so that they add up to zero.

NOTES

EXAMPLE *continued*

	Mon	*Tues*	*Wed*	*Thurs*	*Fri*	*Total*
Estimated average daily variation	–13.00	+16.00	+1.40	+28.30	–32.40	0.30
Adjustment to reduce total variation to 0	–0.06	–0.06	–0.06	–0.06	–0.06	–0.30
Final estimate of average daily variation	–13.06	+15.94	+1.34	+28.24	–32.46	0.00

These might be rounded up or down as follows.

Monday –13; Tuesday +16; Wednesday +1; Thursday +28; Friday –32; Total 0

Activity 3

Calculate a four-quarter moving average trend centred on actual quarters and then find seasonal variations from the following.

Sales in £'000

	Spring	*Summer*	*Autumn*	*Winter*
19X7	200	120	160	280
19X8	220	140	140	300
19X9	200	120	180	320

Seasonal variations using the multiplicative model

4.4 The method of estimating the seasonal variations in the above example was to use the differences between the trend and actual data. This is called the *additive model.*

Definition

The *additive model* for time series analysis assumes that the components of the series are independent of each other, an increasing trend not affecting the seasonal variations, for example.

4.5 The alternative is to use the *multiplicative model.* Sometimes this method is called the *proportional model.*

Definition

The *multiplicative* or *proportional model* for time series analysis expresses each actual figure as a proportion of the trend.

The model summarises a time series as Y = T × S × R. Note that the trend component will be the same whichever model is used but the values of the seasonal and residual components will vary according to the model being applied.

NOTES

4.6 The example following paragraph 4.3 on seasonal variations can be reworked on this alternative basis. The trend is calculated in exactly the same way as before but we need a different approach for the seasonal variations.

The multiplicative model is $Y = T \times S \times R$ and, just as we calculated $S = Y - T$ for the additive model (Paragraph 4.2) we can calculate $Y/T = S$ for the multiplicative model.

		Actual (Y)	*Trend* (T)	*Seasonal percentage* (Y/T)
Week 1	Monday	80		
	Tuesday	104		
	Wednesday	94	92.0	1.022
	Thursday	120	92.4	1.299
	Friday	62	93.6	0.662
Week 2	Monday	82	94.2	0.870
	Tuesday	110	95.2	1.155
	Wednesday	97	95.6	1.015
	Thursday	125	96.0	1.302
	Friday	64	97.2	0.658
Week 3	Monday	84	97.8	0.859
	Tuesday	116	98.8	1.174
	Wednesday	100	99.2	1.008
	Thursday	130		
	Friday	66		

The summary of the seasonal variations expressed in proportional terms is as follows.

	Monday %	*Tuesday* %	*Wednesday* %	*Thursday* %	*Friday* %
Week 1			1.022	1.299	0.662
Week 2	0.870	1.155	1.015	1.302	0.658
Week 3	0.859	1.174	1.008		
Total	1.729	2.329	3.045	2.601	1.320
Average	0.8645	1.1645	1.0150	1.3005	0.6600

Instead of summing to zero, as with the absolute approach, these should sum (in this case) to 5 (an average of 1).

They actually sum to 5.0045 so 0.0009 has to be deducted from each one. This is too small to make a difference to the figures above, so we should deduct 0.002 and 0.0025 from each of two seasonal variations. We could arbitrarily decrease Monday's variation to 0.8625 and Tuesday's to 1.162.

NOTES

Activity 4

A company's quarterly sales figures have been analysed into a trend and seasonal variations using moving averages. Here is an extract from the analysis.

Year	*Quarter* *£'000*	*Actual* *£'000*	*Trend*
19X1	1	350	366
	2	380	370
	3	400	380
	4	360	394
19X2	1	410	406
	2	430	414
	3	450	418
	4	370	423

Required

Find the average seasonal variation for each quarter, using the multiplicative model.

5 FORECASTING

5.1 Forecasting is an essential, but difficult task of management. Many forecasts are made by guessing, but they are unlikely to be reliable.

5.2 There are several mathematical techniques of forecasting which could be used. These techniques will not necessarily provide accurate forecasts but, on the whole, they are likely to provide more reliable estimates than guesswork. Techniques cannot eliminate uncertainty about the future, but they can help to ensure that managers take account of all currently-known facts in the preparation of their forecasts.

5.3 The technique which will be discussed here is that of extrapolating a trend and then adjusting for seasonal variations.

5.4 Forecasts of future values should be made as follows.

(a) Calculate a trend line using moving averages or regression analysis. You may be asked to plot the trend line on a scatter diagram. It should be drawn as a straight line using the first and last available trend line figures.)

(b) Use the trend line to forecast future trend line values. (You can insert the appropriate value for x (= time) into a regression equation or calculate an average seasonal increase (or decrease) as the following example shows.)

(c) Adjust these values by the average seasonal variation applicable to the future period, to determine the forecast for that period. With the additive model, add (or subtract for negative variations) the variation. With the multiplicative model, multiply the trend value by the variation proportion.

5.5 Extending a trend line outside the range of known data, in this case forecasting the future from a trend line based on historical data, is known as extrapolation.

EXAMPLE: FORECASTING

Sales of product X each quarter for the last three years have been as follows (in thousands of units). Trend values, found by a moving averages method, are shown in brackets.

Year	*1st quarter*	*2nd quarter*	*3rd quarter*	*4th quarter*
1	18	30	20 (18.75)	6 (19.375)
2	20 (20)	33 (20.5)	22 (21)	8 (21.5)
3	22 (22.125)	35 (22.75)	25	10

Average seasonal variations for quarters 1 to 4 are –0.1, +12.4, +1.1 and –13.4 respectively.

Required

Use the trend line and estimates of seasonal variations to forecast sales in each quarter of year 4.

Solution

The trend line indicates an increase of about 0.6 per quarter. This can be confirmed by calculating the average quarterly increase in trend line values between the third quarter of year 1 (18.75) and the second quarter of year 2 (22.75). The average rise is

$$\frac{22.75 - 18.75}{7} = \frac{4}{7} = 0.57, \text{ say } 0.6$$

Taking 0.6 as the quarterly increase in the trend, the forecast of sales for year 4, before seasonal adjustments (the trend line forecast) would be as follows.

Year	*Quarter*			*Trend line*
3	*2nd	(actual trend)	22.75, say	22.8
	3rd			23.4
	4th			24.0
4	1st			24.6
	2nd			25.2
	3rd			25.8
	4th			26.4

* last known trend line value.

Seasonal variations should now be incorporated to obtain the final forecast.

	Quarter	*Trend line forecast '000 units*	*Average seasonal variation '000 units*	*Forecast of actual sales '000 units*
Year 4	1st	24.6	–0.1	24.5
	2nd	25.2	+12.4	37.6
	3rd	25.8	+1.1	26.9
	4th	26.4	–13.4	13.0

If we had been using the multiplicative model, with an average variation for (for example) quarter 3 of 1.057, our prediction for the third quarter of year 4 would have been 25.8 × 1.057 = 27.3.

5.6 Note that the multiplicative model is better than the additive model for forecasting when the trend is increasing or decreasing over time. In such circumstances, seasonal variations are likely to be increasing or decreasing too. The additive model simply adds absolute and unchanging seasonal variations to the trend figures whereas the multiplicative model, by multiplying increasing or decreasing trend values by a constant seasonal variation factor, takes account of changing seasonal variations.

5.7 All forecasts are, however, subject to error, but the likely errors vary from case to case.

(a) The further into the future the forecast is for, the more unreliable it is likely to be.

(b) The less data available on which to base the forecast, the less reliable the forecast.

(c) The pattern of trend and seasonal variations cannot be guaranteed to continue in the future.

(d) There is always the danger of random variations upsetting the pattern of trend and seasonal variation.

Activity 5

The percentage of employees absent from work was recorded over a four-week period as follows.

Week	*Mon*	*Tues*	*Weds*	*Thurs*	*Fri*
1	8.4	5.1	5.7	4.8	6.3
2	8.1	5.5	6.0	4.6	6.5
3	8.4	5.6	6.2	5.0	6.8
4	8.6	5.6	6.3	4.9	6.9

Required

(a) Draw a graph of the time series of absenteeism.

(b) By means of a moving average and the additive model, find the trend and the seasonal adjustments.

(c) Plot the trend line by eye and use it as a basis to forecast daily absenteeism for week 5.

(d) Personnel have suggested that the absenteeism figure for Friday of week 8 could be as high as 8%. Discuss whether or not you would support this.

Residuals

Definition

A *residual* is the difference between the results which would have been predicted (for a past period for which we already have data) by the trend line adjusted for the average seasonal variation and the actual results.

5.8 The residual is therefore the difference which is not explained by the trend line and the average seasonal variation. The residual gives some indication of how much actual results were affected by other factors. Large residuals suggest that any forecast is likely to be unreliable. It is a good idea to calculate the residual series (Y – T – S) in order to assess the adequacy of predictions. This will also test whether the assumption (made in Paragraph 4.2) is reasonable.

NOTES

5.9 In the example following Paragraph 5.5, the 'prediction' for the third quarter of year 1 would have been 18.75 + 1.1 = 19.85. As the actual value was 20, the residual was only 20 – 19.85 = 0.15. The residual for the fourth quarter of year 2 was 8 – (21.5 – 13.4) = 8 – 8.1 = –0.1. An analysis of all the residuals associated with a particular time series will indicate whether the predictions based on the time series are reliable.

6 DESEASONALISATION

6.1 Economic statistics, such as unemployment figures, are often 'seasonally adjusted' or 'deseasonalised' so as to ensure that the overall trend (rising, falling or stationary) is clear. All this means is that seasonal variations (S) (derived from previous data) have been taken out, to leave a figure (Y – S) which might be taken as indicating the trend.

Definition

Deseasonalisation is the process of removing seasonal variations from data to leave a figure indicating the trend.

EXAMPLE: DESEASONALISATION

Actual sales figures for four quarters, together with appropriate seasonal adjustment factors derived from previous data, are as follows.

		Seasonal adjustments	
Quarter	*Actual sales £'000*	*Additive model £'000*	*Multiplicative model*
1	150	+3	1.02
2	160	+4	1.05
3	164	–2	0.98
4	170	–5	0.95

Required

Deseasonalise these data.

Solution

We are reversing the normal process of applying seasonal variations to trend figures, so with the additive model we subtract positive seasonal variations (and add negative ones), and with the multiplicative model we divide by the seasonal variation factors (expressed as proportions).

		Deseasonalised sales	
Quarter	*Actual sales £'000*	*Additive model £'000*	*Multiplicative model £'000*
1	150	147	147
2	160	156	152
3	164	166	167
4	170	175	179

Chapter roundup

- A time series is a series of figures or values recorded over time.
- A time series has four features: a trend, seasonal variations, cyclical variations and random variations (residuals).
- A time series can be summarised by the additive model ($Y = T + S + R$) or the multiplicative (or proportional) model ($Y = T \times S \times R$).
- The most commonly used method in practice for finding the trend is the moving averages method. Once the trend has been established, the seasonal component can be calculated as $Y - T$ (if the additive model is being used) or Y/T (if the multiplicative model is being used).
- A process of averaging and adjusting the individual seasonal components is necessary to remove the effect of any residuals and to arrive at seasonal components for each season of the year, day of the week as necessary.
- By extrapolating the trend line and adjusting the resulting figures for the seasonal component of the time series, forecasts can be obtained
- Calculating the residuals of the time series assesses the adequacy and reliability of the predictions made using the trend and seasonal components.
- Deseasonalised data ($Y - S$) are often used by economic commentators.

Quick quiz

1 What is the definition of a time series?

2 What are the four components that combine to form a time series?

3 How can trend lines be found?

4 How are trend values calculated when moving averages of an even number of results are taken?

5 Why are average seasonal variations adjusted to sum to zero?

6 Distinguish between the additive model and the multiplicative model of time series.

7 In what circumstances should the proportional model rather than the additive model be used?

8 Describe how the additive model may be used in forecasting.

9 What is extrapolation?

10 What is the term for the difference which is not explained by the trend line and the average seasonal variation?

NOTES

Answers to activities

1 Sales of video recorders might peak at Christmas and also before major sporting events such as Wimbledon.

2 $\frac{700 + 900 + 1,250}{3} = 950$

3

		Sales (Y)	4-quarter total	8-quarter total	Moving average (T)	Seasonal variation (Y-T)
19X7	Spring	200				
	Summer	120				
			760			
	Autumn	160		1,540	192.5	–32.5
			780			
	Winter	280		1,580	197.5	+82.5
			800			
19X8	Spring	220		1,580	197.5	+22.5
			780			
	Summer	140		1,580	197.5	–57.5
			800			
	Autumn	140		1,580	197.5	–57.5
			780			
	Winter	300		1,540	192.5	+107.5
			760			
19X9	Spring	200		1,560	195.0	+5.0
			800			
	Summer	120		1,620	202.5	–82.5
			820			
	Autumn	180				
	Winter	320				

We can now average the seasonal variations.

	Spring	Summer	Autumn	Winter	Total
19X7			–32.5	+82.5	
19X8	+22.5	–57.5	–57.5	+107.5	
19X9	+5.0	–82.5			
	+27.5	–140.0	–90.0	+190.0	
Average variation (in £'000)	+13.75	–70.00	–45.00	+95.00	–6.25
Adjustment so sum is zero	+1.5625	+1.5625	+1.5625	+1.5625	+6.25
Adjusted average variations	+15.3125	–68.4375	–43.4375	+96.5625	0

These might be rounded up or down to:

Spring £15,000, Summer –£68,000, Autumn –£43,000, Winter £96,000

NOTES

4

Quarter	*1*	*2*	*3*	*4*
	%	%	%	%
Variation, 19X1	0.956	1.027	1.053	0.914
Variation, 19X2	1.010	1.039	1.077	0.875
Average variation	0.983	1.033	1.065	0.895
Adjustment	0.006	0.006	0.006	0.006
Adjusted average variation	0.989	1.039	1.071	0.901

5 (a)

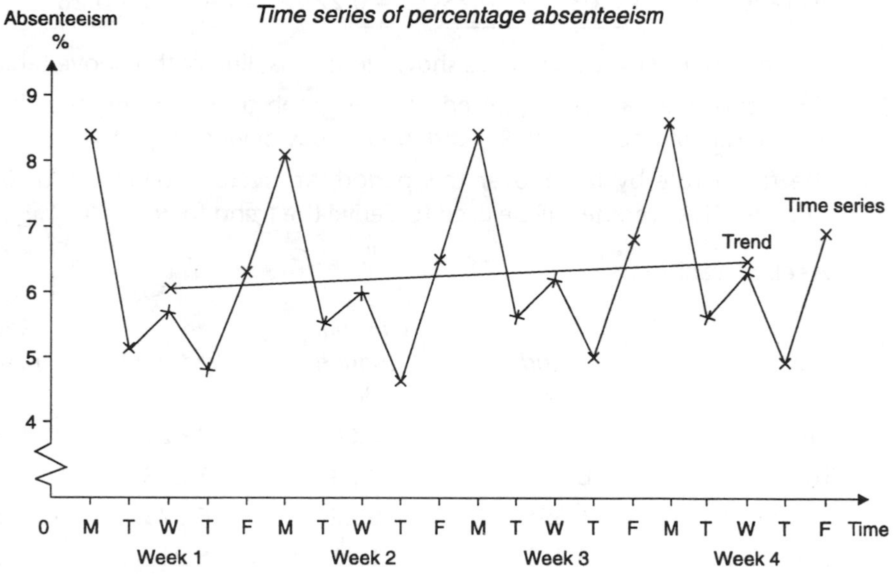

(b)

Week	Day	Data %	Five-day total %	Five-day average (trend) %	Seasonal variation %
1	M	8.4			
	T	5.1			
	W	5.7	30.3	6.06	– 0.36
	T	4.8	30.0	6.00	– 1.20
	F	6.3	30.4	6.08	+ 0.22
2	M	8.1	30.7	6.14	+ 1.96
	T	5.5	30.5	6.10	– 0.60
	W	6.0	30.7	6.14	– 0.14
	T	4.6	31.0	6.20	– 1.60
	F	6.5	31.1	6.22	+ 0.28
3	M	8.4	31.3	6.26	+ 2.14
	T	5.6	31.7	6.34	– 0.74
	W	6.2	32.0	6.40	– 0.20
	T	5.0	32.2	6.44	– 1.44
	F	6.8	32.2	6.44	+ 0.36
4	M	8.6	32.3	6.46	+ 2.14
	T	5.6	32.2	6.44	– 0.84
	W	6.3	32.3	6.46	– 0.16
	T	4.9			
	F	6.9			

NOTES

Week	*M*	*T*	*W*	*T*	*F*	*Total*
	%	%	%	%	%	
1			– 0.36	– 1.20	+ 0.22	
2	+ 1.96	– 0.60	– 0.14	– 1.60	+ 0.28	
3	+ 2.14	– 0.74	– 0.20	– 1.44	+ 0.36	
4	+ 2.14	– 0.84	– 0.16			
	6.24	–2.18	–0.86	–4.24	0.86	
Average	+ 2.08	– 0.73	– 0.22	– 1.41	+ 0.29	+ 0.01
Adjustment					– 0.01	– 0.01
Adjusted average	+ 2.08	– 0.73	– 0.22	– 1.41	+ 0.28	0

The seasonal adjustments are as shown in the last line of the above table.

(c) The trend line has been plotted on the graph above, using the figures for Wednesday of week 1 (6.06%) and Wednesday of week 4 (6.46%).

The trend rose by 0.4% over this period, an average daily rise of 0.4/15 = 0.027%. This average will be used to derive the trend for week 5.

Week 5 predictions

Day	*Trend* %	*Seasonal variation* %	*Prediction* %	*Rounded prediction* %
Monday	6.541*	+ 2.08	8.621	8.6
Tuesday	6.568	– 0.73	5.838	5.8
Wednesday	6.595	– 0.22	6.375	6.4
Thursday	6.622	– 1.41	5.212	5.2
Friday	6.649	+ 0.28	6.929	6.9

* 6.46 + (3 × 0.027)

(d) A forecast for Friday of week 8, based on the above computations, would be 6.46 + (22 × 0.027) + 0.28 = 7.334%, which is significantly below the personnel department's forecast. It is probable that the personnel department have estimated a more steeply rising trend. However, no forecast so far into the future and based on only four weeks data is likely to be reliable. The estimate of 8% cannot be supported.

Further question practice

Now try the following practice questions at the end of this text.

Multiple choice questions **72–77**

Exam style question **10**

Chapter 11

LINEAR PROGRAMMING

Introduction

In this chapter we will be looking at a technique which can be used to allocate resources (which might be materials, labour, money and so on) in order to achieve the best possible results. The name 'linear programming' sounds rather formidable and the technique *can* get quite complicated. But don't worry. You are only expected to be able to analyse *fully* the simplest examples, using a graphical technique (ie draw lines!). The more complex approach, the Simplex method, is usually carried out on a computer and we will only be considering the construction of what is called the initial tableau and the interpretation of the final tableau.

Your objectives

After completing this chapter you should:

(a) understand the circumstances in which linear programming can be used;

(b) be able to set up a linear programming model;

(c) be able to graph the model;

(d) be able to find the feasible solutions to the problem and the best solution;

(e) be able to apply sensitivity analysis;

(f) understand and be able to calculate dual/shadow prices;

(g) be aware of the circumstances in which the Simplex method of linear programming should be used;

(h) be able to set up and interpret an initial tableau;

(i) be able to interpret the final tableau and objective function.

EXAMPLE: WHEN LINEAR PROGRAMMING CAN HELP

Suppose that Jack Russell is the production manager of Barkers Ltd, a small company which manufactures dog kennels. The company produces a number of different types of kennel but has a flexible workforce that can be switched easily from one production line to another. Much of the machinery is used in the production of more than one type of kennel, as are many of the raw materials, wood, paint, fleece and fur (for lining the kennels), plastic (for water and food bowls inside the kennels) and so on. Profit earned depends on the type of kennel sold. Pooch's Parlour (a model for small breeds such as poodles) does not generate as much profit as the Penthouse (centrally heated, and suitable for the most pampered of pets). The time taken to produce a kennel and the potential market also depend on the type of kennel in question.

Jack Russell's problem is to decide how the company should divide up its production among the various types of kennel it manufactures in order to obtain the maximum possible profit, taking the factors mentioned above into account. In other words, he cannot simply produce as many as possible of each model of kennel because there will be limitations or constraints within which the production must operate. Such constraints could be limited quantities of raw materials available, a fixed number of man-hours per week for each type of worker, limited machine hours and so on. Moreover, since the profits generated by each model of kennel vary, it may be better not to produce any of a less profitable line, but to concentrate all resources on producing the more profitable ones. On the other hand limitations in market demand could mean that all those kennels produced may not be sold.

You can see from this brief outline of the problem that the chances of Jack Russell arriving at the 'best solution' (the one giving maximum possible profits) by simply thinking about it are minimal. What Jack needs is a systematic way of tackling the problem which guarantees that he will end up with the most profitable solution and ensures that the company operates within the constraints of staff hours, machine hours, quantities of raw materials and so on. Linear programming is that 'systematic way of tackling the problem'.

Definition

Linear programming is a technique for solving problems of profit maximisation (or cost minimisation) and resource allocation. The word programming is simply used to denote a series of events. The various aspects of the problem are expressed as linear equations.

1 FORMULATING THE PROBLEM

1.1 In common with many quantitative methods, we need a rather simple example to illustrate the basic linear programming techniques. Let us imagine that Barkers Ltd makes just two models, the Super and the Deluxe, and that monthly machine capacity is restricted to 400 hours. The Super requires 5 hours of machine time per unit and the Deluxe 1.5 hours. Government restrictions mean that the maximum number of kennels that can be sold each month is 150, that number being made up of any combination of the Super and the Deluxe.

1.2 Let us now work through the steps involved in setting up a linear programming model.

Setting up a linear programming model

Step 1: define variables

1.3 What are the quantities that the company can vary? Obviously not the number of machine hours or the maximum sales, which are fixed by external circumstances beyond the company's control. The only things which it can determine are the number of each type of kennel to manufacture. It is these numbers which Jack Russell has to determine in such a way as to get the maximum possible profit. Our variables will therefore be as follows.

Let x = the number of units of the Super kennel manufactured.

Let y = the number of units of the Deluxe kennel manufactured.

Step 2: establish constraints

1.4 Having defined these two variables we can now translate the two constraints into inequalities involving the variables.

1.5 Let us first consider the machine hours constraint. Each Super requires 5 hours of machine time. Producing five Supers therefore requires $5 \times 5 = 25$ hours of machine time and, more generally producing x Supers will require 5x hours. Likewise producing y Deluxes will require 1.5y hours. The total machine hours needed to make x Supers and y Deluxes is $5x + 1.5y$. We know that this cannot be greater than 400 hours so we arrive at the following inequality.

$$5x + 1.5y \leq 400$$

1.6 We can obtain the other inequality more easily. The total number of Supers and Deluxes made each month is $x + y$ but this has to be less than 150 due to government restrictions. The sales order constraint is therefore as follows.

$$x + y \leq 150$$

1.7 The variables in linear programming models should usually be non-negative in value. In this example, for instance, you cannot make a negative number of kennels and so we need the following constraints.

$$x \geq 0; y \geq 0$$

Do not forget these non-negativity constraints when formulating a linear programming model.

Step 3: establish objective function

Definition

An *objective function* is the mathematical expression of the aim of a linear programming exercise.

1.8 We have yet to introduce the question of profits. Let us assume that the profit on each type of kennel is as follows.

	£
Super	100
Deluxe	200

1.9 The objective of Barkers Ltd is to maximise profit and so the objective function to be maximised is as follows.

$$\text{Profit (P)} = 100x + 200y$$

Note that another organisation might have, for example, the minimisation of costs or the maximisation of contribution as its objective.

NOTES

1.10 The problem has now been reduced to the following four inequalities and one equation.

$$5x + 1.5y \leq 400$$
$$x + y \leq 150$$
$$x \geq 0$$
$$y \geq 0$$
$$P = 100x + 200y$$

1.11 Have you noticed that the inequalities are all linear expressions? If plotted on a graph, they would all give straight lines. This explains why the technique is called linear programming and also gives a hint as to how we should proceed with trying to find the solution to Jack's problem.

1.12 Before we progress to the next step, let us look at an example.

EXAMPLE: FORMULATING A PROBLEM

Maxim Wise Ltd makes three products, A, B and C. Each product is made by the same grades of labour, and the time required to make one unit of each product is as follows.

	A	*B*	*C*
Skilled labour	3 hours	4 hours	1 hour
Unskilled labour	2.5 hours	2 hours	6 hours

The variable costs per unit of A, B and C are £28, £30 and £26 respectively. The products sell for £40, £40 and £34 respectively.

In March 19X3 the company expects to have only 600 hours of skilled labour and 2,000 hours of unskilled labour available. There is a minimum requirement for 40 units of B and 120 units of C in the month.

Monthly fixed costs are £1,500.

Required

Formulate a linear programming problem.

Solution

The variables are the products A, B and C. We want to decide how many of each to produce in the month.

Let the number of units of product A made be a.
Let the number of units of product B made be b.
Let the number of units of product C made be c.

The objective is to maximise the monthly profit. Since fixed costs are a constant value of £1,500, which will be incurred regardless of which production plan is selected, these are irrelevant to the objective function, which can be stated as 'to maximise profit by maximising contribution'. The contribution per unit is £12 for A, £10 for B and £8 for C.

The objective is therefore to maximise 12a + 10b + 8c (contribution).

There are constraints relating to the availability of skilled labour and unskilled labour, and the minimum requirements for B and C. In addition, there are the constraints that A, B and C cannot have negative values, but since B and C must exceed 40 and 120 respectively, the non-negativity constraints are redundant for these two variables.

EXAMPLE *continued*

The programme may therefore be formulated as follows.

Objective: maximise 12a + 10b + 8c (contribution)

subject to the constraints:

3a + 4b + c	≤	600	(skilled labour)
2.5a + 2b + 6c	≤	2,000	(unskilled labour)
b	≥	40	(requirement for B)
c	≥	120	(requirement for C)
a	≤	0	

2 GRAPHING THE MODEL

2.1 We have looked at how to formulate a problem and in this section we will look at solving a problem using (as hinted in Paragraph 1.11) graphs.

2.2 A graphical solution is only possible when there are two variables in the problem. One variable is represented by the x axis and one by the y axis of the graph. Since non-negative values are not usually allowed, the graph shows only zero and positive values of x and y.

2.3 A linear equation with one or two variables is shown as a straight line on a graph. Thus y = 6 would be shown as follows.

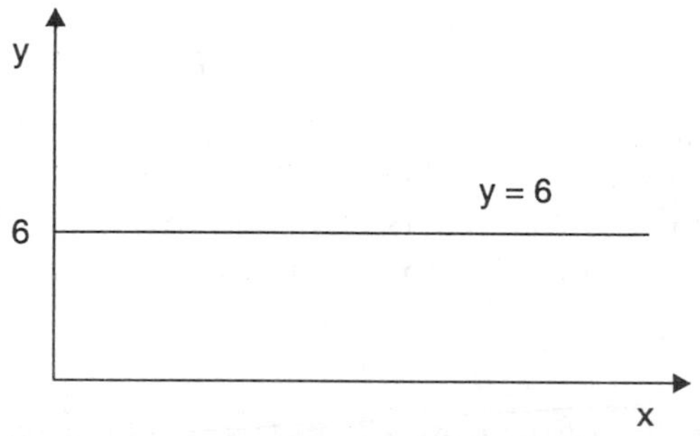

Figure 11.1 Linear equation where y = 6

If the problem included a constraint that y could not exceed 6, the *inequality* y ≤ 6 would be represented by the shaded area of the graph below.

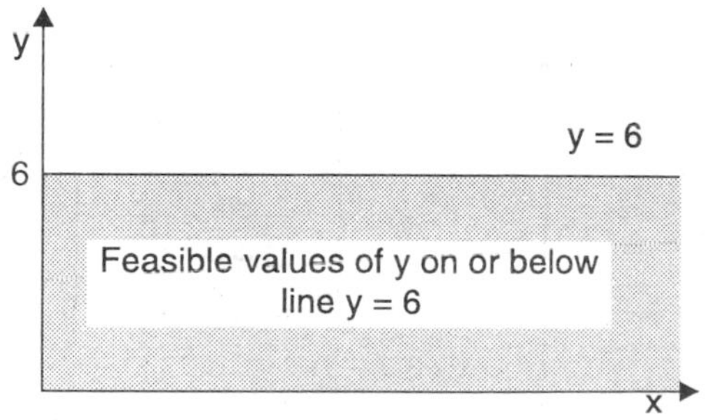

Figure 11.2 Constraint y ≤ 6

2.4 The equation 4x + 3y = 24 is also a straight line on a graph. To draw any straight line, we need only to plot two points and join them up. The easiest points to plot are the following.

(a) x = 0 (in this example, if x = 0, 3y = 24, y = 8)

(b) y = 0 (in this example, if y = 0, 4x = 24, x = 6)

By plotting the points, (0, 8) and (6, 0) on a graph, and joining them up, we have the line for $4x + 3y = 24$.

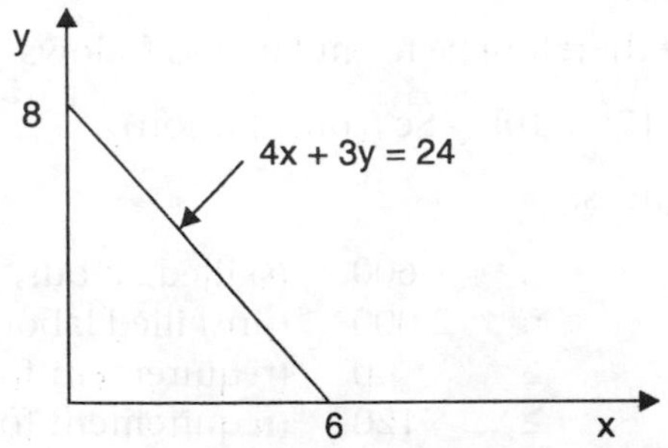

Figure 11.3 Linear equation where $4x + 3y = 24$

2.5 If we had a constraint $4x + 3y \leq 24$, any combined value of x and y within the shaded area below (on or below the line) would satisfy the constraint.

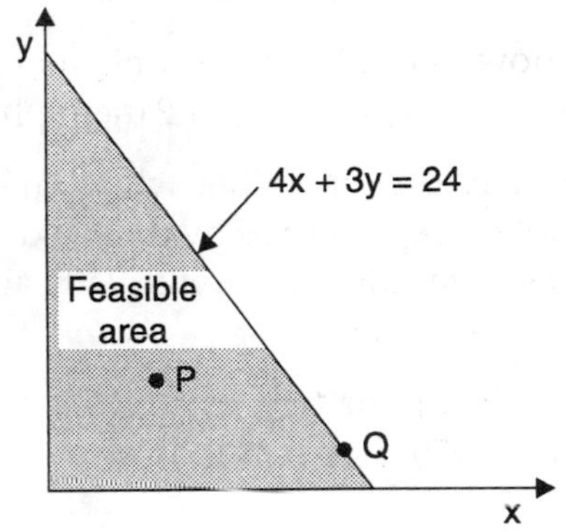

Figure 11.4 Constraint $4x + 3y \leq 24$

For example, at point P ($x = 2$, $y = 2$), $4x + 3y = 14$ which is less than 24; and at point Q ($x = 5.5$, $y = 2/3$), $4x + 3y = 24$. Both P and Q lie within the *feasible area* (the area where the inequality is satisfied, also called the feasible region). A *feasible area* enclosed on all sides may also be called a *feasible polygon.*

Definition

The area on a graph of a linear programming problem within which all of the inequalities are satisfied is known as a *feasible area.*

2.6 The inequalities $y \geq 6$, $x \geq 6$ and $4x + 3y \geq 24$, would be shown graphically as follows.

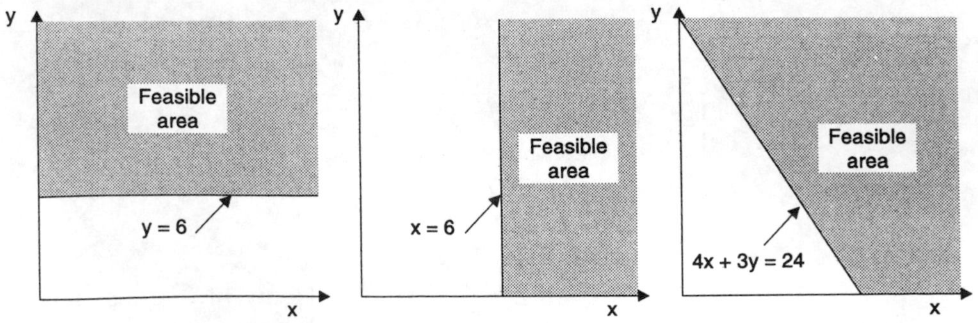

Figure 11.5 Graphical representations of inequalities

2.7 When there are several constraints, the feasible area of combinations of values of x and y must be an area where all the inequalities are satisfied.

Thus, if $y \leq 6$ *and* $4x + 3y \leq 24$ the feasible area would be the shaded area in Figure 11.6.

NOTES

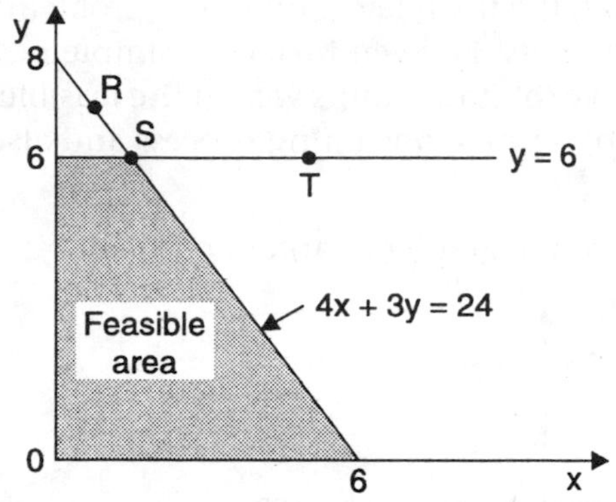

Figure 11.6 Graph showing more than one constraint (1)

(a) Point R (x = 0.75, y = 7) is not in the feasible area because although it satisfies the inequality $4x + 3y \leq 24$, it does not satisfy $y \leq 6$.

(b) Point T (x = 5, y = 6) is not in the feasible area, because although it satisfies the inequality $y \leq 6$, it does not satisfy $4x + 3y \leq 24$.

(c) Point S (x = 1.5, y = 6) satisfies both inequalities and lies just on the boundary of the feasible area since y = 6 exactly, and 4x + 3y = 24. Point S is thus at the intersection of the two equation lines.

2.8 Similarly, if $y \geq 6$ and $4x + 3y \geq 24$ but $x \leq 6$, the feasible area would be the shaded area in the graph below.

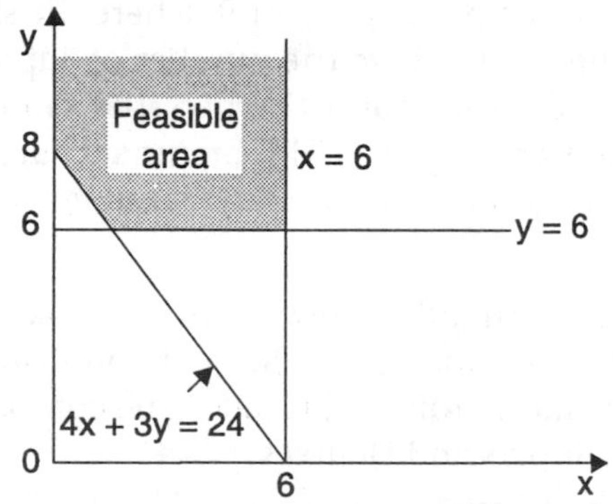

Figure 11.7 Graph showing more than one constraint (2)

Activity 1

Draw the feasible region which arises from the constraints facing Barkers.

Activity 2

Draw the feasible area for the following inequalities.

$$2x + 3y \leq £12$$
$$y \geq 2x$$
$$x, y \geq 0$$

3 FINDING THE BEST SOLUTION

3.1 Having found the feasible region (which includes all the possible solutions to the problem) we need to find which of these possible solutions is 'best' in the sense that it yields the maximum possible profit. We could do this by finding out what profit each of the possible solutions would give, and then choosing as our 'best' combination the one for which the profit is greatest.

3.2 Consider, however, the feasible region of the problem faced by Barkers Ltd (see the solution to Activity 1). Even in such a simple problem as this, there are a great many possible solution points within the feasible area. Even to write them all down would be a time-consuming process and also an unnecessary one, as we shall see.

3.3 Let us look again at the graph of Barker's problem.

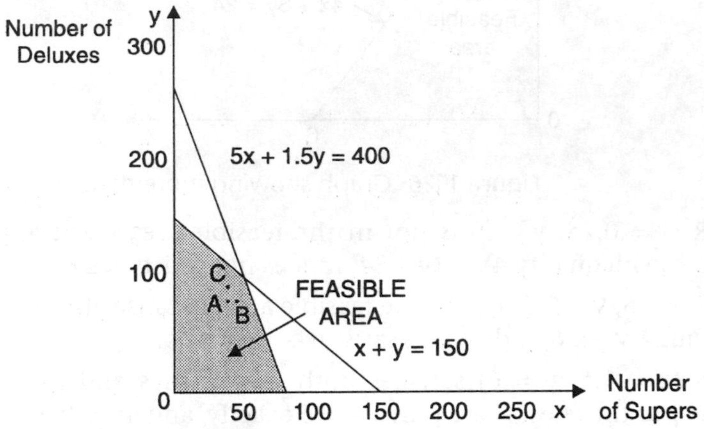

Figure 11.8 Barker's problem

Consider, for example, the point A at which 40 Supers and 80 Deluxes are being manufactured. This will yield a profit of ((40 × 100) + (80 × 200)) = £20,000. We would clearly get more profit at point B, where the same number of Deluxes are being manufactured but where the number of Supers being manufactured has increased by five, or from point C where the same number of Supers but 10 more Deluxes are manufactured. This argument suggests that the 'best' solution is going to be a point on the edge of the feasible area rather than in the middle of it.

3.4 This still leaves us with quite a few points to look at but there is a way we can narrow down the candidates for the best solution still further. Suppose that Barkers wish to make a profit of £10,000. The company could sell the following combinations of Supers and Deluxes.

(a) 100 Super, no Deluxe

(b) No Super, 50 Deluxe

(c) A proportionate mix of Super and Deluxe, such as 80 Super and 10 Deluxe or 50 Super and 25 Deluxe

3.5 The possible combinations of Supers and Deluxes required to earn a profit of £10,000 could be shown by the straight line 100x + 200y = 10,000.

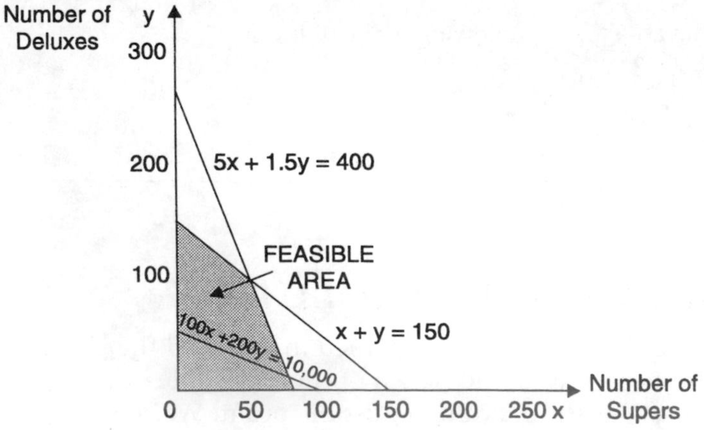

Figure 11.9 Combinations earning a profit of £10,000

NOTES

3.6 For a total profit of £15,000, a similar line 100x + 200y = 15,000 could be drawn to show the various combinations of Supers and Deluxes which would achieve the total of £15,000.

Similarly a line 100x + 200y = 8,000 would show the various combinations of Supers and Deluxes which would earn a total profit of £8,000.

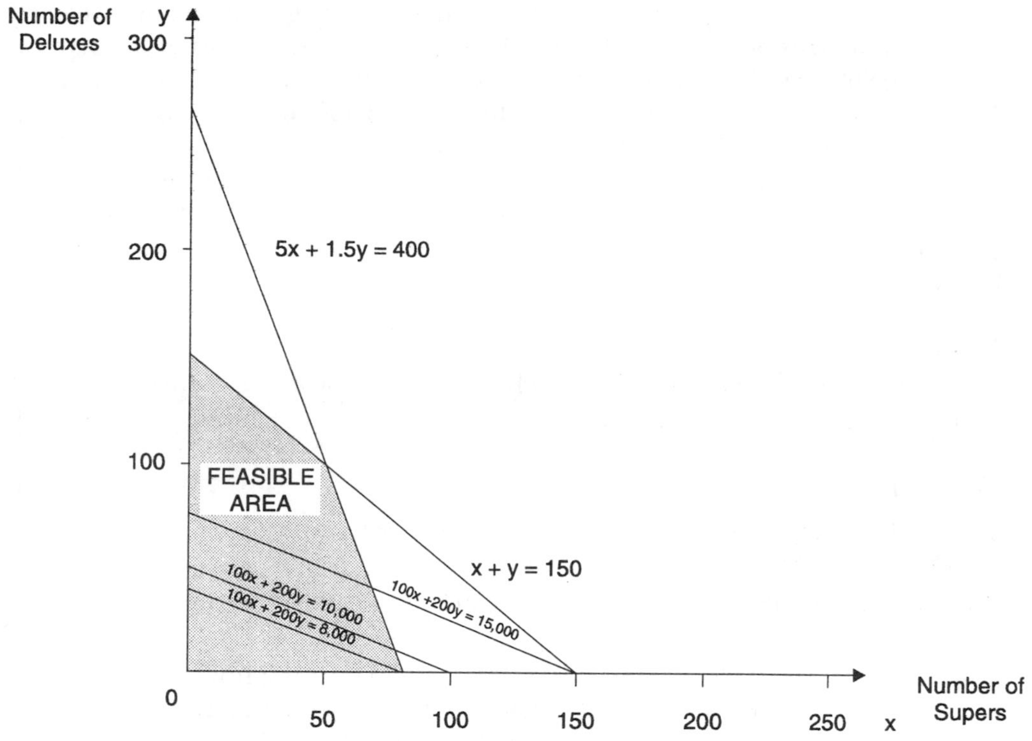

Figure 11.10 Combinations earning various profits

3.7 These profit lines are all parallel. (They are called *iso-profit lines*, 'iso' meaning equal.) A similar line drawn for any other total profit would also be parallel to the three lines shown here. This means that if we wish to know the slope or gradient of the profit line, for any value of total profit, we can simply draw one line for any convenient value of profit, and we will know that all the other lines will be parallel to the one drawn: they will have the same slope.

3.8 Bigger profits are shown by lines further from the origin (100x + 200y = 15,000), smaller profits by lines closer to the origin (100x + 200y = 8,000). As Barkers try to increase possible profit we need to slide the profit line outwards from the origin, while always keeping it parallel to the other profit lines.

3.9 As we do this there will come a point at which, if we were to move the profit line out any further, it would cease to lie in the feasible region and therefore larger profits could not be achieved in practice because of the constraints. In our example concerning Barkers this will happen, as you should test for yourself, where the profit line is just passing through the intersection of x + y = 150 with the y axis (at (0, 150)). The point (0, 150) will therefore give us the best production combination of the Super and the Deluxe, that is, to produce 150 Deluxe models and no Super models.

NOTES

EXAMPLE: A MAXIMISATION PROBLEM

Brunel Ltd manufactures plastic-covered steel fencing in two qualities, standard and heavy gauge. Both products pass through the same processes, involving steel-forming and plastic bonding.

Standard gauge fencing sells at £18 a roll and heavy gauge fencing at £24 a roll. Variable costs per roll are £16 and £21 respectively. There is an unlimited market for the standard gauge, but demand for the heavy gauge is limited to 1,300 rolls a year. Factory operations are limited to 2,400 hours a year in each of the two production processes.

	Processing hours per roll	
Gauge	*Steel-forming*	*Plastic-bonding*
Standard	0.6	0.4
Heavy	0.8	1.2

Required

Determine the production mix which will maximise total contribution. Calculate the total contribution.

Solution

Let S be the number of standard gauge rolls per year.
Let H be the number of heavy gauge rolls per year.

The objective is to maximise 2S + 3H (contribution) subject to the following constraints.

$$\begin{aligned} 0.6S + 0.8H &\leq 2{,}400 && \text{(steel-forming hours)} \\ 0.4S + 1.2H &\leq 2{,}400 && \text{(plastic-bonding hours)} \\ H &\leq 1{,}300 && \text{(sales demand)} \\ S, H &\geq 0 \end{aligned}$$

Note that the constraints are *inequalities*, and are not equations. There is no requirement to use up the total hours available in each process, nor to satisfy all the demand for heavy gauge rolls.

If we take the production constraint of 2,400 hours in the steel-forming process

$$0.6S + 0.8H \leq 2{,}400$$

it means that since there are only 2,400 hours available in the process, output must be limited to a maximum of:

(a) $\frac{2{,}400}{0.6}$ = 4,000 rolls of standard gauge;

(b) $\frac{2{,}400}{0.8}$ = 3,000 rolls of heavy gauge; or

(c) a proportionate combination of each.

This maximum output represents the boundary line of the constraint, where the inequality becomes the equation

$$0.6S + 0.8H = 2{,}400$$

The line for this equation may be drawn on a graph by joining up two points on the line (such as S = 0, H = 3,000; H = 0, S = 4,000).

The other constraints may be drawn in a similar way with lines for the following equations.

$$\begin{aligned} 0.4S + 1.2H &= 2{,}400 && \text{(plastic-bonding)} \\ H &= 1{,}300 && \text{(sales demand)} \end{aligned}$$

NOTES

EXAMPLE *continued*

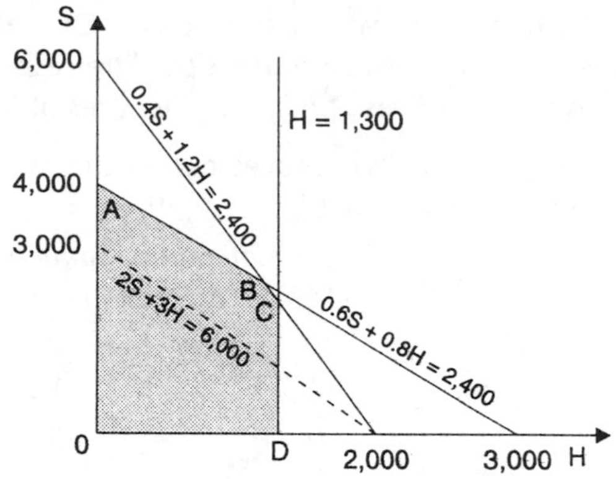

To satisfy all the constraints simultaneously, the values of S and H must lie on or below each constraint line. The outer limits of the feasible polygon are the lines, but all combined values of S and H within the shaded area are feasible solutions.

The next step is to find the optimal solution, which maximises the objective function. Since the objective is to maximise contribution, the solution to the problem must involve relatively high values (within the feasible polygon) for S, or H or a combination of both.

If, as is likely, there is only one combination of S and H which provides the optimal solution, this combination will be one of the outer corners of the feasible polygon. There are four such corners, A, B, C and D. However, it is possible that any combination of values for S and H on the boundary line between two of these corners might provide solutions with the same total contribution.

To solve the problem we establish the slope of the iso-contribution lines, by drawing a line for any one level of contribution. In our solution, a line 2S + 3H = 6,000 has been drawn. (6,000 was chosen as a convenient multiple of 2 and 3.) This line has no significance except to indicate the slope, or gradient, of every iso-contribution line for 2S + 3H.

Using a ruler, we can draw an iso-contribution line which is as far to the right as possible (that is, away from the origin) but which still touches the feasible polygon.

This occurs at corner B where the constraint line 0.4S + 1.2H = 2,400 crosses with the constraint line 0.6S + 0.8H = 2,400. At this point, there are simultaneous equations, from which the exact values of S and H may be calculated.

$$
\begin{array}{rcll}
0.4S + 1.2H & = & 2,400 & (1) \\
0.6S + 0.8H & = & 2,400 & (2) \\
1.2S + 3.6H & = & 7,200 & (3)\ ((1) \times 3) \\
1.2S + 1.6H & = & 4,800 & (4)\ ((2) \times 2) \\
2H & = & 2,400 & (5)\ ((3) - (4)) \\
H & = & 1,200 & (6)
\end{array}
$$

Substituting 1,200 for H in either equation, we can calculate that S = 2,400.

The contribution is maximised where H = 1,200 and S = 2,400.

	Units	*Contribution per unit*	*Total contribution*
		£	*£*
Standard gauge	2,400	2	4,800
Heavy gauge	1,200	3	3,600
			8,400

Activity 3

The Dervish Chemical Company operates a small plant. Operating the plant requires two raw materials, A and B, which cost £5 and £8 per litre respectively. The maximum available supply per week is 2,700 litres of A and 2,000 litres of B.

The plant can operate using either of two processes, which have differing contributions and raw materials requirements, as follows.

Process	*Raw materials consumed (litres per processing hour)*		*Contribution per hour*
	A	*B*	*£*
1	20	10	70
2	30	20	60

The plant can run for 120 hours a week in total, but for safety reasons, process 2 cannot be operated for more than 80 hours a week.

Required

Formulate a linear programming model, and then solve it, to determine how many hours process 1 should be operated each week and how many hours process 2 should be operated each week.

Minimisation problems in linear programming

3.10 Although decision problems with limiting factors usually involve the maximisation of contribution, there may be a requirement to minimise costs. A graphical solution, involving two variables, is very similar to that for a maximisation problem, with the exception that instead of finding a contribution line touching the feasible area as far away from the origin as possible, we look for a total cost line touching the feasible area as close to the origin as possible.

EXAMPLE: A MINIMISATION PROBLEM

Bilton Sandys Ltd has undertaken a contract to supply a customer with at least 260 units in total of two products, X and Y, during the next month. At least 50% of the total output must be units of X. The products are each made by two grades of labour, as follows.

	X	*Y*
	Hours	*Hours*
Grade A labour	4	6
Grade B labour	4	2
Total	8	8

Although additional labour can be made available at short notice, the company wishes to make use of 1,200 hours of Grade A labour and 800 hours of Grade B labour which has already been assigned to working on the contract next month. The total variable cost per unit is £120 for X and £100 for Y.

Bilton Sandys Ltd wishes to minimise expenditure on the contract next month.

Required

Calculate how much of X and Y should be supplied in order to meet the terms of the contract.

NOTES

EXAMPLE *continued*

Solution

Let the number of units of X supplied be x, and the number of units of Y supplied be y.

The objective is to minimise 120x + 100y (costs), subject to the following constraints.

x + y	≥	260	(supply total)
x	≥	0.5 (x + y)	(proportion of x in total)
4x + 6y	≥	1,200	(Grade A labour)
4x + 2y	≥	800	(Grade B labour)
x, y	≥	0	

The constraint x ≥ 0.5 (x + y) needs simplifying further.

x	≥	0.5 (x + y)
2x	≥	x + y
x	≥	y

In a graphical solution, the line will be x = y. Check this carefully in the following diagram.

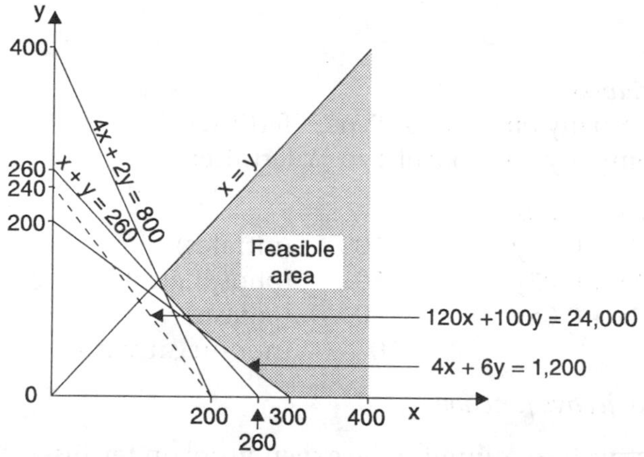

The cost line 120x + 100y = 24,000 has been drawn to show the slope of every cost line 120x + 100y. Costs are minimised where a cost line touches the feasible area as close as possible to the origin of the graph. This occurs where the constraint line 4x + 2y = 800 crosses the constraint line x + y = 260. This point is found as follows.

x + y	=	260	(1)
4x + 2y	=	800	(2)
2x + y	=	400	(3) ((2) ÷ 2)
x	=	140	(4) ((3) – (1))
y	=	120	(5)

Costs will be minimised by supplying the following.

	Unit cost	*Total cost*
	£	*£*
140 units of X	120	16,800
120 units of Y	100	12,000
		28,800

The proportion of units of X in the total would exceed 50%, and demand for Grade A labour would exceed the 1,200 hours minimum. The minimum amount of Grade B labour would be used.

NOTES

3.11 Another format of the cost minimisation problem incorporates quality requirements. An example will serve to illustrate this type of problem.

EXAMPLE: QUALITY REQUIREMENTS

J Farms Ltd can buy two types of fertiliser which contain the following percentages of chemicals.

	Nitrates	*Phosphates*	*Potash*
Type X	18	5	2
Type Y	3	2	5

For a certain crop the following minimum quantities (kg) are required.

Nitrates 100 Phosphates 50 Potash 40

Type X costs £10 per kg and Type Y costs £5 per kg. J Farms Ltd currently buys 1,000 kg of each type and wishes to minimise its expenditure on fertilisers.

Required

Recommend the quantity of each type of fertiliser which should be bought and the cost of these amounts.

Solution

Define variables

Let the company buy x kg of Type X fertiliser.
Let the company buy y kg of Type Y fertiliser.

Establish constraints

$0.18x + 0.03y$	$\geq$	100	(nitrates)
$0.05x + 0.02y$	$\geq$	50	(phosphates)
$0.02x + 0.05y$	$\geq$	40	(potash)
x, y	$\geq$	0	(non-negativity)

Establish objective function

The objective is to minimise the expenditure on fertilisers.

Minimise $10x + 5y$

Graph the model (see following page)

Determine optimal solution

If we move a ruler up the graph parallel to the objective function, the first point reached in the feasible region is point A. We find the co-ordinates of this point by solving the simultaneous equations below.

$0.05x + 0.02y$	=	50	(1)
$0.02x + 0.05y$	=	40	(2)
$0.05x + 0.125y$	=	100	(3) ((2) × 2.5)
$0.105y$	=	50	(4) ((3) – (1))
y	=	476.2	

$0.05x + (0.02 \times 476.2)$	= 50	(5) (Substitute in (1))
$0.05x + 9.52$	= 50	
$0.05x$	= 40.48	
x	= 809.6	

So the company should buy 809.6 kg of Type X fertiliser and 476.2 kg of Type Y fertiliser

EXAMPLE *continued*

The total cost is (10 × 809.6) + (5 × 476.2) = £10,477.

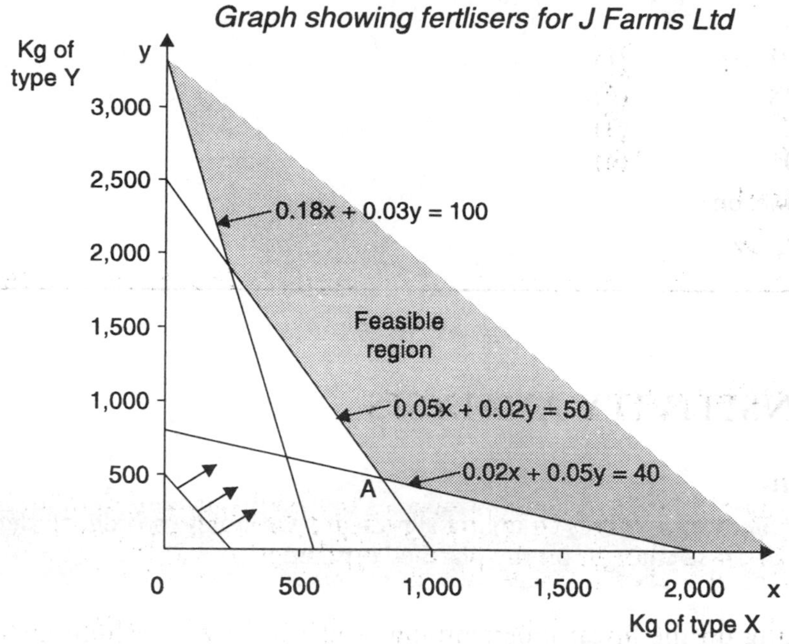

The use of simultaneous equations

3.12 You might think that a lot of time could be saved if we started by solving the simultaneous equations in a linear programming problem and did not bother to draw the graph. Certainly, this procedure may give the right answer, but in general (unless the example is very straightforward) it is *not* recommended until you have shown graphically which constraints are effective in determining the optimal solution. (In particular, if a question requires 'the graphical method', you *must* draw a graph.) To illustrate this point, consider the graph below.

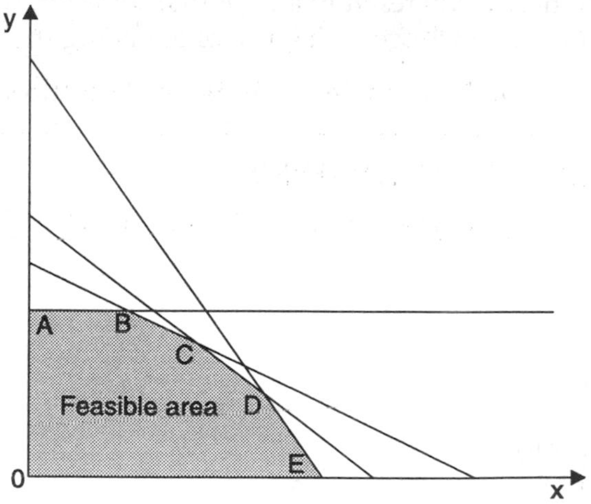

Figure 11.11 Graph showing feasible solutions

No figures have been given on the graph but the feasible area is OABCDE. When solving this problem, we would know that the optimum solution would be at one of the corners of the feasible area. We need to work out the profit at each of the corners of the feasible area and pick the one where the profit is greatest.

Once the optimum point has been determined graphically, simultaneous equations can be applied to find the exact values of x and y at this point.

NOTES

Activity 4

Given the following constraints and objective function, determine the optimal production level of product X and product Y.

Constraints

$Y \leq {}^{-X}/_{2} + 5$ (1)

$Y \leq 2X$ (2)

$X \geq 0$ (3)

$Y \geq 0$ (4)

Objective function

Profit = 3X + 4Y

4 SENSITIVITY ANALYSIS

Definition

Sensitivity analysis involves changing significant variables in order to determine the effect of these changes on the planned outcome.

4.1 In setting up the linear programming model we had to assume that we had adequate information about the amounts of the various resources by which production is constrained and about the profits which would be generated by the sale of the products. In practice, of course, these can be quite difficult to estimate, particularly when planning production not just for a week or two in advance, but for a whole year ahead. We may expect to be able to use a certain machine for 400 hours a month, only to find that, due to breakdowns, the figure is closer to 350 hours. We may hope to sell the Super at a price which will give us a profit of £100 per kennel, and then discover that a competitor has put a cheap new alternative on the market and we must cut our profit margins if we are to maintain our market share.

4.2 These circumstances could result in an optimal solution, worked out for a set of assumptions that are no longer valid, no longer being the optimal solution.

4.3 To examine this topic further a new example will be introduced.

EXAMPLE: SENSITIVITY ANALYSIS

Dual Ltd makes two products, X and Y, which have the following selling prices and costs.

	X		*Y*	
	£	£	£	£
Unit selling price		14		15
Costs				
Materials (at £1 per kg)	3		2	
Labour (at £3 per hr)	6		9	
		9		11
Unit profit		5		4

What production plan would maximise profit in the next period, given that the supply of materials will be restricted to 600 kg, only 450 labour hours will be available, and a minimum demand for 150 units of product X must be met?

How would changes in the selling prices affect the solution?

NOTES

EXAMPLE *continued*

Solution

The problem could be solved graphically, as follows.

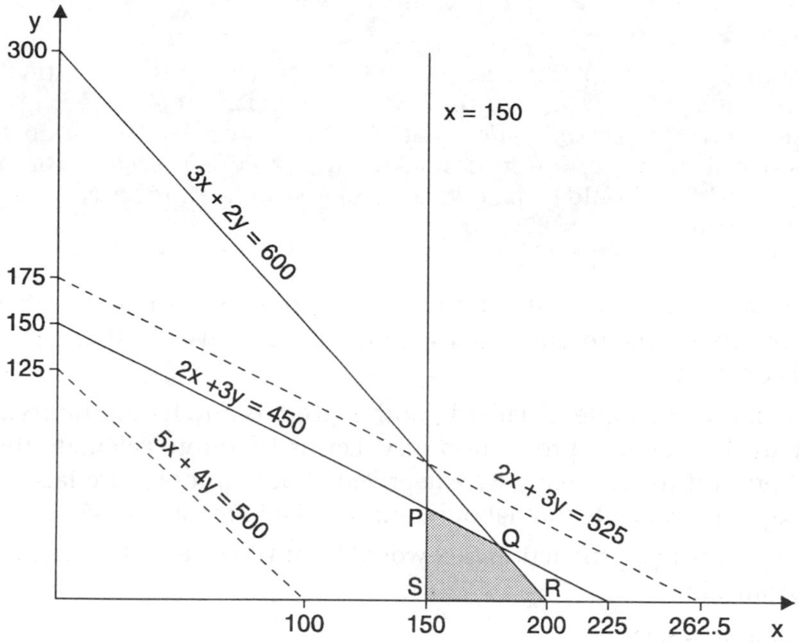

The feasible polygon is PQRS, and profit would be maximised at point Q, where

$$3x + 2y = 600$$

$$2x + 3y = 450$$

Therefore x = 180, y = 30, and total profit is £1,020.

The optimum will shift to point R (x = 200, y = 0) if X becomes sufficiently more profitable. It will shift when the iso-profit line becomes steeper than the line 3x + 2y = 600. That line's gradient is –1.5, and the iso-profit line's gradient is

$$\frac{-\text{ unit profit from X}}{\text{unit profit from Y}}$$

Thus the optimum will shift to R if the unit profit from Y remains at £4 but the unit profit from X increases to more than £6, corresponding to an increase in the unit selling price of more than £1 to more than £15.

Activity 5

In the above example, if the unit profit from X remains at £5, what would the unit profit from Y have to increase to in order to shift the optimum to point P? What unit selling price of Y does this new profit correspond to?

4.4 The point of sensitivity analysis is that it indicates the risk of our selecting the wrong solution. If small changes in prices would lead to a different optimum applying, there is a high risk of our selecting the wrong solution. If, on the other hand, large changes in prices would leave the optimum unchanged, errors in predicting prices are unlikely to lead to our selecting the wrong solution.

NOTES

Dual prices

Definition

The *dual price* (also called the *shadow price*) of a resource which is fully used at the optimum is the amount by which:

(a) total profit would fall if the company were deprived of one unit of the resource;

(b) total profit would rise if the company were able to obtain one extra unit of the scarce resource, *provided that* the resource remains an effective constraint on production and *provided also* that the extra unit of the resource can be obtained at its normal unit cost. The dual price is therefore the maximum amount which should be paid *in excess of the normal rate* for each extra unit of the resource.

4.5 The dual price is calculated on the assumption that there is a change in the availability of one resource, but with the availability of other resources being held constant.

4.6 In the above example (Dual Ltd), both materials and labour hours are used up fully in the planned production mix. Let us therefore calculate the effect on total profit if the company were deprived of one unit of materials, so that only 599 kg were available (but labour hours available remain at 450).

The new optimal production mix would be at the intersection point of the two constraint lines:

$$3x + 2y = 599$$

$$2x + 3y = 450$$

Solving the simultaneous equations, x = 179.4 units and y = 30.4 units:

	Product	*Units*	*Profit* £
	X	179.4 (× £5)	897.00
	Y	30.4 (× £4)	121.60
			1,018.60
Profit in original problem			1,020.00
Reduction in profit from loss of 1 kg of materials			1.40

The dual price of materials is therefore £1.40 per kg.

4.7 Suppose that materials available are 600 kg, but that the labour supply is reduced by 20 hours to 430 hours. The optimal production mix occurs at the intersection of the two constraints:

$$2x + 3y = 430;$$

$$3x + 2y = 600.$$

Solving the simultaneous equations, x = 188 units and y = 18 units.

	Product	*Units*	*Profit* £
	X	188 (× £5)	940
	Y	18 (× £4)	72
			1,012
Profit in original problem			1,020
Reduction in profit from loss of 20 labour hours			8

The dual price of labour is therefore 8/20 = £0.40 an hour.

4.8 The dual price of a resource also shows by how much profit would increase if an additional unit of the resource were made available. In our example, if the materials available were 600 kg but the labour supply were raised to 451 hours, the optimum production mix would be 179.6 units of X and 30.6 units of Y.

	Product	*Units*	*Profit*
			£
	X	179.6 (× £5)	898.00
	Y	30.6 (× £4)	122.40
			1,020.40
Profit in original problem			1,020.00
Increase in profit from one extra unit of labour			0.40

Once again, the dual price of labour is £0.40 an hour.

4.9 The increase in contribution of £0.40 per extra labour hour is calculated on the assumption that the extra labour hour would be paid for at the normal variable cost, which is £3 an hour in the problem.

(a) The management of the company should be prepared to pay up to £0.40 extra per extra hour of labour in order to obtain more labour hours (perhaps through overtime working: the maximum value of overtime premium would then be £0.40 per hour). We assume that the existing 450 hours of labour are still paid only £3 an hour.

(b) This value of labour only applies as long as labour remains fully used. If more and more labour hours are made available, there will eventually be so much labour that it is no longer a scarce resource. In our problem, this will occur when the third constraint, $x \geq 150$, prevents a further reduction in the output of X in order to increase output of Y.

4.10 We can calculate how many hours must be available before labour ceases to be fully used. This will happen when the new labour constraint passes through the intersection of $x = 150$ and $y = 75$ (the intersection of $3x + 2y = 600$ and $x = 150$), when it no longer forms a boundary to the feasible area. The labour constraint $2x + 3y$ would therefore be

$$2x + 3y = ?$$

If $x = 150$ and $y = 75$, $2x + 3y = (2 \times 150) + (3 \times 75) = 525$

This is shown as the upper right dotted line on the graph on Page 263.

The dual price of labour is £0.40 per hour in the initial problem, but only up to a maximum supply of 525 labour hours (75 hours more than the original 450 hours). Extra labour above 525 hours would not have any use, and the two limiting factors would now be materials and the minimum demand for x. Beyond 525 hours, labour would have a dual price of zero. Once the labour constraint ceases to matter in this way, it becomes an *ineffective, non-binding* or *non-critical* constraint.

Any resource which is not fully used has a dual price of zero: losing one unit will not matter, and there is no point in paying over the normal rate for extra units.

Activity 6

A linear programming problem is as follows.

Maximise profit, $4x + 2y$, subject to the following constraints.

$3x + 6y$	$\leq$	12,000 (hours of labour)
$5x + 2y$	$\leq$	10,000 (hours of machine time)
x,y	$\geq$	0

The optimum is at the intersection of the labour constraint and the machine time constraint. What is the dual price per hour of machine time?

5 SIMPLEX FORMULATION

5.1 The linear programming problems in the previous sections included only two decision variables. In practice, few problems will be this simple. We therefore need to look at another technique.

Definition

The *simplex method* is a method of solving linear programming problems with two or more decision variables. It is a repetitive step by step process (and therefore an ideal computer application) that tests a number of feasible solutions in turn. If the manual process is used this is done in the form of a tableau (or table or matrix) of figures.

5.2 The formulation of the linear programming problem is identical whether it is the Simplex method or the graphical approach which is being used. It is in the solution of the problem that the diference lies.

5.3 Rather than explaining in words what is involved, the Simplex method is best illustrated by an example.

EXAMPLE: SIMPLEX METHOD

Shore Toffer Lott Ltd produces and sells two products, X and Y. Products X and Y require the following resources.

	Materials	*Labour*	*Machine time*	*Contribution per unit*
	Units	*Hours*	*Hours*	*£*
X, per unit	5	1	3	20
Y, per unit	2	3	2	16
Total available, each week	3,000 units	1,750 hours	2,100 hours	

Although we have just two decision variables, we can still use the Simplex method to solve the problem. We begin by formulating the problem in the usual way.

Define variables Let x = the number of units of X that should be produced and sold
Let y = the number of units of Y that should be produced and sold

Establish constraints

Materials	$5x + 2y \leq 3{,}000$
Labour	$x + 3y \leq 1{,}750$
Machine time	$3x + 2y \leq 2{,}100$
Non-negativity	$x \geq 0, \quad y \geq 0$

Establish objective function Maximise contribution (C) = $20x + 16y$

5.4 Now we change our approach and introduce the Simplex method.

Slack variables

5.5 Using the Simplex technique, we begin by turning each constraint (ignoring the non-negativity constraints now) into an equation. This is done by introducing slack variables.

Definition

A *slack variable* represents the amount of a constraining resource or item that is unused.

Let a be the quantity of unused materials
b be the number of unused labour hours
c be the number of unused machine hours

5.6 We can now express the original constraints as equations.

$$5x + 2y + a = 3{,}000$$
$$x + 3y + b = 1{,}750$$
$$3x + 2y + c = 2{,}100$$

5.7 The slack variables a, b and c will be equal to 0 in the final solution only if the combined production of X and Y uses up all the available materials (a), labour hours (b) and machine hours (c).

5.8 If there are n constraints, there will be n variables with a value greater than 0 in any feasible solution. In this example, there are five variables (x, y, a, b and c) in the problem and three equations. In any feasible solution that is tested, three variables will therefore have a non-negative value (since there are three equations) which means that two variables will have a value of zero.

5.9 It is also usual to express the objective function as an equation with the right hand side equal to zero. In order to keep the problem consistent, the slack (or surplus) variables are inserted into the objective function equation, but as the quantities they represent should have no effect on the objective function they are given zero coefficients. In our example, the objective function will be expressed as follows.

Maximise contribution (C) given by $C - 20x - 16y + 0a + 0b + 0c = 0$.

6 THE INITIAL TABLEAU

6.1 The first feasible solution that we test has a zero value for all of the decision variables and a non-negative value for all the slack variables. Obviously this will not be the optimal solution but it gives us a starting point from which we can develop other feasible solutions.

6.2 Simplex tableaux can be drawn in several different ways but the general rules of construction are as follows.

(a) There should be a column for each variable (decision and slack). In our example there should be five columns.

(b) There should also be a solution column (on the right).

(c) It helps to add a further column the left, to indicate the variable in the solution (the non-negative value variables) to which the corresponding value in the solution column relates. In our example there will be three non-negative value variables.

(d) There is a row for each equation in the problem. Our example will therefore have three rows (for the three constraints).

(e) There is also a solution row.

NOTES

6.3 The initial tableau for the Shore Toffer Lott Ltd problem is therefore as follows.

Variable in solution	*x*	*y*	*a*	*b*	*c*	*Solution*
a	5	2	1	0	0	3,000
b	1	3	0	1	0	1,750
c	3	2	0	0	1	2,100
Solution	–20	–16	0	0	0	0

6.4 Let us look at how this tableau was put together.

(a) The figures in each row correspond with the coefficients of the variables in each of the revised constraints. The bottom row or solution row holds the coefficients of the revised objective function. For example the materials constraint 5x + 2y + a = 3,000 gives us the first row, 5 (number of x's), 2 (number of y's), 1 (number of a's) then zeros in the b and c columns (since these do not feature in the constraint equation) and finally 3,000 in the solution column.

(b) The variables in the solution are a, b and c (as indicated by the left hand column).

  (i) The value of each variable is shown in the solution column.

  (ii) The column values for each *variable in the solution* are as follows.

    (1) 1 in the variable's own solution row

    (2) 0 in every other row, including the solution row.

(c) The contribution per unit obtainable from x and y are given in the solution row. These are called the *shadow prices* or *dual values* of the products X and Y. The minus signs are of no particular significance. An optimal solution has been reached when all the elements of the solution row have become positive.

Interpretation of the tableau

6.5 Interpreting the tableau, we can see that the solution is testing a = 3,000, b = 1,750 and c = 2,100, contribution = 0.

6.6 The shadow prices in the initial solution (tableau) indicate the following.

(a) The profit would be increased by £20 for every extra unit x produced (because the shadow price of x is £20 per unit).

(b) Similarly, the profit would be increased by £16 for every extra unit of y produced (because its shadow price is £16).

6.7 Since the solution is not optimal, the contribution may be improved by introducing either x or y into the solution.

Activity 7

D Electronics produces three models of satellite dishes – Alpha, Beta and Gamma –which have contributions per unit of £400, £200 and £100 respectively.

There is a two-stage production process and the number of hours per unit for each process are as follows.

	Alpha	*Beta*	*Gamma*
Process 1	2	3	2.5
Process 2	3	2	2.0

There is an upper limit on process hours of 1,920 per period for Process 1 and 2,200 for Process 2.

The Alpha dish was designed for a low-power satellite which is now fading and the sales manager thinks that sales will be no more than 200 per period.

Fixed costs are £40,000 per period.

Required

(a) Formulate these data into a linear programming model using the following notation.

x_1: number of Alphas
x_2: number of Betas
x_3: number of Gammas

(b) Formulate (but do not attempt to solve) the initial Simplex tableau using

x_4 as slack for Process 1
x_5 as slack for Process 2
x_6 as slack for any sales limit

7 INTERPRETING THE FINAL TABLEAU AND OBJECTIVE FUNCTION

7.1 The following tableau is the final solution to the Short Toffer Lott Ltd problem.

Variable in solution	*x*	*y*	*a*	*b*	*c*	*Solution*
x	1	0	0	–0.2857	0.4286	400
a	0	0	1	0.5714	-1.8571	100
y	0	1	0	0.4286	-0.1429	450
Solution	0	0	0	1.1428	6.2858	15,200

7.2 The solution in this tableau is the optimal one because the shadow prices on the bottom row are all positive. The optimal solution is to make and sell 400 units of X and 450 units of Y, to earn a contribution of £15,200. The solution will leave 100 units of materials unused, but will use up all available labour and machine time.

The values in the solution row indicate the shadow price (or dual value) of the variables.

The shadow price of labour time (b) is £1.1428 per hour (bottom of column (b)), which indicates the amount by which contribution would increase/decrease if more/less labour time could be made available at its normal variable cost.

The shadow price of machine time (c) is £6.2858 per hour (bottom of column (c)), which indicates the amount by which contribution would increase/decrease if more/less machine time could be made available, at its normal variable cost.

The shadow price of materials is nil (bottom of column (a)) because there are 100 units of unused materials in the solution and therefore the materials constraint is not critical. Note, however, that if either x or y had a shadow price, this would indicate the amount by which the overall contribution would decrease if one more unit of x or y were produced.

7.3 You will usually be asked to interpret the final objective function rather than the final tableau.

7.4 The final objective function of our example is

CONTRIBUTION = 15,200 – 1.1428 (slack labour time) – 6.2858 (slack machine time)

Activity 8

When solved by the Simplex method, the final objective function of the problem set out in Activity 7 is:

CONTRIBUTION = 181,333.3 – 66.67 (Gammas) – 66.67 (slack process 1) – 266.7 (slack sales limit)

Discuss the information contained in this equation.

8 SENSITIVITY ANALYSIS

8.1 We looked at sensitivity analysis in Section 4. You might be required to carry out some sensitivity analysis on the solution to a problem solved by the Simplex method. You might have to work out how the value of the objective function might change if there were either more or less of a scarce resource. Alternatively you might have to test whether it would be worthwhile to obtain more of a scarce resource by paying a premium for the additional resources, for example by paying an overtime premium for extra labour hours, or by paying a supplier a higher price for extra raw materials.

8.2 Let us go back to our original example and the objective function of the optimal solution:

CONTRIBUTION = 15,200 – 1.1428 (slack labour time) – 6.2858 (slack machine time)

The effect of having more or less of a scarce resource

8.3 The objective function gives us information about the effect on contribution if additional labour hours or machine time becomes available. For example, if three additional labour hours became available, contribution would increase by $3 \times$ £1.1428 = £3.4284. Note, however, that if extra materials become available contribution would be unaffected because materials availability is not a critical constraint.

8.4 There must be a limit to the number of extra labour hours that would earn an extra £1.1428 towards contribution. As we saw earlier in the chapter, there will be a point when there is so much labour available that it is no longer a scarce resource. You can use the same process as before to determine this point.

Activity 9

Draw a graph of the linear programming problem facing Short Toffer Lott Ltd and determine the number of additional labour hours (over and above the original 1,750 hours) over which the shadow price of £1.1428 per hour is valid.

Obtaining extra resources at a premium on cost

8.5 The shadow price, or dual price, of a scarce resource indicates the amount by which the value of the objective function would change if more or less units of the scarce resource were available *at their normal variable cost per unit.* It follows that if more units of a scarce resource were available at a premium over their normal variable cost, we can decide whether it would be worthwhile paying the premium in order to obtain the extra units.

8.6 Returning for the last time to the example of Shore Toffer Lott Ltd, we are given the following information.

(a) The normal variable cost of labour hours is £4 per hour, but extra labour hours could be worked as overtime, when the rate of pay would be time-and-a-half.

(b) The normal variable cost of machine time is £1.50 per hour, but some extra machine time could be made available by renting another machine for 40 hours per week, at a rental cost of £160. Variable running costs of this machine would be £1.50 per hour.

8.7 We know that the shadow price of labour hours is £1.1428 and of machine hours, £6.2858. We can therefore deduce the following.

(a) Paying an overtime premium of £2 per hour for labour would not be worthwhile, because the extra contribution of £1.1428 per hour would be more than offset by the cost of the premium, leaving the company worse off by £0.8572 per hour worked in overtime.

(b) Renting the extra machine would be worthwhile, but only by £91.43 (which is perhaps too small an amount to bother with).

	£
Extra contribution from 40 hours of machine time (× £6.2858)	251.43
Rental cost	160.00
Net increase in profit	91.43

Note that the variable running costs do not enter into this calculation since they are identical to the normal variable costs of machine time. We are concerned here only with the *additional* costs.

Activity 10

A company manufactures three products, tanks, trays and tubs, each of which passes through three processes, X, Y and Z.

Process	*Process hours per unit* *Tanks*	*Trays*	*Tubs*	*Total process hours available*
X	5	2	4	12,000
Y	4	5	6	24,000
Z	3	5	4	18,000

The contribution to profit of each product is £2 for each tank, £3 per tray and £4 per tub.

Required

(a) Formulate these data into a linear programming model using the following notation.

Let a be the number of units of tanks produced
b be the number of units of trays produced
c be the number of units of tubs produced

(b) Formulate the initial Simplex tableau using the slack variables x, y and z to represent the number of unused hours in processes X, Y and Z respectively.

(c) When the problem is solved by the Simplex method, the final objective function is found to be:

CONTRIBUTION = 14,000 – 2.33 (tanks) – 0.667 (slack Process X) – 0.333 (Slack Process Z)

(i) Discuss the information contained in this equation.

(ii) What would happen to budgeted contribution if an order were received for 300 units of tanks which the company felt that it had to accept, because of the importance of the customer?

NOTES

Chapter roundup

- Linear programming, at least at this fairly simple level, is a technique that can be carried out in a fairly 'handle-turning' manner once you have got the basic ideas sorted out. The steps in that technique are as follows.

  Define variables
  Establish constraints (including non-negativity)
  Construct objective function
  Draw a graph of the constraints
  Establish the feasible region
  Add an iso-profit/contribution line
  Determine optimal solution

  The apparent simplicity of the technique should not, however, allow you to disregard the following practical limitations of linear programming.

- In all practical situations there are likely to be substantial problems involved in estimating the total quantities of scarce resources available. Furthermore, the final estimates used are likely to be subject to considerable uncertainty.
- There is an assumption of linearity. Each extra unit of a given product is supposed to change the contribution and the consumption of resources by the same amount. In practice, this assumption may be invalid except over small ranges. For example, in a profit maximisation problem, it may well be found that there are substantial changes in unit variable costs arising from increasing or decreasing returns to scale.
- The linear programming model is essentially static and is therefore not really suitable for analysing in detail the effects of changes over time.
- In some circumstances, a solution derived from a linear programming model may be of limited use if, for example, the variables may only take on integer values. A solution can be found by a combination of rounding up or down and trial and error, but this sort of approach is not really suitable for large-scale practical problems.
- The later part of this chapter has described how to solve a linear programming problem using the Simplex method. The method can be used with any number of decision variables, whereas the graphical method can only be applied to problems involving two decision variables.
- Make sure that you can formulate the linear programming problem and then set up an initial tableau. The method for setting up this tableau is as follows.

  Turn each constraint (ignoring non-negativity constraints) into an equation by introducing slack variables (which represent the amount of constraining resource or item that is unused).

  Express the objective function as an equation with the right-hand side equal to zero. Insert the slack variables into the equation, giving them zero coefficients.

  The initial feasible solution tested is that all the decision variables have a zero value but all the slack variables have a non-negative value.

  There should be a column for each variable and also a solution column.

  There is a row for each equation in the problem (which correspond with the coefficients of the variables in each of the revised constraints), and a solution row which holds the coefficients of the revised objective function.

- The final solution is reached when the shadow prices on the solution row are all positive. The shadow price indicates the amount by which contribution/profit would increase/decrease if more/less of the resource could be made available at its normal variable cost.
- Sensitivity analysis allows you to test the effect of having more or less of a scarce resource or of obtaining extra resources at a premium on cost.

Quick quiz

1 What is meant by an objective function?
2 What would the inequality $4x + 3y = 24$ look like when drawn on a graph?
3 What is the feasible region?
4 What is an iso-profit line?
5 How does the graphical solution of minimisation problems differ from that of maximisation problems?
6 Define the dual price of a resource.
7 What is a slack variable?
8 How is it possible to differentiate the final tableau from other tableaux?
9 What is a shadow price?
10 What is involved in doing sensitivity analysis with the Simplex method?

Answers to activities

1 If $5x + 1.5y = 400$, then if $x = 0$, $y = 267$ and if $y = 0$, $x = 80$.

If $x + y = 150$, then if $x = 0$, $y = 150$ and if $y = 0$, $x = 150$.

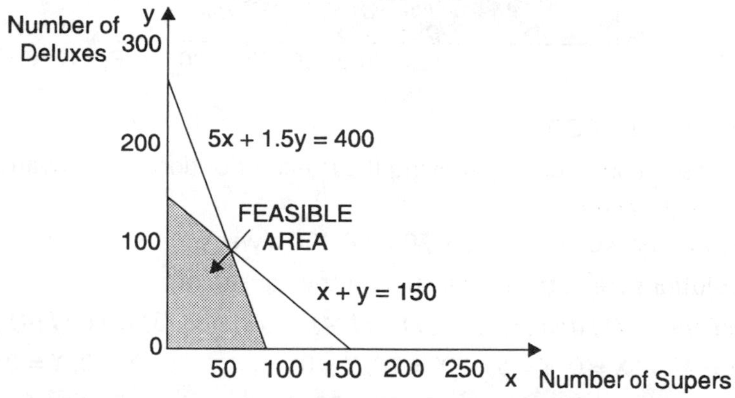

2 The new problem here is the inequality $y \geq 2x$. The equation $y = 2x$ is a straight line, and you need to plot two points to draw it, for example:

(a) when $x = 0$, $y = 0$

(b) when $x = 2$, $y = 4$

Since $y \geq 2x$, feasible combinations of x and y lie above this line (if $x = 2$, y must be 4 or more).

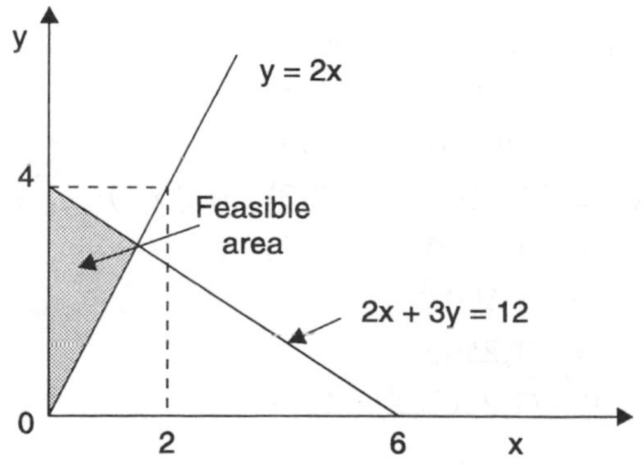

NOTES

3 The decision variables are processing hours in each process. If we let the processing hours per week for process 1 be P_1 and the processing hours per week for process 2 be P_2 we can formulate an objective and constraints as follows.

The objective is to maximise $70P_1 + 60P_2$, subject to the following constraints.

$20P_1 + 30P_2$	$\leq$	2,700	(material A supply)
$10P_1 + 20P_2$	$\leq$	2,000	(material B supply)
P_2	$\leq$	80	(maximum time for P_2)
$P_1 + P_2$	$\leq$	120	(total maximum time)
P_1, P_2	$\geq$	0	

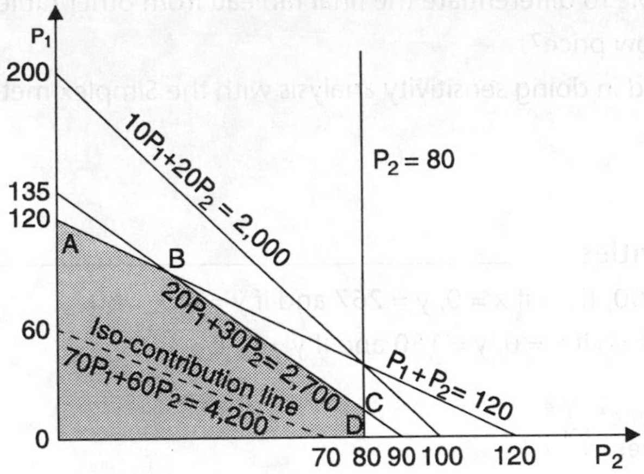

The feasible area is ABCDO.

The optimal solution, found by moving the iso-contribution line outwards, is at point A, where $P_1 = 120$ and $P_2 = 0$.

Total contribution would be 120 × 70 = £8,400 a week.

4 Feasible solutions are at the intersection of the constraints:

(1) and (2)	*(1) and (3)*	*(1) and (4)*	*(2) and (3)*	*(2) and (4)*	*(3) and (4)*
X = 2, Y = 4	X = 0, Y = 5	X = 10, Y = 0			X = 0, Y = 0
Profit = 22	Profit = 20	Profit = 30			Profit = 0

Profit is maximised when 10 units of product X and no units of product Y are produced.

5 The gradient of 2x + 3y = 450 is –2/3. We therefore need:

5/unit profit from Y < 2/3

Unit profit from Y > £7.50

Unit selling price of Y > £18.50

6 The optimum is at the following point.

$3x + 6y$	=	12,000	(1)
$5x + 2y$	=	10,000	(2)
$15x + 6y$	=	30,000	(3) ((2) × 3)
$12x$	=	18,000	(3) – (1)
x	=	1,500	
$\therefore y$	=	1,250	

Profit = (1,500 × 4) + (1,250 × 2) = £8,500.

NOTES

With one extra machine hour, the optimum would be as follows.

$3x + 6y$	=	12,000	(1)	
$5x + 2y$	=	10,001	(2)	
$15x + 6y$	=	30,003	(3)	((2) × 3)
$12x$	=	18,003	(3) – (1)	
x	=	1,500.25		
y	=	1,249.875		

Profit = (1,500.25 × 4) + (1,249.875 × 2) = £8,500.75.

The dual price per machine hour is £(8,500.75 – 8,500.00) = £0.75

7 (a) *Define variables*

Let x_1 be the number of Alphas produced/sold per period
Let x_2 be the number of Betas produced/sold per period
Let x_3 be the number of Gammas purchased/sold per period

Establish constraints

$2x_1 + 3x_2 + 2.5x_3$	$\leq 1{,}920$	(Process 1)
$3x_1 + 2x_2 + 2x_3$	$\leq 2{,}200$	(Process 2)
$0 \leq x_1$	≤ 200	(Sales)
x_2, x_3	≥ 0	(Non-negativity)

Establish objective functions

Maximise $C = 400x_1 + 200x_2 + 100x_3$ (Contribution)

To prepare the initial tableau we need to introduce slack variables.

Let x_4 = quantity of unused process 1 hours
Let x_5 = quantity of unused process 2 hours
Let x_6 = quantity of unused units of Alpha

The revised constraints are as follows.

$2x_1 + 3x_2 + 2.5x_3 + x_4 = 1{,}920$

$3x_1 + 2x_2 + 2x_3 + x_5 = 2{,}200$

$x_1 + x_6 = 200$

The objective function can be redefined as

$C - 400x_1 - 200x_2 - 100x_3 + 0x_4 + 0x_5 + 0x_6 = 0$

(b) The initial Simplex tabulation is as follows.

Variable in solution	x_1	x_2	x_3	x_4	x_5	x_6	*Solution*
x_4	2	3	2.5	1	0	0	1,920
x_5	3	2	2	0	1	0	2,200
x_6	1	0	0	0	0	1	200
Solution	–400	–200	–100	0	0	0	0

8 Overall contribution = £181,333.30.

Since this is the optimal solution, contribution will fall by £66.67 per unit of Gamma produced. (If it were to rise, the solution would not be optimal.)

If the number of Process 1 hours were reduced/increased by one, contribution would fall/rise by £66.67.

If the upper limit on sales of Alpha were reduced/increased by one, contribution would fall/rise by £266.7.

9

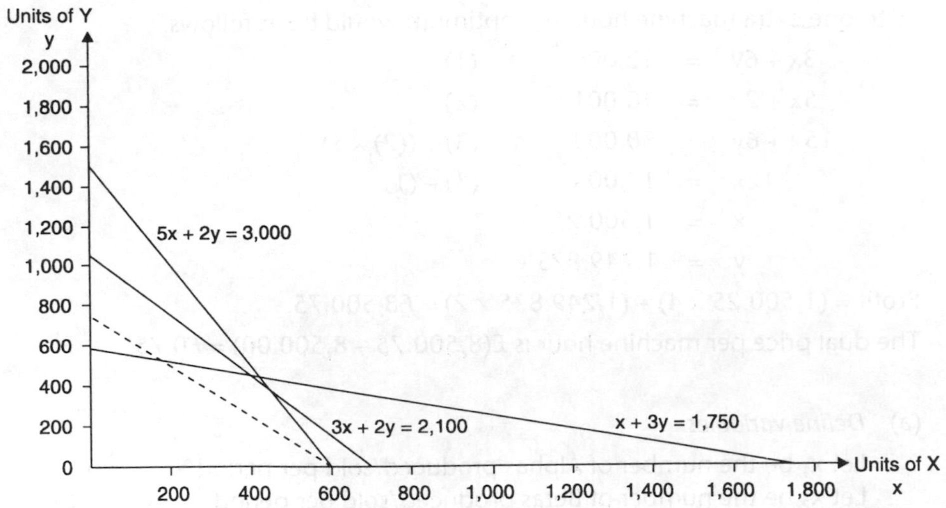

As the number of labour hours available increases, the line on the graph representing the constraint will move up the axes parallel to the original constraint. It will remain part of the boundary of the feasible area and a critical constraint until the point when it passes through the point (0, 1,050). At this point the labour hours available are (1 x 0) + (3 x 1,050) = 3,150. The shadow price of £1.1428 per hour is therefore valid for about 1,400 *extra* labour hours.

10 (a) The objective function is to:

Maximise	2a + 3b + 4c (contribution)	
Subject to the constraints	5a + 2b + 4c	≤ 12,000 (process X hours)
	4a + 5b + 6c	≤ 24,000 (process Y hours)
	3a + 5b + 4c	≤ 18,000 (process Z hours)
	a, b, c	≥ 0

(b) Initial tableau

Variables in the solution	*a*	*b*	*c*	*x*	*y*	*z*	*Solution*
x	5	2	4	1	0	0	12,000
y	4	5	6	0	1	0	24,000
z	3	5	4	0	0	1	18,000
Solution	–2	–3	–4	0	0	0	0

(c) (i) The maximum contribution available is £14,000

Contribution would fall by £2.33 for every tank produced.

If the number of hours in Process X were reduced/increased by one, contribution would fall/rise by £0.667.

If the number of hours in Process Z were reduced/increased by one, contribution would fall/rise by £0.333.

Process Z hours would be fully utilised in the optimal solution.

(ii) If an order were to be received for 300 tanks and they were produced, contribution would fall by 300 × £2.33 = £700.

Further question practice

Now try the following practice questions at the end of this text.

Multiple choice questions **78–85**

Exam style question **11**

Chapter 12

DIFFERENTIAL CALCULUS

Introduction

In this chapter we will be looking at one of the most important branches of mathematics, calculus.

Calculus is concerned with measuring change. It provides the methodology to allow us to calculate the rate of change and determine whether that rate of change is increasing or decreasing.

There are two branches of calculus, differentiation and integration. We will be looking at differentiation, which is also known as differential calculus.

Differential calculus has many business applications. It can, for example, provide additional information about the graphs of equations. It also enables profit-maximising, revenue-maximising and cost-minimising output levels to be calculated and it can be used to derive a cost-minimising stock order quantity formula.

In this chapter we will look at differentiation and its application to graphs of equations and profit and revenue maximisation/cost minimisation.

Your objectives

After completing this chapter you should:

(a) know how to perform differentiation;

(b) be able to find the gradient of a curve using differentiation;

(c) be able to determine whether a gradient is positive or negative;

(d) be able to determine whether a turning point is a maximum or a minimum turning point;

(e) know how to determine the second derivative of a function;

(f) be able to use differentiation in a business context.

1 DIFFERENTIAL CALCULUS

Definition

Differentiation measures the rate of change in one variable (usually denoted y) resulting from a change in another variable (usually denoted x) at a particular point.

1.1 To understand what we mean by 'rate of change' let us consider a simple example.

1.2 Suppose that the annual cost to Sid (in £s) of running his car is described by the function $y = {}^{x}/_{5} + 200$ where y is the total annual cost and x is the number of miles travelled by the car per annum.

1.3 How do we interpret this equation? Let us start by considering the situation in which Sid does not drive his car at all during the year. If the car travels no miles then $x = 0$. Total cost is therefore £200 $({}^{0}/_{5} + 200)$. This £200 represents costs such as road tax and insurance that are incurred even if a car is not driven.

1.4 Suppose that Sid drives 1 mile per annum. His costs are now £200.20 $(y = {}^{1}/_{5} + 200)$. If he drives two miles his costs are £200.40 $(y = {}^{2}/_{5} + 200)$, if he drives three miles his costs are £200.60 $(y = {}^{3}/_{5} + 200)$ and so on. For each additional mile, Sid's costs increase by 20p.

1.5 What is the rate of change of the total cost, y? When the number of miles travelled, x, is 1, costs increases by 20p; when $x = 2$, y increases by 40p; when $x = 3$, y increases by 60p; and when $x = 100$, y increases by £20. It is therefore obvious that y is increasing at ${}^{1}/_{5}$ the rate at which x increases. The rate of change is therefore ${}^{1}/_{5}$.

1.6 Suppose, however, that we were trying to determine the rate at which the population of a country increases or decreases as the average monthly household income (in £) increases or decreases. Suppose that the relationship between population and average household income per month is described by $y = 9x^4 + 3x^3 + 2x^2 + 15x + 952$. It is far more difficult to ascertain a rate of change when faced with such a complicated equation but, using differential calculus, we can work out the rate of change in a matter of moments.

How to differentiate

1.7 If we have a function $y = ax^n$ where x is the independent variable and y is the dependent variable, we can find the rate of change of y with respect to changes in x by *differentiating y with respect to x* to get dy/dx (pronounced 'dee-y by dee-x').

When $y = ax^n$, $dy/dx = nax^{n-1}$.

dy/dx, the result of differentiating, is called the first derivative of y with respect to x and gives the rate of change of y for any given value of x.

1.8 Let us go back to our example about Sid. The cost function was $y = {}^{x}/_{5} + 200$. Rewrite this (for ease of comprehension) as $y = {}^{1}/_{5}.x^1 + 200\,x^0$ (where $x^0 = 1$)

Differentiating, we have $dy/dx \;=\; 1.{}^{1}/_{5}.x^{1-1} + 0.200.x^{0-1}$

$= {}^{1}/_{5}.x^0 + 0$

$= {}^{1}/_{5}$ (as before)

1.9 Here are two examples.

(a) If $y = 3x^4$, $dy/dx = 4 \times 3 \times x^{4-1} = 12x^3$

So when $x = 1$, y rises $12 \times 1^3 = 12$ times as fast as x; when $x = 2$, y rises $12 \times 2^3 = 96$ times as fast as x, and so on.

(b) If $p = 5q^2$, we can differentiate p with respect to q (in exactly the same way as differentiating y with respect to x) such that $dp/dq = 2 \times 5 \times q^{2-1} = 10q$.

1.10 The following points should be noted.

(a) On differentiation, any constant disappears. For example, if $y = 3x^2 + 8$, the constant, 8, disappears on differentiation, and

$dy/dx = 2 \times 3 \times x^{2-1} = 6x$

(b) If the 'power' of x is one, the corresponding value on differentiation is the coefficient of x in the original function. Thus, if $y = 7x$

$dy/dx = 1 \times 7 \times x^{1-1} \quad = 7 \times x^0 = 7 \times 1 = 7$

(c) If there are several expressions in the function, each element in the function may be differentiated separately.

For example, if $y = 3x^4 - 2x^3 + 6x^2 - 8x + 24$

$$dy/dx = (4 \times 3 \times x^3) - (3 \times 2 \times x^2) + (2 \times 6 \times x) - (8)$$
$$= 12x^3 - 6x^2 + 12x - 8$$

(d) The rule also applies when negative powers are involved. For example, if

$y = 3/x^2 = 3x^{-2}$,

$dy/dx = -2 \times 3 \times x^{-3} = -6x^{-3} = -6/x^3$

Activity 1

Differentiate the following.

(a) $y = 6x + 9$

(b) $p = q^3 + 2q$

(c) $s = 3t^3 + 4t^2 - 2t + 5$

(d) $2y = 5x^2 - 4x + 7$

(e) $y = \frac{1}{x^2} - \frac{3}{2x^3} + \frac{5}{4x^4}$

---

2 DIFFERENTIATION AND QUADRATIC EQUATIONS

2.1 If we draw a graph of the linear equation $y = 3x + 2$, we get a straight line as follows.

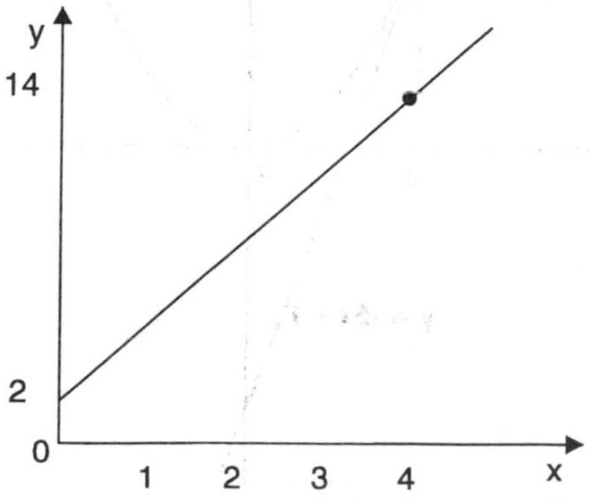

Figure 12.1 Linear equation $y = 3x + 2$

We can differentiate $y = 3x + 2$, such that $dy/dx = 3$. In other words, the rate of change in y at any point on the graph is equal to a constant amount of 3 per extra unit of x. Another way of expressing this idea is that the gradient or slope of the line at any point on the line shows a constant ratio between increases in y and increases in x of +3 : 1.

NOTES

2.2 Similarly, if we draw a curve of $y = x^2$

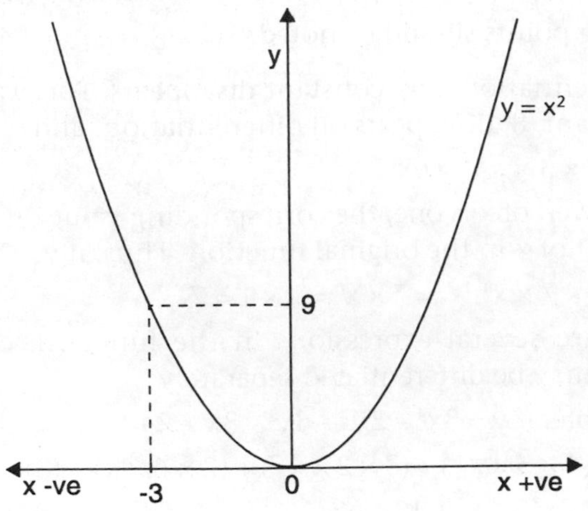

Figure 12.2 Curve of $y = x^2$

$dy/dx = 2x$. The rate of change in y at any point on the curve is shown by the gradient or slope of the curve at that point. This gradient is equal to twice the value of x at that point. Thus at the point (–3,9) the rate of change in y at that point is twice the value of x, $2 \times (-3) = -6$, and the gradient of the curve is –6.

2.3 You may find it difficult to picture the gradient of a curve at a particular point since gradients are normally associated with straight lines. If, however, you were to draw what is known as a tangent at (–3,9) (a tangent being a straight line that just touches the curve at the point in question) then the gradient of the curve at that point would be the same as the gradient of the tangent at that point.

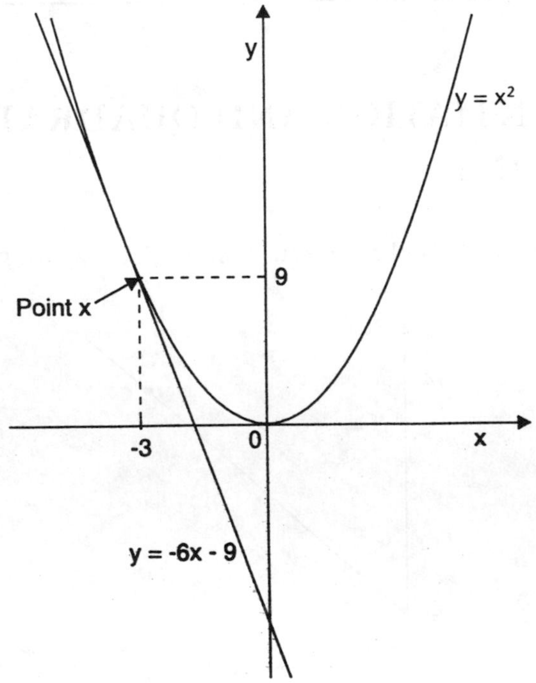

Figure 12.3 Tangent showing gradient at x

NOTES

Positive and negative gradients

2.4 The gradient of a straight line that is upward sloping (when travelling from left to right) is positive, whereas the gradient of a straight line that is downward sloping (when travelling from left to right) is negative. For example, if $y = 3x^2 + 4x - 6$, then $dy/dx = 6x + 4$. When $x = 1$, the gradient of the curve, and hence of a tangent to the curve at $x = 1$, is 10 $((6 \times 1) + 4)$. This means that the tangent at $x = 1$ would be upward sloping since the gradient is positive (+ 10).

Turning points

2.5 Suppose that $y = 5x - 0.001x^2$, then $dy/dx = 5 - 0.002x$.

Now if $x = 1{,}000$, $dy/dx = 5 - 2 = 3$ which is positive. This means that when x is 1,000, the value of y is still increasing as x increases, and the gradient of the curve at that point is positive.

However if $x = 3{,}000$, $dy/dx = 5 - 6 = -1$, which is negative. This means that when x is 3,000, the value of y is decreasing as x increases, and the gradient of the curve is negative.

2.6 Clearly the curve 'flips over' at a turning point somewhere between $x = 1{,}000$ and $x = 3{,}000$.

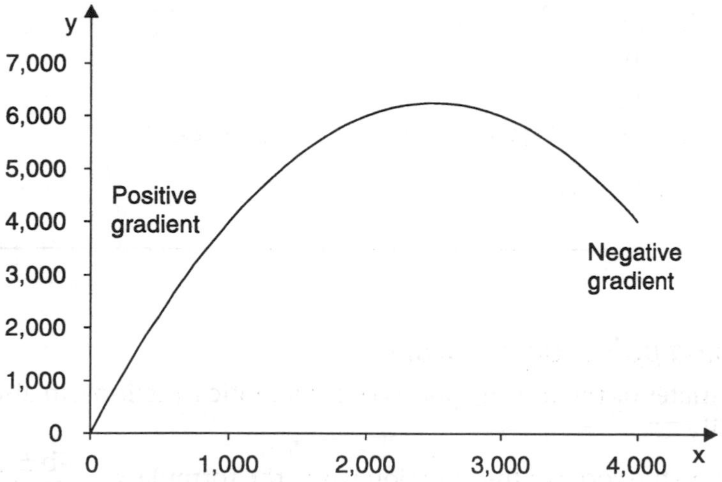

Figure 12.4 The turning point

Definition

A 'flip over' point on the graph of a function is known as a *turning point* or stationary point and occurs when dy/dx (in other words, the gradient of the curve) is zero.

2.7 To find the turning points of an equation we follow a number of steps.

(a) Differentiate the equation.

(b) Let $dy/dx = 0$.

(c) Solve the resulting equation for x.

(d) Substitute the value for x into the original equation to determine the value for y.

NOTES

EXAMPLE: TURNING POINTS

Find the turning points of the following equations.

(a) $y = x^2 - 4x + 3$

(b) $4y = 20x^2 - 48x + 32$

Solution

(a)
$$\begin{aligned} y &= x^2 - 4x + 3 \\ dy/dx &= 2x - 4 \\ 0 &= 2x - 4 \\ 4 &= 2x \\ 2 &= x \\ \therefore y &= 4 - 8 + 3 = -1 \end{aligned}$$

Turning point at (2, –1)

(b)
$$\begin{aligned} 4y &= 20x^2 - 48x + 32 \\ y &= 5x^2 - 12x + 8 \\ dy/dx &= 10x - 12 \\ 0 &= 10x - 12 \\ 12 &= 10x \\ {}^6/_5 &= x \end{aligned}$$

$\therefore y = (5 \times {}^6/_5 \times {}^6/_5) - (12 \times {}^6/_5) + 8 = {}^{36}/_5 - {}^{72}/_5 + {}^{40}/_5 = {}^4/_5.$

Turning point at $({}^6/_5, {}^4/_5)$

Finding turning points algebraically

2.8 The coordinates of the turning points of a quadratic function can also be found algebraically.

(a) Calculate the roots of the equation using the formula $x = \dfrac{-b \pm \sqrt{b^2 - 4ac}}{2a}$

(b) Calculate the midpoint between the two roots, which will be the turning point.

$$\text{Turning point (x coordinate)} = \frac{\text{Lowest root + highest root}}{2}$$

Let us use the example which follows Paragraph 2.7.

If $y = x^2 - 4x + 3$, then the roots of the equation are

$$x = \frac{4 \pm \sqrt{16 - (4 \times 1 \times 3)}}{2} = \frac{4 \pm 2}{2} = 1 \text{ or } 3$$

$$\therefore \text{Turning point (x coordinate)} = \frac{1+3}{2} = 2$$

$\therefore$ Turning point (y coordinate) = 4 – 8 + 3 = –1

$\therefore$ Turning point = (2, –1) (the result we arrived at in the example in Paragraph 2.7)

Maximum and minimum points

2.9 A turning point is either a maximum turning point or a minimum turning point. A maximum turning point is 'the top of a hill' on the graph of a curve, whereas a minimum turning point is 'the bottom of a ditch' on the graph of a curve.

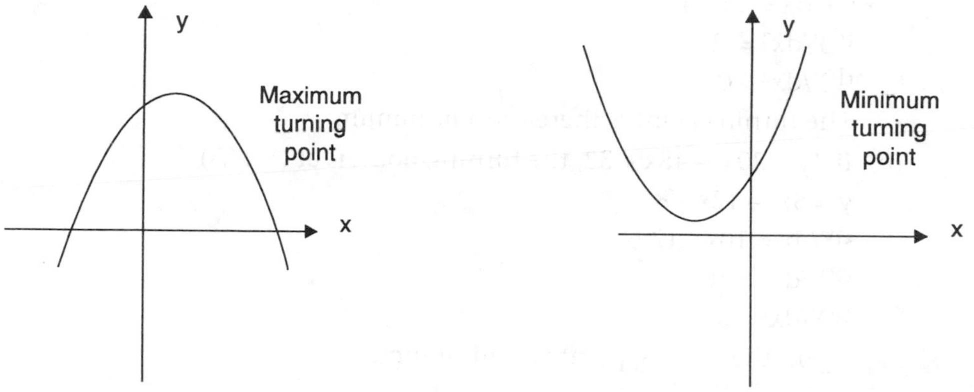

Figure 12.5 Maximum and minimum turning points

2.10 We can see from the graph in Paragraph 2.5 that there is a maximum point and not a minimum point but we cannot tell if the turning points determined in the example following Paragraph 2.7 are maximum or minimum turning points. To do this we need to calculate the second derivative of the function.

The second derivative

2.11 The first derivative of a function $y = ax^n$ is $dy/dx = nax^{n-1}$

This can be used to calculate the gradient of the curve on a graph of $y = ax^n$ for any given value of x.

Definition

The *second derivative* or *differential* of a function is the derivative of dy/dx, and is written as d^2y/dx^2 (pronounced 'dee – squared – y by dee – x – squared').

2.12 The second derivative may be used to calculate the *rate* at which the *gradient* of the curve $y = ax^n$ is increasing or decreasing.

(a) If $y = 3x^3 - 2x^2 + 4x - 20$

then $dy/dx = 9x^2 - 4x + 4$

and $d^2y/dx^2 = 18x - 4$

(b) If $y = 28/x - 3/x^2 + 5x^4$

then $dy/dx = -28/x^2 + 6/x^3 + 20x^3$

and $d^2y/dx^2 = 56/x^3 - 18/x^4 + 60x^2$

The second derivative is then used to test for maximum or minimum points.

The rule for testing maximum and minimum points

2.13 The rules for testing whether a point is a maximum or a minimum are as follows.

(a) If $d^2y/dx^2 > 0$ there is a minimum point.

(b) If $d^2y/dx^2 < 0$ there is a maximum point.

Definitions

If the second differential at a turning point is less that zero, the turning point is a *maximum turning point*.

If the second differential at a turning point is greater than zero, the turning point is a *minimum turning point*.

NOTES

EXAMPLE: MAXIMUM AND MINIMUM TURNING POINTS

Let us look again at the two equations in the example following Paragraph 2.7.

(a) If $y = x^2 - 4x + 3$, the turning point is at (2, –1)
$dy/dx = 2x - 4$
$d^2y/dx^2 = 2$
$d^2y/dx^2 > 0$
The turning point is therefore a minimum.

(b) If $4y = 20x^2 - 48x + 32$, the turning point is at $(^6/_5, ^4/_5)$
$y = 5x^2 - 12x + 8$
$dy/dx = 10x - 12$
$d^2y/dx^2 = 10$
$d^2y/dx^2 > 0$
Again the turning point is a minimum.

Points of inflexion

Definition

Occasionally, the second derivative of a function is zero when the first derivative is zero. Where this occurs, the point on the graph is neither a maximum nor a minimum point, but is a *'point of inflexion'*.

EXAMPLE: A POINT OF INFLEXION

Consider the graph of $y = x^3$

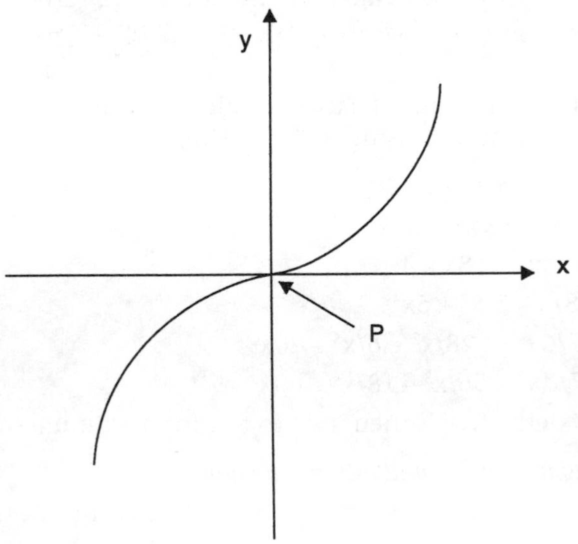

Point P is a point of inflexion for the following reasons.

(a) $dy/dx = 3x$: this is zero when $x = 0$.

(b) $d^2y/dx^2 = 6x$: when $x = 0$, this also equals 0.

3 THE USE OF DIFFERENTIATION IN A BUSINESS CONTEXT

3.1 Business situations and economic relationships can often be described mathematically. The point at which an organisation makes neither a profit or a loss can be determined using equations and, by expressing total overheads as an equation, the split between fixed and variable overheads can be calculated mathematically.

3.2 We are not, however, always interested in what is happening at a certain level of output or at a certain price. We may be interested in the rate at which total sales revenue changes with the volume of units sold or how demand for a product varies with its price. This is where differential calculus can help.

3.3 We have looked at the basic rules for differentiating functions, so we will now consider these more practical uses of differential calculus by working through a number of examples. Make sure you are aware of the following definitions before you begin, however.

Definitions

Marginal cost comprises the additional costs which arise when one exta unit is produced.

Marginal revenue is the additional revenue from selling one extra unit.

EXAMPLE: MARGINAL COST

A company's total production costs are fixed costs of £30,000 and variable costs of £5 per unit.

Required

Use differential calculus to find the marginal cost.

Solution

The first step is to translate the above situation into an equation. The equation obviously has to include costs as the dependent variable but what affects the level of costs (and is therefore the independent variable)? Costs increase and decrease according to the level of output: output is therefore the independent variable.

Let total costs = c and output = x

Total costs = 30,000 + 5x because for every additional unit produced costs increase by £5 but if no units are produced the company still incurs costs of £30,000.

This being a simple example we have already arrived at the marginal cost of £5. Let us try to get the same answer using differential calculus.

Differential calculus will find the rate at which total costs (c) change as output (x) changes (in other words the marginal cost).

$$c = 30{,}000 + 5x$$

$$dc/dx = 5$$

Marginal cost = £5

NOTES

3.4 Let us look at a more difficult example.

EXAMPLE: MARGINAL REVENUE

Wib Ltd's total revenue (R) from producing the Wibbet can be expressed as

$4x^3 - 9x^2 - 10x - 13$, where x is the number of Wibbets sold.

Required

Use differential calculus to find the marginal revenue when 10 Wibbets are sold.

Solution

We can use differential calculus to find the rate at which total revenue (R) changes as the number of Wibbets sold (x) changes.

$R = 4x^3 - 9x^2 - 10x - 13$

$dR/dx = 12x^2 - 18x - 10$

Marginal revenue $= 12x^2 - 18x - 10$

We are interested in the marginal revenue when 10 Wibbets are sold (x = 10)

Marginal revenue $(12 \times 10^2) - (18 \times 10) - 10 = 1{,}200 - 180 - 10 =$ £1,010.

The marginal revenue function still contains x's. Different values of x substituted into the equation will therefore give different marginal revenues.

3.5 We will now go on to look at how we use differential calculus to find maximum and minimum profits.

EXAMPLE: PROFIT MAXIMISATION

Cat Ltd believes that demand for its product can be represented by $P = 10 - 0.003Q$, where P is the unit price in pounds and Q is the quantity of sales. The total cost function is (in £s) $C = 1{,}000 + 3Q + 0.004Q^2$.

Required

(a) Calculate the level of output and the unit price at which profit will be maximised.

(b) Calculate the amount of profit at this level.

Solution

(a) If $P = 10 - 0.003Q$, then total revenue R is found by multiplying the number of units sold by the price per unit.

$R = PQ = (10 - 0.003Q)Q = 10Q - 0.003Q^2$

The marginal revenue function (the rate of change of revenue with quantity) is found by differentiating R with respect to Q.

$dR/dQ = MR = 10 - 0.006Q$

Since $C = 1{,}000 + 3Q + 0.004Q^2$, the marginal cost function (the rate of change of cost with quantity) is $dC/dQ = MC = 3 + 0.008Q$

EXAMPLE *continued*

Profit is maximised where MC = MR, as above that point each additional unit will increase total costs by more than total revenue.

$3 + 0.008Q$	=	$10 - 0.006Q$
$0.014Q$	=	7
Q	=	500

The unit price is P $= 10 - 0.003Q$

$= 10 - 0.003(500)$

$= £8.50$

(b)

	£
Revenue (500×8.50)	4,250
Less costs $(1,000 + 3(500) + 0.004(500)^2)$	3,500
Profit	750

EXAMPLE: MARGINAL COST AND MARGINAL REVENUE

The costs of selling a product are $c = x^2 - 2x + 20$ where

x = output in batches

c = costs, in thousands of pounds

The revenue from the product is $r = 8.5x^2 - x^3 + 20x$ where

r = value in thousands of pounds

x = sales in batches

Required

(a) Calculate the volume of output at which total costs would be minimised.

(b) Calculate the volume of sales at which total revenue would be maximised.

(c) Using the principle that profits are maximised where marginal cost equals marginal revenue (MC = MR), calculate the volume of output and sales which will maximise profits.

(d) Prove your solution in (c) by formulating the profit function, and calculating where this has a maximum point.

Solution

(a) $c = x^2 - 2x + 20$

$dc/dx = 2x - 2$

This is a maximum or minimum point when $2x - 2 = 0$

$2x = 2$

$x = 1$

$d^2c/dx^2 = 2$

This is a positive number, therefore when x = 1, there is a minimum point.

NOTES

EXAMPLE *continued*

(b) $r = 8.5x^2 - x^3 + 20x$

$dr/dx = 17x - 3x^2 + 20$

This is a maximum or minimum point when $-3x^2 + 17x + 20 = 0$

$$x = \frac{-17 \pm \sqrt{[289 - (4 \times (-3) \times 20)]}}{-6}$$

$$= \frac{-17 - 23}{-6} \text{ or } \frac{-17 + 23}{-6}$$

$= 6^2/_3$ or -1

Since output cannot be negative, we have a maximum or minimum point when $x = 6^2/_3$

$d^2r/dx^2 = -6x + 17$

When $x = 6^2/_3$, this equals $-40 + 17 = -23$. This is a negative number, therefore when $x = 6^2/_3$, there is a maximum point. Total revenue is maximised when $6^2/_3$ batches are sold.

(c) Marginal cost (MC) = $dc/dx = 2x - 2$

Marginal revenue (MR) = $dr/dx = -3x^2 + 17x + 20$

Profits are maximised when MC = MR: $2x - 2 = -3x^2 + 17x + 20$

$$-3x^2 + 15x + 22 = 0, \text{ or } 3x^2 - 15x - 22 = 0$$

$$x = \frac{+15 \pm \sqrt{[225 - (4 \times 3 \times (-22))]}}{6}$$

$$= \frac{+15 + 22.1}{6} \text{ or } \frac{+15 - 22.1}{6}$$

$= 6.2$ or -1.2

Since x cannot be negative, profit is maximised when $x = 6.2$.

(d) Profit equals revenue minus costs.

Revenue	$= -x^3 + 8.5x^2 + 20x$
Costs	$= x^2 - 2x + 20$
Profit (p)	$= -x^3 + 7.5x^2 + 22x - 20$
dp/dx	$= -3x^2 + 15x + 22$

There is a maximum or minimum point when $-3x^2 + 15x + 22 = 0$.

As in (c) above, $-3x^2 + 15x + 22 = 0$ when $x = 6.2$ (or -1.2)

$d^2p/dx^2 = -6x + 15$

When $x = 6.2$, $d^2p/dx^2 = -22.2$. This is a maximum point. Profits must therefore be at a maximum when $x = 6.2$.

NOTES

Activity 2

A building firm has won a contract to build a new sports centre. The contract profit will be determined by the size of the work force involved; if the workforce is too small, it is unlikely that the work will be finished on time and the firm will incur penalty payments; if the workforce is too large there are likely to be high rectification costs due to using unskilled labour.

The profit function has been determined as

Profit (£'000) = $x^2 - 80x + 1{,}431$

where x is the number of workers.

Required

(a) Calculate the limits on the size of the workforce which will ensure that the firm makes a profit.

(b) Calculate the number of workers which will result in minimum profit.

The graphical approach to finding the profit-maximising output

3.6 Instead of equating the equations for MC and MR and solving algebraically we could plot the two equations on a graph and find the point where the two lines intersect.

EXAMPLE: GRAPHICAL APPROACH

Draw a graph showing marginal cost and marginal revenue as calculated in the marginal cost and marginal revenue example which follows paragraph 3.5 above, for output between 0 and 9 batches, clearly indicating the profit-maximising output.

Solution

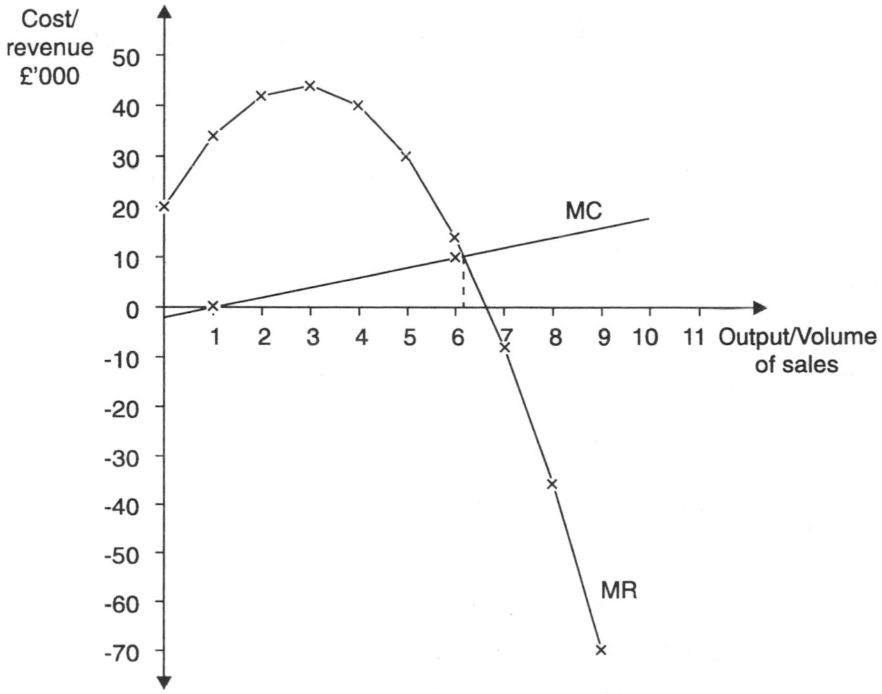

NOTES

EXAMPLE *continued*

Workings

x	*MC*	*MR*
0	–2	20
1	0	34
2	2	42
3	4	44
4	6	40
5	8	30
6	10	14
7	12	–8
8	14	–36
9	16	–70

We need to find the turning point of the MR curve.

MR $= -3x^2 + 17x + 20$

dMR/dx $= -6x + 17$

0 $= -6x + 17$

17 $= 6x$

17/6 $= x$

$\therefore$ MR $= 44.08$

The profit-maximising output is at an output level of 6.2 batches.

Activity 3

(a) A company manufactures a product. For the accounting period, the total costs are £1,050 when the output is 20 units and £1,850 when the output is 40 units. Assuming linearity, find an expression for total costs in terms of q, the quantity of output.

(b) When the price is £20, the demand in the accounting period is 40 units. If the price is reduced to £10, the demand increases to 45 units. Assuming linearity, obtain the relationship between price and demand (q).

(c) Obtain an expression for the revenue function and hence show that the profit function is

$P = -2q^2 + 60q - 250$

By a graphical method or otherwise find the output which maximises profits.

Activity 4

A firm has analysed its operating conditions, prices and costs and has developed the following functions, where Q is the number of units sold.

Revenue (£): R $= 200Q - 3Q^2$

Cost (£): C $= 2Q^2 + 50Q + 10$

The firm's objective is to maximise profit.

Required

(a) Calculate the quantity that should be sold.

(b) Calculate the price at which the product should be sold.

(c) Calculate the profit that the company will earn.

NOTES

Cost minimisation and revenue maximisation

3.7 We know that by differentiating a function we can find turning points and then by determining the second differential we can ascertain whether the turning point is a maximum or minimum point. This being the case we can:

(a) differentiate a function representing an organisation's costs, determine the second differential and ascertain the production level at which costs are minimised; or

(b) differentiate a function representing an organisation's revenue, determine the second differential and ascertain the sales level at which revenue is maximised.

3.8 We could, of course, also find the point at which costs are maximised or the point at which revenue is minimised. Sounds complicated? Don't worry, it's not! Let us have a look at an example.

EXAMPLE: COST MINIMISATION

A company's costs are given by the function

$$C = 2{,}000q + \frac{27{,}000}{q^2}$$

where q is the quantity produced.

Required

Use differential calculus to determine the production level at which costs are minimised and hence calculate the minimum costs.

Solution

$$C = 2{,}000q + \frac{27{,}000}{q^2} = 2{,}000q + 27{,}000q^{-2}$$

$$\frac{dC}{dq} = 2{,}000 - 54{,}000q^{-3}$$

To find a maximum or minimum point we let $dC/dq = 0$

$$0 = 2{,}000 - 54{,}000q^{-3} = 2{,}000 - \frac{54{,}000}{q^3}$$

$$\therefore \frac{54{,}000}{q^3} = 2{,}000$$

$$\therefore \frac{54{,}000}{2{,}000} = q^3 = 27$$

$$\therefore q = 3$$

We now need to see whether a production quantity of 3 leads to minimum costs.

$$\frac{d^2C}{dq^2} = 162{,}000\ q^{-4}$$

If $q = 3$, $\frac{d^2C}{dq^2} = 2{,}000 > 0$

When $\frac{d^2C}{dq^2} > 0$ we have a minimum point, so costs are at a minimum.

NOTES

EXAMPLE *continued*

Let us calculate the minimum costs.

$$C = 2{,}000q + \frac{27{,}000}{q^2}$$

When q = 3, C = £9,000

At a production level of 3, minimum costs of £9,000 are incurred.

3.9 The approaches to finding maximum revenue, maximum cost and minimum revenue are exactly the same. Try this activity which requires you to determine maximum revenue.

Activity 5

The demand for AB Ltd's product X is dependent on price, the price function for product X being

$$P = \frac{q^2}{3} - \frac{45q}{2} + 450, \text{ where q is the quantity sold.}$$

Use differential calculus to find both the sales volume at which revenue is maximised and the maximum revenue available from the sales of product X.

Chapter roundup

- Differential calculus may at first seem to be a very abstract branch of mathematics but, as the examples in this chapter demonstrate, it has very practical applications in business.
- After reading this chapter you should be able to differentiate functions, using the fact that if $y = ax^n$, then $dy/dx = nax^{n-1}$.
- You should also be able to determine the gradient of a curve at a particular point since gradient = dy/dx and you should be able to identify whether a curve is upward sloping at a particular point ($dy/dx > 0$) or downward sloping ($dy/dx < 0$) at a particular point.
- The distinction between maximum and minimum turning points should now be clear to you. Remember we find a turning point by letting dy/dx = 0 and then we identify the type of turning point by letting d^2y/dx^2 (the second derivative) = 0. If $d^2y/dx^2 > 0$ there is a minimum point and if $d^2y/dx^2 < 0$ there is a maximum point. A point of inflexion occurs if $d^2y/dx^2 = 0$.
- As far as using calculus in a business context is concerned, you should be able to calculate marginal costs, marginal revenues, the point at which profits are maximised (when MC = MR), maximum/minimum revenues and maximum/minimum costs.

NOTES

Quick quiz

1 If $y = ax^n$, what is the formula for the first derivative of y with respect to x?

2 Does a positive first derivative at a particular point indicate that a graph is upwards sloping (from left to right) or downward sloping (from left to right) at that point?

3 What is a turning point?

4 If the second derivative is greater than 0, does this indicate a maximum or minimum point?

5 What is a point of inflexion?

6 At what point are profits maximised?

Answers to activities

1 (a) $dy/dx = 6$

(b) $dp/dq = 3q^2 + 2$

(c) $ds/dt = 9t^2 + 8t - 2$

(d) $y = {}^5/_2\, x^2 - 2x + {}^7/_2$

$dy/dx = 5x - 2$

(e) $y = x^{-2}\ {}^3/_2 x^{-3} + {}^5/_4 x^{-4}$

$dy/dx = -2x^{-3} + {}^9/_2\, x^{-4} - 5x^{-5}$

$= {}^{-2}/_{x^3} + {}^9/_{2x^4} - {}^5/_{x^5}$

2 (a) Profit (p) = $x^2 - 80x + 1{,}431$

$$x = \frac{80 \pm \sqrt{(-80)^2 - (4 \times 1 \times 1{,}431)}}{2}$$

$$= \frac{80 \pm \sqrt{676}}{2} = 27 \text{ or } 53$$

∴ Provided that the number of workers is more than 27 and less than 53, the firm will make a profit. (When there are 27 or 53 workers the firm breaks even.)

(b) Profit is minimised when $dp/dx = 0$ and $d^2p/dx^2 > 0$.

$dp/dx = 2x - 80$ and so profit is minimised when $0 = 2x - 80$ and $d^2p/dx^2 > 0$.

$d^2p/dx^2 = 2 > 0$

∴ Profit is minimised when $0 = 2x - 80$

∴ Profit is minimised if there are 40 workers.

3 (a) When q rises by 20 units (from 20 units to 40 units) total costs rise by £800 (from £1,050 to £1,850). This is a rise of £800/20 = £40 a unit, so variable costs are £40 a unit. At 20 units, we have:

Fixed costs + 20 × £40 = £1,050

Fixed costs = £1,050 – £800 = £250

The required expression for total costs is therefore T = 250 + 40q.

(b) Let p = price, and assume that p = a + bq

Then	20	=	a + 40b	(1)
	10	=	a + 45b	(2)
	10	=	–5b	(3) (subtract (2) from (1))
	b	=	–2	(4)
	20	=	a –80	(5) (from (1))
	a	=	100	(6)

The required relationship is p = 100 – 2q.

(c) Revenue = pq = q(100 –2q) = $100q - 2q^2$

NOTES

Profit $= P$ = revenue – costs
$= 100q - 2q^2 - (250 + 40q)$
$= -2q^2 + 60q - 250$

A graph may be plotted using the following values.

q	$-2q^2 + 60q - 250$
5	0
10	150
15	200
20	150
25	0

Graph of profit against quantity

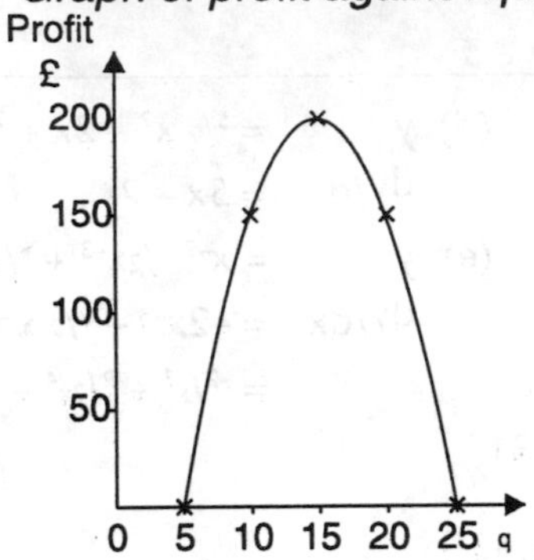

We can see from the graph that profit is maximised at $q = 15$. At this point, profit = £200.

4 (a) $R = 200Q - 3Q^2$

$dR/dQ = 200 - 6Q$ = marginal revenue

$C = 2Q^2 + 50Q + 10$

$dC/dQ = 4Q + 50$ = marginal cost

Profit is maximised when MR = MC

ie when
$$200 - 6Q = 4Q + 50$$
$$200 - 50 = 10Q$$
$$150 = 10Q$$
$$15 = Q$$

(b) $R = 200Q - 3Q^2$

$R = Q(200 - 3Q)$ = quantity × price

Price $= 200 - 3Q = 200 - (3 \times 15) =$ £155

(c)

		£
Revenue	$= ((200 \times 15) - (3 \times 225))$	2,325
Cost	$= ((2 \times 15^2) + (50 \times 15) + 10))$	1,210
Profit		1,115

5 Revenue (R) = price × quantity sold = Pq

$$R = \left(\frac{q^2}{3} - \frac{45q}{2} + 450\right) \times q = \frac{q^3}{3} - \frac{45}{2}q^2 + 450q$$

$$\frac{dR}{dq} = \frac{3q^2}{3} - \frac{90}{2}q + 450 = q^2 - 45q + 450$$

NOTES

For a maximum or minimum $0=q^2 - 45q + 450$. We therefore need to use the formula for solving a quadratic equation to determine values for q.

$$q = \frac{+45 \pm \sqrt{(-45)^2 - (4 \times 1 \times 450)}}{2} = \frac{+45 \pm \sqrt{225}}{2} = \frac{45 \pm 15}{2}$$

$\therefore$ q = 30 or 15

To find the revenue-maximising sales volume we calculate $\frac{d^2R}{dq^2}$.

$$\frac{d^2R}{dq^2} = 2q - 45$$

When q = 15, $\frac{d^2R}{dq^2} = -15 < 0$ and so revenue is maximised when q = 15

(because if q = 30, $\frac{d^2R}{dq^2} > 0$)

If q = 15, R = £2,812.50

$\therefore$ When 15 units are sold maximum revenue of £2,812.50 can be earned.

Further question practice

Now try the following practice questions at the end of this text.

Multiple choice questions	**86–90**
Exam style question	**12**

Chapter 13

BREAKEVEN ANALYSIS

Introduction

The knowledge gained from Chapter 1 on equations is used in this chapter to enable us to construct breakeven analysis models. Breakeven analysis attempts to represent the behaviour of total costs and revenues and so provide information about profit levels, breakeven points and so on.

Your objectives

After completing this chapter you should:

(a) understand the concept of contribution;

(b) be able to calculate a breakeven point;

(c) be able to construct algebraic breakeven models;

(d) know how to account for non-linear relationships when using breakeven analysis.

1 AN INTRODUCTION TO BREAKEVEN ANALYSIS

1.1 Managers like to be able to assess and plan their future profits (profit planning), so they need to be able to forecast future costs and revenues.

1.2 One way of presenting information about expected future costs and revenues for management decision making is breakeven analysis. Breakeven analysis is sometimes called CVP or cost–volume–profit analysis. It uses marginal costing.

1.3 The basic idea of marginal costing is that if one extra unit is produced, then the costs which vary with production will all go up slightly. It therefore makes sense to identify those costs as the costs of production, the marginal costs. On the other hand, overheads such as rent, rates and heating will remain the same even if an extra unit is produced. They are fixed costs, and are not linked directly to the level of production.

1.4 The marginal cost per unit of production of an item will consist of the following.

(a) Direct materials
(b) Direct labour
(c) Variable production overheads, such as power costs

Contribution

Definition

Contribution is the difference between sales value and the marginal cost of sales.

1.5 If a stock item has a marginal cost of £10 a unit, and is sold for £12 a unit, each sale generates a contribution of £2. This contribution will go towards covering the fixed overheads of the business, and once these have been covered, the excess is profit. If the business has fixed overheads of £10,000 a year, the first 5,000 units sold will generate enough contribution to pay the fixed overheads of the year, and any further sales contribute £2 a unit clear profit. In any business, the total contribution from all sales during a period can be compared with the fixed costs for that period; any excess of contribution over fixed costs or of fixed costs over contribution represents the profit or loss respectively for the period.

The breakeven point

Definition

The *breakeven point* is the point at which neither a profit nor a loss occurs.

1.6 The management of an organisation usually wishes to know not only the profit likely to be made if the aimed-for production and sales for the year are achieved, but also the point at which neither profit nor loss occurs (the breakeven point), and the amount by which actual sales can fall below anticipated sales without a loss being incurred.

1.7 The breakeven point can be calculated arithmetically. The number of units which must be sold in order to break even will be the total fixed costs divided by the contribution per unit. This is because the contribution required to break even must be an amount which exactly equals the amount of fixed costs.

NOTES

EXAMPLE: THE BREAKEVEN POINT

Expected sales	10,000 units at £8 = £80,000
Variable cost	£5 a unit
Fixed costs	£21,000

Required

Compute the breakeven point.

Solution

The contribution per unit is £ (8 – 5) = £3

Breakeven point (BEP) = £21,000 ÷ £3

= 7,000 units

In revenue, BEP = 7,000 × £8 = £56,000

Sales above £56,000 will result in profit of £3 for each unit of additional sales and sales below £56,000 will mean a loss of (7,000 units – actual units sold) × £3.

	Sales	
	7,000 units	*7,001 units*
	£	£
Revenue	56,000	56,008
Less variable costs	35,000	35,005
Contribution	21,000	21,003
Less fixed costs	21,000	21,000
Profit	0	3

The margin of safety

Definition

The *margin of safety* is the difference in units between budgeted sales volume and breakeven sales volume, and it is sometimes expressed as a percentage of the budgeted sales volume. It may also be expressed as the difference between the budgeted sales revenue and breakeven sales revenue, expressed as a percentage of the budgeted sales revenue.

2 CONSTRUCTING ALGEBRAIC BREAKEVEN ANALYSIS MODELS

2.1 Before we begin our examination of the construction of algebraic breakeven analysis models, we need to set out the assumptions upon which breakeven analysis is based.

(a) It is assumed that fixed costs are the same in total and variable costs are the same per unit at all levels of output. This assumption is a great simplification.

(b) It is assumed that selling prices will be constant at all levels of activity. This may not be true, especially at high volumes of output, where the price may have to be reduced to win extra sales.

(c) Production and sales are assumed to be the same; therefore the consequences of any increases in stock levels (when production exceeds sales) or de-stocking (when sales exceed production) are ignored.

2.2 Although these assumptions limit the extent to which breakeven analysis reflects reality, we can still use the technique to enable us to build up formulae which explain, in simplified general terms, how costs and revenues behave.

The total revenue formula

2.3 We assume that the selling price is constant at all levels of activity. Total revenue is therefore equal to the selling price per unit multiplied by the quantity sold.

We can write this as $R = pq$

where R = total revenue
p = selling price per unit
q = sales volume or quantity sold

The total cost formula

2.4 Total costs are made up of fixed costs and variable costs. Since we are assuming that fixed costs are the same in total and variable cost per unit remain the same whatever the level of output, we can write

$$C = F + vq$$

where C = total costs
F = fixed costs
v = variable cost per unit
q = quantity sold

The total profit formula

2.5 Total profit (P) is the difference between total revenue and total cost and so we can write

$$P = R - C$$

We can, however, substitute our formulae for R and C into the formula for P.

$$\begin{aligned} P &= R - C \\ &= pq - (F + vq) \\ &= (p - v)q - F \end{aligned}$$

The total contribution formula

2.6 Contribution per unit, as we have already seen, is the difference between the selling price per unit and the variable cost per unit (or marginal cost). We can therefore write

$$k = (p - v)$$

where k = contribution per unit

The formula for total contribution, K, can therefore be written as

$$K = (p - v)q$$

2.7 A comparison of the formulae for total contribution and total profit reveals that the difference between them is, obviously, F, fixed costs. If you cannot see why the difference had to be F, reread the explanation of contribution at the beginning of the chapter.

NOTES

What happens at the breakeven point?

2.8 We have now established the formulae necessary to solve any breakeven analysis problem. Before we tackle a few questions, let us just consider what happens to the formulae at breakeven point.

2.9 At the breakeven point neither profit nor loss occurs and so P = 0.

We know that P = R – C

If P = 0 then 0 = R – C and so R = C, that is, total revenue equals total costs.

If R = pq and C = F + vq, at the breakeven point pq = F + vq and so (p – v)q = F

Remember that K = (p – v)q and so, at the breakeven point, K = F.

EXAMPLE: USING THE FORMULAE

The budgeted annual output of a factory is 120,000 units. The fixed overheads amount to £40,000 and the variable costs are 50p a unit. The selling price is £1 a unit.

Required

(a) Calculate the budgeted profit.

(b) Ascertain the breakeven point.

(c) Determine the margin of safety in units and as a percentage of budgeted sales revenue.

Solution

(a) Budget

	£
Sales (120,000 units)	120,000
Less variable costs	60,000
Contribution	60,000
Less fixed costs	40,000
Profit	20,000

(b) F = £40,000

v = £0.50

p = £1

q = breakeven quantity

At the breakeven point K = F

but K = (p – v)q

and so (p – v)q = F

Substituting in the values given we find

(1 – 0.5)q = 40,000

and so q = 80,000

(c) Margin of safety = (120,000 – 80,000) units

= 40,000 units = £40,000 of revenue

= $33^1/_3$ % of expected revenue

EXAMPLE: THE FORMULAE APPROACH AGAIN

Butterfingers Ltd makes a product which has a variable cost of £7 a unit. Fixed costs are £63,000 a year.

Required

Calculate the selling price per unit if the company wishes both to break even and to sell 12,000 units of the product.

Solution

Required contribution to break even = K = F	= £63,000	
Volume of sales	= 12,000 units	£
Required contribution per unit	= £63,000 ÷ 12,000 =	5.25
Variable cost per unit		7.00
Required selling price per unit		12.25

Target profits

2.10 A similar approach may be applied where a company wishes to achieve a certain profit during a period. To achieve this profit, sales must cover all costs and leave the required profit.

$R = C + P$

We can rewrite this as $pq = F + vq + P$

Subtracting vq from each side of the equation, we get the following.

$pq - vq = F + P$

$(p - v)q = F + P$

Total contribution required = F + P

EXAMPLE: A REQUIRED PROFIT

Riding Breeches Ltd makes and sells a single product, for which variable costs are as follows.

	£
Direct materials	10
Direct labour	8
Variable production overhead	4
Variable sales overhead	2
	24

The selling price is £30 a unit, and fixed costs are £68,000 a year. The company wishes to make a profit of £16,000 a year.

Required

Calculate the sales required to achieve this profit.

Solution

Required contribution	=	F + P
	=	£68,000 + £16,000 = £84,000

£6 profit is made per unit and so 84,000/6 = 14,000 units must be sold to recover the £84,000.

Each unit sells for £30 and so required revenue is £30 × 14,000	=	£420,000 of sales

Activity 1

Seven League Boots Ltd wishes to sell 14,000 units of its product, which has a variable cost of £15. Fixed costs are £47,000 and the required profit is £23,000.

Required

Calculate the required price per unit.

Activity 2

(a) A company manufactures a product and finds that the fixed costs are £10,000, the labour costs are £6 per unit and other variable costs are £14 per unit. The selling price is fixed at £40.

Required

Find the following levels of sales.

(i) At breakeven point

(ii) To produce a profit of £2,200

(b) The company can purchase a new machine for £2,100 (this would increase the fixed costs by this amount). The new machine would mean that labour costs could be reduced by a third. Assume that other costs and the selling price remain unchanged.

Required

(i) Find the following levels of sales.

(1) At breakeven point

(2) To produce a profit of £2,200

(ii) Advise the company on the level of output at which it would be economic to purchase the new machine.

3 BREAKEVEN ANALYSIS AND NON-LINEAR RELATIONSHIPS

3.1 In the problems we have looked at so far, the relationships have been linear. In other words, the variables in the formulae were all to the power of one.

3.2 You may, however, be asked to deal with non-linear relationships. The basic principles still hold (for example total revenue equals the product of the selling price and quantity sold) but you may be provided with algebraic expressions for the components of the original formulae. Do not worry, it sounds a lot more complicated than it actually is.

3.3 Such questions often involve plotting a graph and extracting information from that graph. The method is perhaps best illustrated with a comprehensive example.

NOTES

EXAMPLE: NON-LINEAR RELATIONSHIPS

A company manufactures a product. The total fixed costs are £75 and the variable cost per unit is £5. The total revenue function is given by R = (25 – q)q, where q is the quantity sold.

Required

(a) Find an expression for total costs in terms of q, the quantity produced.

(b) The unit selling price function is in the form p = a + bq, where q is the quantity sold. Calculate the values of a and b.

(c) Plot on the same axes the revenue function and the total cost function found in part (a). Shade the region where profits are made.

(d) Using the graph, or otherwise, obtain the output levels where total revenue equals total costs. For these output levels find the corresponding price.

(e) Calculate the profit-maximising level of output and the profit at this output level.

Solution

(a) Let C = total costs
C = total variable costs + total fixed costs
C = 5q + 75

(b) We are given that R = (25 – q)q.

We know that R = pq and hence pq = (25 – q)q.

Dividing both sides by q gives p = 25 – q.

If p = a + bq, a = 25 and b = –1.

(c) *Workings for graph*

	C	*R*
q	*5q + 75*	*(25 – q)q*
0	75	0
3		66
6		114
9		144
12		156
15		150
18		126
21		84
24		24
25	200	0

Note that as the total cost function is a straight line (it is a linear function of q), only two points are needed. On the other hand, R = (25 – q)q = 25q – q^2, which is non-linear and so several points are needed.

NOTES

EXAMPLE *continued*

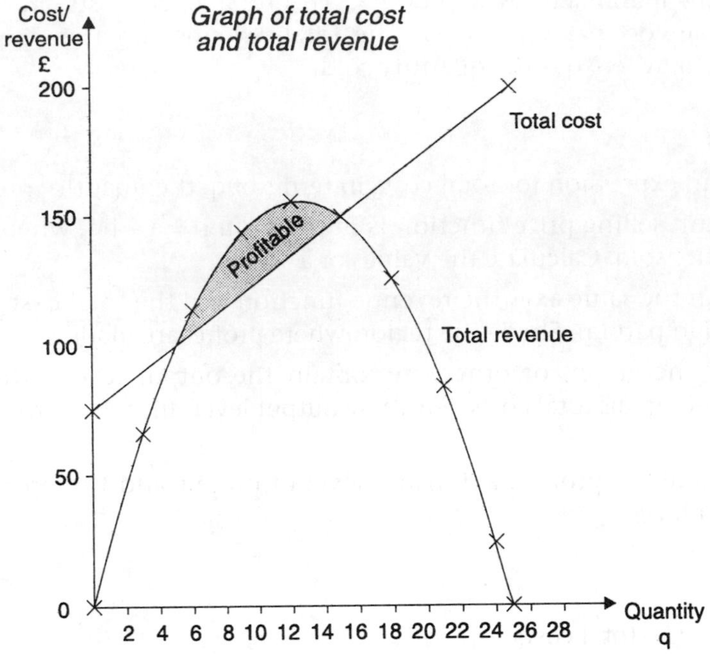

(d) Total revenue = total costs at the point where the total costs line crosses the total revenue curve. The coordinates of these two points may be found approximately from the graph, or may be found by solving the following equation:

C = R
5q + 75 = (25 – q)q
5q + 75 = 25q – q^2
q^2 – 20q + 75 = 0

This is a quadratic equation of the form $ax^2 + bx + c = 0$. We can solve the equation as follows.

$$q = 20 \pm \frac{\sqrt{\left(20^2 - \left(4 \times 1 \times 75\right)\right)}}{2 \times 1}$$

$$q = \frac{20 \pm 10}{2}$$

q = 5 or 15

Using p = 25 – q, we have the following two points

Quantity *q*	*Price* £
5	20
15	10

(e) Profit = total revenue – total costs. Profit is therefore represented by the vertical gap between the total revenue curve and the total cost line on the graph. This gap is maximised at q = 10.

Profit = R – C

= (25 – q) q – (5q + 75)

The profit at this level is therefore ((25 – 10) × 10) – ((5 × 10) + 75) = £25.

NOTES

This example has covered the majority of techniques which are likely to come up in a breakeven analysis question dealing with non-linear relationships. Ensure that you attempt the exam style question recommended at the end of this chapter as it too covers non-linear relationships.

Activity 3

(a) A company manufactures a product. For the accounting period, the total costs are £1,050 when the output is 20 units and £1,850 when the output is 40 units. Assuming linearity, find an expression for total costs in terms of q, the quantity of output.

(b) When the price of the company's product is £20, the demand in the accounting period is 40 units. If the price is reduced to £10, the demand increases to 45 units. Assuming linearity, obtain the relationship between price and demand (q).

(c) Obtain an expression for the company's revenue function and hence show that the profit function is

$P = -2q^2 + 60q - 250$

By a graphical method or otherwise find the output which maximises profits.

Chapter roundup

- Breakeven analysis has a number of purposes: to provide information to management about cost behaviour for routine planning and 'one-off' decision making; to determine what volume of sales is needed at any given budgeted sales price in order to break even; to identify the 'risk' in the budget by measuring the margin of safety; to calculate the effects on profit of changes in variable costs, sales price and so on.
- The algebraic approach to breakeven analysis relies on three principal equations.

  $R = pq$
  $C = F + vq$
  $P = R - C$
- At the breakeven point, $P = 0$ and $R = C$.
- The margin of safety is the difference between budgeted sales volume/revenue and breakeven sales volume/revenue.
- As well as dealing with linear relationships, you might also have to tackle problems which involve non-linear relationships. Such questions often involve plotting a graph of the total cost and total revenue functions and extracting information from the graph.

Quick quiz

1 What is contribution?

2 At the breakeven point, will total contribution equal fixed costs?

3 What are the assumptions upon which breakeven analysis is based?

4 What is the total revenue formula?

5 What is the total cost formula?

6 How is profit represented on the graph of a total revenue curve and total cost line?

NOTES

Answers to activities

1 Required contribution = F + P = £47,000 + £23,000 = £70,000

Required sales = 14,000 units

		£
Required contribution per unit sold	= £70,000 ÷ 14,000 =	5
Variable cost per unit, v		15
Required price per unit, p		20

2 (a) Let q = quantity sold.

Then profit = revenue – costs
= 40q – (6q + 14q + 10,000)
= 20q – 10,000

(i) At breakeven point, profit = 0
20q – 10,000 = 0
20q = 10,000
q = 500

(ii) At a profit of £2,200,
20q – 10,000 = 2,200
20q = 12,200
q = 610

(b) Fixed costs will rise to £12,100, and labour costs per unit will fall to £6 × $^2/_3$ = £4.

Then profit = 40q – (4q + 14q + 12,100)
= 22q – 12,100

(i) (1) At breakeven point,
profit = 0
22q – 12,100 = 0
22q = 12,100
q = 550

(2) At a profit of £2,200
22q – 12,100 = 2,200
22q = 14,300
q = 650

(ii) The machine is clearly worth purchasing so long as quantity produced is above some critical level, since the machine increases fixed costs but decreases variable costs. This level will be that at which profits both with and without the machine are equal. This will be at:

20q – 10,000 = 22q – 12,100
2,100 = 2q
q = 1,050

The machine should be bought if output will exceed 1,050 units. At precisely 1,050 units, profit will be the same both with and without the machine.

NOTES

3 (a) When q rises by 20 units (from 20 units to 40 units) total costs rise by £800 (from £1,050 to £1,850). This is a rise of £800/20 = £40 a unit, so variable costs are £40 a unit. At 20 units, we have:

Fixed costs + 20 × £40 = £1,050

Fixed costs = £1,050 – £800 = £250

The required expression for total costs is therefore C = 250 + 40q.

(b) Let p = price, and assume that p = a + bq

Then	20	=	a + 40b	(1)
	10	=	a + 45b	(2)
	10	=	–5b	(3) (subtract (2) from (1))
	b	=	–2	(4)
	20	=	a –80	(5) (from (1))
	a	=	100	(6)

The required relationship is p = 100 – 2q.

(c) Revenue = pq = q(100 –2q) = $100q - 2q^2$

Profit = P = revenue – costs
= $100q - 2q^2 - (250 + 40q)$
= $-2q^2 + 60q - 250$

A graph may be plotted using the following values.

q	$-2q^2 + 60q - 250$
5	0
10	150
15	200
20	150
25	0

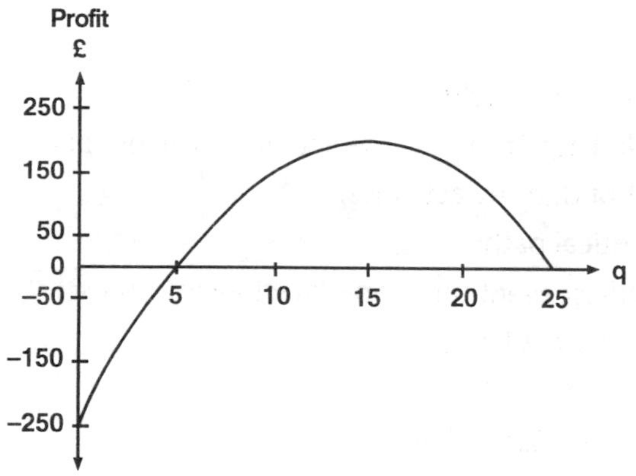

We can see from the graph that profit is maximised at q = 15. At this point, profit = £200.

Further question practice

Now try the following practice questions at the end of this text.

Multiple choice questions **91–92**

Exam style question **13**

Chapter 14

NETWORK ANALYSIS

Introduction

A large project, such as building a bridge, will comprise many activities, which must be done in the right order. Network analysis is a way of mapping out the activities in a project, and showing their interrelationships: we will see how to draw a type of network diagram called an activity on arrow diagram.

Timing is often crucial in large projects. We will see how to find the critical path, which is a sequence of those activities which, were any of them to run late, would mean that the whole project was delayed. We will also see how to find the earliest time each activity might be able to start (an earliest event time) and the latest time by which it must be finished (a latest event time). We can then work out by how much an activity might be allowed to overrun (its float). Activities may take more or less time than anticipated, and so we will look at PERT, a method of dealing with such uncertainties. Finally we will look at Gantt charts, which can be used to estimate the amount of resources required for a project.

Your objectives

After completing this chapter, you should:

(a) be able to draw network diagrams using the activity on arrow presentation;

(b) understand the concept of dummy activities;

(c) be able to identify the critical path;

(d) be able to determine earliest event times and latest event times;

(e) be able to calculate an activity's float;

(f) be able to use PERT;

(g) be able to construct and use Gantt charts.

NOTES

1 PRESENTING PROJECTS AS NETWORKS

1.1 Network analysis is a technique for planning and controlling large projects, such as construction work, research and development projects or the computerisation of business systems. Network analysis helps managers to plan when to start various tasks, to allocate resources so that the tasks can be carried out within schedule, to monitor actual progress and to find out when control action is needed to prevent a delay in completion of the project. The events and activities making up the whole project are represented in the form of a diagram or chart. Network analysis is sometimes called critical path analysis (CPA) or critical path method (CPM).

Definition

Network analysis is basically concerned with the deployment of available resources for the completion of a complex task.

Drawing a network diagram: the activity on arrow presentation

1.2 Here is an example of a network for building the Channel Tunnel, with the whole project simplified to just three activities.

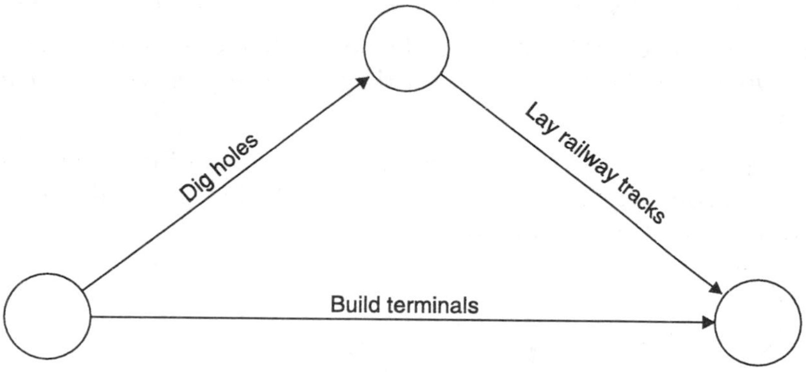

Figure 14.1 Channel Tunnel network diagram

The holes must be dug before the tracks can be laid, which is why laying the tracks follows on from digging the holes in the diagram. However, building the terminals in France and England can be done at the same time as the other two activities, which is why building the terminals runs across the page alongside those other activities in the diagram.

This form of network diagram is an activity on arrow diagram, which means that each activity within a project is represented on the diagram by an arrowed line. An alternative form of diagram is activity on node, but we shall use the activity on arrow presentation because it is easier to follow.

1.3 A project is analysed into its separate activities and the sequence of activities is presented in a network diagram. The flow of activities in the diagram is from left to right.

1.4 An *activity* within a network is represented by an arrowed line, running between one event and another event. An event is simply the start and/or completion of an activity, which is represented on the network diagram by a circle (called a *node*).

1.5 Let us suppose that in a certain project there are two activities A and B, and activity B cannot be started until activity A is completed. Activity A might be building the walls of a house, and activity B might be putting the roof on. This would be represented as follows.

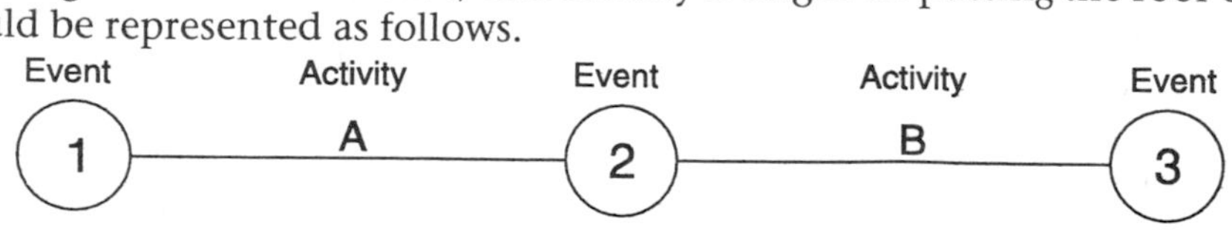

Figure 14.2 Construction of network diagrams (1)

NOTES

The rule is that an activity cannot start until all activities leading into the event at its start have been completed.

1.6 Events are usually numbered, just to identify them. In this example, event 1 is the start of Activity A, event 3 is the completion of Activity B, and event 2 is both the completion of A and the start of B.

1.7 Let us now suppose that another project includes three activities, C, D and E. Neither activity D nor E can start until C is completed, but D and E could be done simultaneously if required. This would be represented as follows.

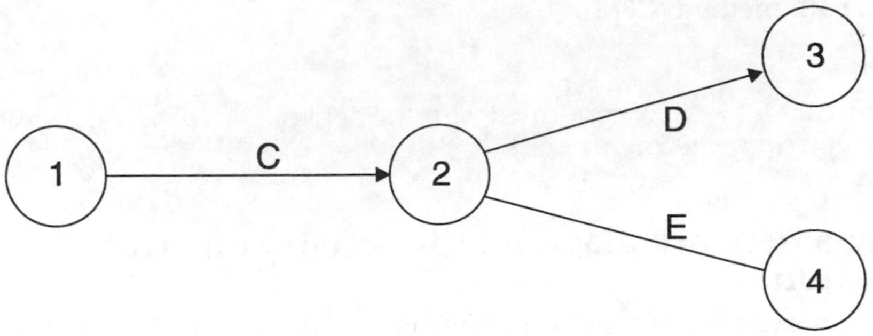

Figure 14.3 Construction of network diagrams (2)

In this diagram, event 2 represents the point when C is completed and also the point when D and E can start, so the diagram clearly shows that D and E must follow C.

1.8 A third possibility is that an activity cannot start until two or more activities have been completed. If H cannot start until F and G are both complete, then we would represent the situation like this.

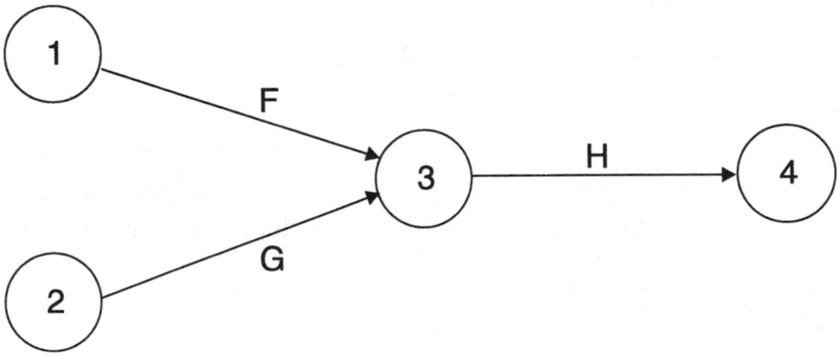

Figure 14.4 Construction of network diagrams (3)

EXAMPLE: NETWORK DIAGRAMS

Draw the network for the following project to build a factory.

Activity	*Preceding activity*
A: lay foundations	–
B: build walls	A
C: lay drains	A
D: install electricity cables	A
E: fit window frames	B
F: fit door frames	B
G: fit windows	E
H: fit doors	F
I: plaster inside walls	G,H
J: lay floor	C
K: fit power outlets	D
L: install machines	I, J, K

NOTES

EXAMPLE *continued*

Solution

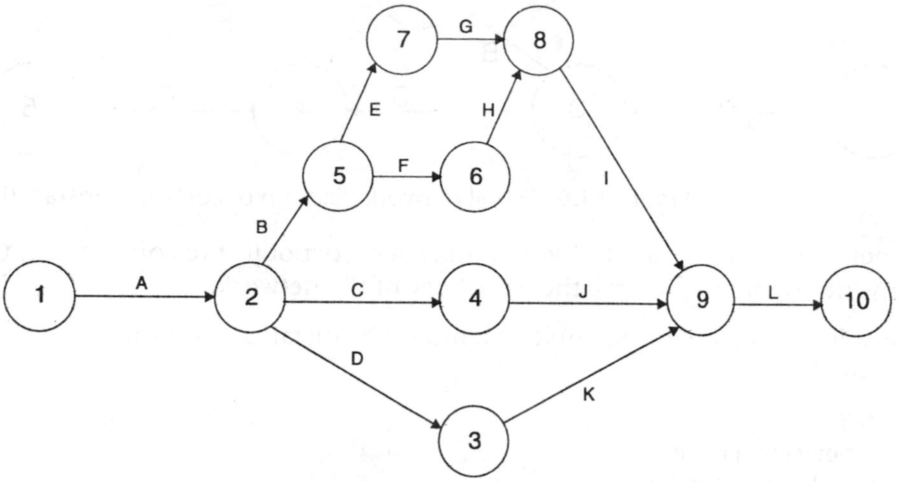

Activity 1

In the above network, could activities E and H be carried on simultaneously?

The identification of activities

1.9 Activities may be identified as either:

(a) activities A, B, C, D and so on; or

(b) activities 1–2, 2–5, 2–4, 2–3 and so on.

Dummy activities

1.10 It is a convention in network analysis that two activities are not drawn between the same events. The convention makes diagrams clearer.

To avoid having two activities running between the same events, we use a dummy activity. A dummy activity takes no time and no resources to complete.

Definition

A *dummy activity* is used in network analysis when two activities could start at the same time and finish at the same time too. It is represented by a broken arrowed line.

1.11 For example, suppose that the sequence of activities in a project to install a computer system is as follows.

Activity	*Preceding Activity*
A: install computer	–
B: write programs	A
C: hire trained staff	A
D: test system	B, C

In theory, we could draw the network as follows.

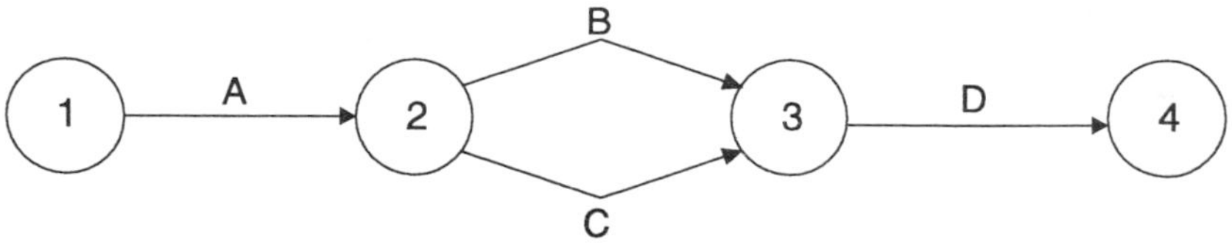

Figure 14.5 Theoretical network diagram of computer installation

NOTES

By convention, this would be incorrect. Two separate activities must not start and end with the same events. The correct representation is shown below.

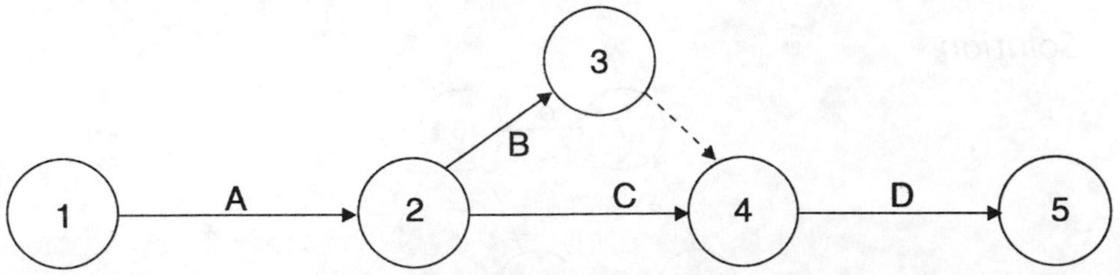

Figure 14.6 Actual network diagram of computer installation

1.12 Sometimes it is necessary to use a dummy activity not just to comply with the convention, but to preserve the basic logic of the network.

1.13 Consider the following example of a project to install a new office telephone system.

Activity	*Preceding Activity*
A: buy equipment	–
B: allocate extension numbers	–
C: install switchboard	A
D: install wiring	B, C
E: print office directory	B

The project is finished when both D and E are complete.

The problem arises because D can only start when both B and C have been finished, whereas E is only required to follow B. The only way to draw the network is to use a dummy activity.

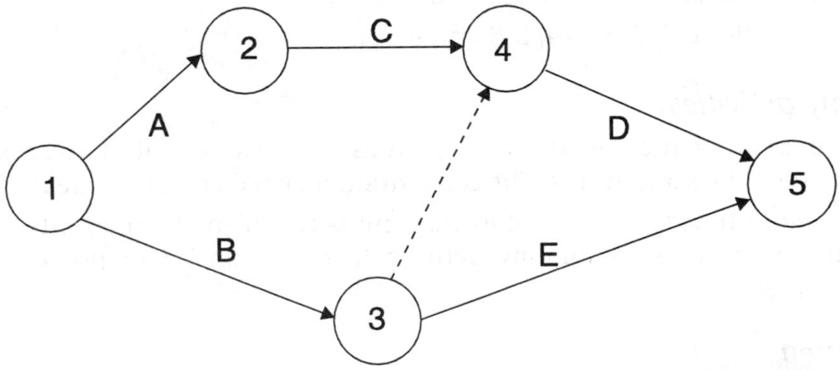

Figure 14.7 Network diagram with dummy activity

Paths through the network

1.14 Any network can be analysed into a number of different paths or routes. A path is simply a sequence of activities from the start to the end of the network. In the example above, there are just three paths.

(a) A C D;

(b) B Dummy D;

(c) B E.

Activity 2

List the paths through the network in the earlier example to build a factory with activities A – L.

NOTES

2 THE CRITICAL PATH, EVENT TIMES AND FLOATS

Definition

The *critical path* is the path through the network with the greatest total duration.

2.1 The time needed to complete each individual activity in a project must be estimated. This time is shown on the network above or below the line representing the activity. The duration of the whole project will be fixed by the time taken to complete the path through the network with the greatest total duration. This path is called the *critical path* and activities on it are known as *critical activities*. A network can have more than one critical path, if several paths tie for the greatest duration.

2.2 Activities on the critical path must be started and completed on time, otherwise the total project time will be extended. The method of finding the critical path is illustrated in the example below.

EXAMPLE: THE CRITICAL PATH

The following activities comprise a project to renovate a block of flats.

Activity	*Preceding Activity*	*Duration (weeks)*
A: replace windows in lounges	–	5
B: rewire	–	4
C: replaster walls of lounges	A	2
D: fit lights in lounges	B	1
E: decorate bedrooms	B	5
F: install plumbing	B	5
G: decorate lounges	C,D	4
H: decorate kitchens	F	3
I: decorate bathrooms	F	2

(a) What are the paths through the network?

(b) What is the critical path and what is its duration?

Solution

The first step in the solution is to draw the network diagram, with the time for each activity shown.

A network should have just one start node and one completion node, and in the diagram below, this is achieved by introducing a dummy activity after activity I. Dummy activities always have zero duration.

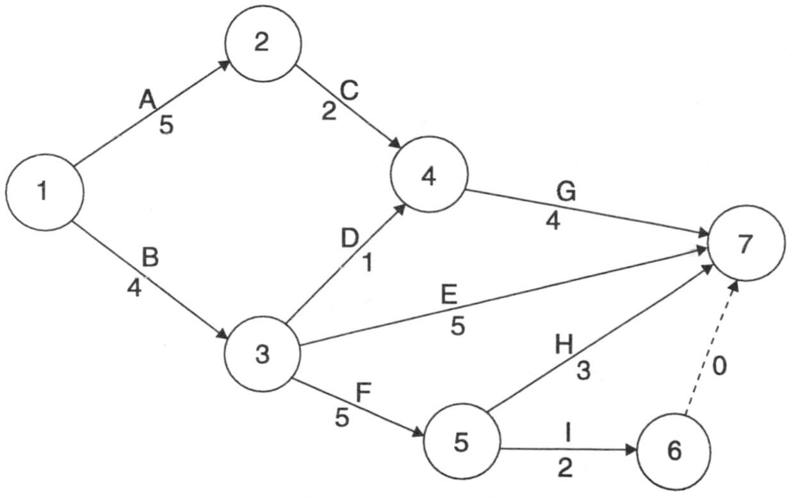

NOTES

EXAMPLE *continued*

We could list the paths through the network and their durations as follows.

Path	*Duration (weeks)*	
A C G	(5 + 2 + 4)	11
B D G	(4 + 1 + 4)	9
B E	(4 + 5)	9
B F H	(4 + 5+ 3)	12
B F I Dummy	(4 + 5 + 2 + 0)	11

The critical path is the longest path, BFH, with a duration of 12 weeks. This is the minimum time needed to complete the project. Note that a network may have more than one critical path, if two or more paths have equal highest durations.

Activity 3

The following activities comprise a project to agree a price for some land to be bought for development.

Activity		*Preceded by*	*Duration Days*
P:	get survey done	–	4
Q:	draw up plans	–	7
R:	estimate cost of building work	Q	2
S:	get tenders for site preparation work	P	9
T:	negotiate price	R, S	3

Within how many days could the whole project be completed?

2.3 Listing paths through the network in this way is easy for small networks, but it becomes tedious for bigger and more complex networks.

Earliest event times and latest event times

2.4 Another way to find the critical path is to include earliest times and latest times for each event, showing them on the network diagram.

(a) The earliest event time is the earliest time that any subsequent activities can start.

(b) The latest event time is the latest time by which all preceding activities must be completed if the project as a whole is to be completed in the minimum time.

One way of showing earliest and latest event times is to divide each event node into three sections. These will record:

(a) the event number;

(b) the earliest event time. For the starting node in the network, this is time 0;

(c) the latest event time.

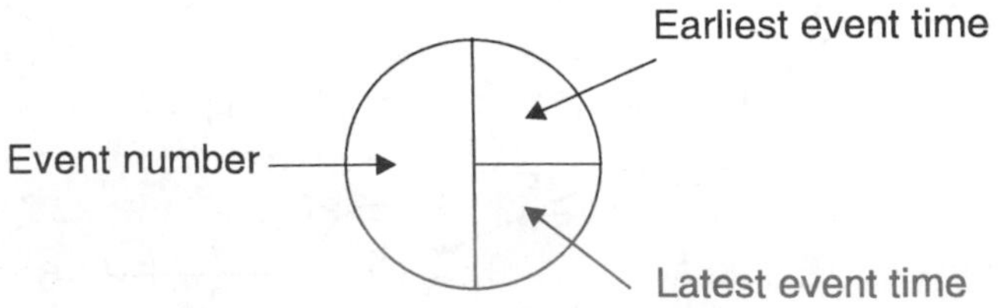

Figure 14.8 Earliest and latest event times

Earliest event times

2.5 The next step is to calculate the earliest event times. Always start at event 1 with its earliest starting time of 0. We will continue the previous example to show how times are calculated.

Work from left to right through the diagram calculating the earliest time that the next activity following the event can start. For example, the earliest event time at event 2 is the earliest time activity C can start. This is week 0 + 5 = 5. Similarly, the earliest event time at event 3 is the earliest time D, E and F can start, which is week 0 + 4 = 4, and the earliest time at event 5 is the earliest time activities H and I can start, which is 4 + 5 = week 9.

A slight problem occurs where more than one activity ends at the same node. For example, event 4 is the completion node for activities C and D. Activity G cannot start until both C and D are complete, therefore the earliest event time at event 4 is the higher of:

(a) earliest event time, event 2 + duration of C = 5 + 2 = 7 weeks;

(b) earliest event time, event 3 + duration of D = 4 + 1 = 5 weeks.

The earliest event time at event 4 is 7 weeks.

Similarly, the earliest event time at event 7 is the highest of:

Earliest event time, event 3 + duration of E	= 4 + 5 = 9
Earliest event time, event 4 + duration of G	= 7 + 4 = 11
Earliest event time, event 5 + duration of H	= 9 + 3 = 12
Earliest event time, event 6 + duration of dummy activity	= 11 + 0 = 11

The highest value is 12 weeks. This also means that the minimum completion time for the entire project is 12 weeks.

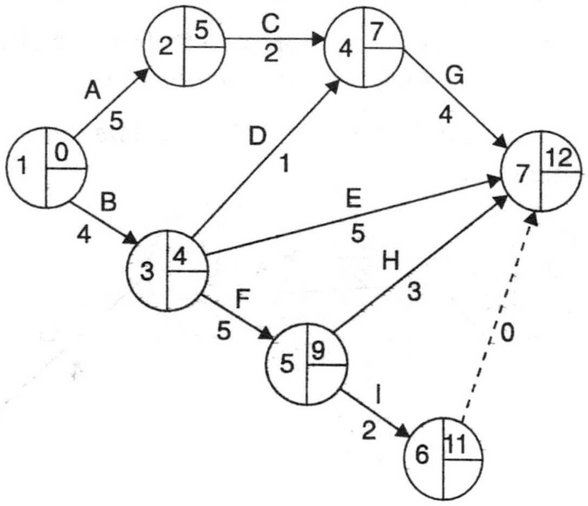

Figure 14.9 Calculating earliest event times

Activity 4

If activity C had taken four weeks, which earliest event times would have been affected, and what would they have changed to?

Latest event times

2.6 The next step is to calculate the latest event times. These are the latest times at which each event can occur if the project as a whole is to be completed in the shortest possible time, 12 weeks. The latest event time at the final event must be the same as the earliest event time, which in this example is 12 weeks.

Work from right to left through the diagram calculating the latest time at which each activity can start, if it is to be completed by the latest event time of the event at its end. The latest event time for:

(a) event 4 is 12 – 4 = week 8;
(b) event 6 is 12 – 0 = week 12;
(c) event 2 is 8 – 2 = week 6.

Event 5 might cause difficulties as two activities, H and I lead back to it.
(a) Activity H must be completed by week 12, and so must start at week 9.
(b) Activity I must also be completed by week 12, and so must start at week 10.

The latest event time at node 5 is the earlier of week 9 or week 10, that is, week 9. All activities leading up to node 5, which in this case is just F, must be completed by week 9 so that both H and I can be completed by week 12.

The latest event time at event 3 is calculated in the same way. It is the earliest time which enables all subsequent activities to be completed within the required time. Thus, at event 3, we have the following.

Subsequent event	Latest time of that event (a)	Intermediate activity	Duration of the activity (b)	Required event time at event 3 (a) – (b)
4	8	D	1	7
5	9	F	5	4
7	12	E	5	7

All activities before event 3 must be completed by week 4, to enable all subsequent activities to be completed within the required time.

Similarly, the latest event time at event 1 is the lower of:
Latest event time, event 2 minus duration of A = 6 – 5 = 1
Latest event time, event 3 minus duration of B = 4 – 4 = 0

The latest event time at event 1 is therefore 0. It must always be 0. If your calculations give any other value, you have made an error.

The final network diagram is now as follows. The critical path has been indicated by a double line.

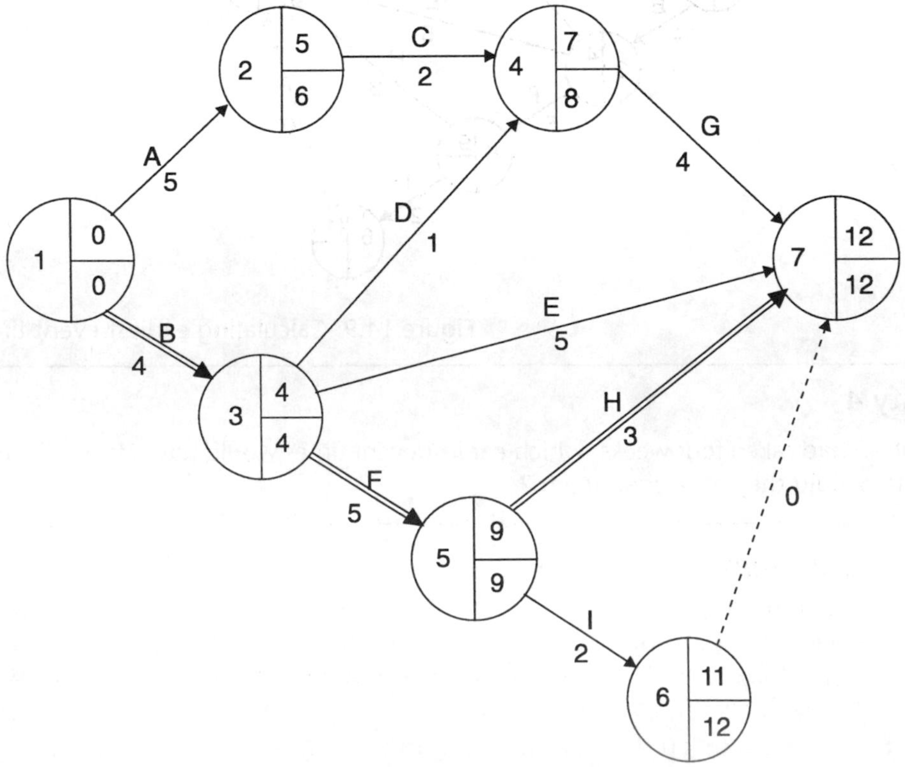

Figure 14.10 Final network diagram

NOTES

Finding the critical path

2.7 Critical activities are those activities which must be started on time, otherwise the total project time will be increased. It follows that each event on the critical path must have the same earliest and latest times. The critical path for the above network is therefore B F H (events 1,3,5,7). An event with the same earliest and latest times is called a *critical event*.

Activity 5

The following activities comprise a project to make a film.

Activity		*Preceded by*	*Duration Weeks*
J:	negotiate distribution	–	6
K:	arrange publicity	J	5
L:	write screenplay	–	3
M:	hire cast and crew	L	5
N:	shoot and edit	M, Q	4
P:	design sets	L	2
Q:	build sets	P	1

What are the earliest and latest event times of the event at the end of activity P?

2.8 You may find that an activity connects two events each of which has the same earliest and latest event times, but that the activity itself is not critical.

For example, in the following extract from the example following paragraph 2.2, events 3 and 7 are on the critical path.

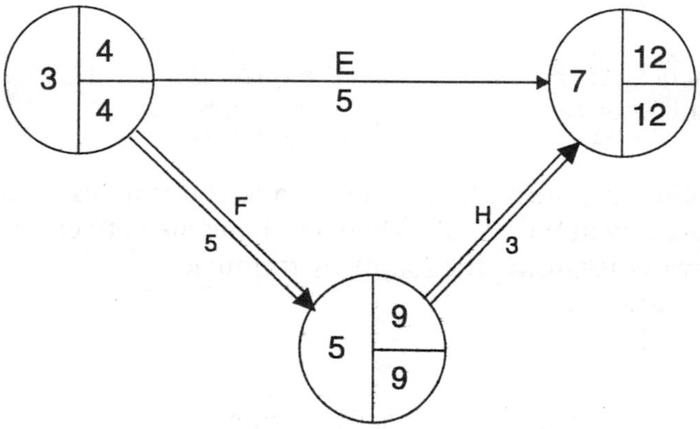

Figure 14.11 The critical path

Activity E, however, is not critical: the critical path goes through event 5. If you are in doubt as to whether an activity is on the critical path you should check to see whether it has any float (see below). All critical activities have zero float.

Float

2.9 Activities which are not on the critical path are non–critical, and they can, within limits:

(a) start late; and/or

(b) take longer than the time specified,

without holding up the completion of the project as a whole.

The float for any activity is the amount of time by which its duration could be extended up to the point where it would become critical. This is the same as the amount of time by which its duration could be extended without affecting the total project time.

The effect on the time available for preceding and subsequent activities is ignored. The total float for an activity is therefore equal to its latest finishing time minus its earliest starting time minus its duration.

For example, look at activity C in the above example to renovate a block of flats. This must be completed by week 8 if the total project time is not to be extended. It cannot be started until week 5 at the earliest, but as it only takes two weeks there is one spare week available. The float for activity C is (8 – 5 – 2) = 1 week.

Activity 6

What are the floats for activities D and G in the above example?

3 UNCERTAIN ACTIVITY DURATIONS

3.1 Network problems may be complicated by uncertainty in the durations of individual activities. For example, building works can easily be delayed by bad weather.

Definition

PERT (project evaluation and review technique) is a form of network analysis which takes account of uncertainty.

3.2 Using PERT, optimistic, most likely and pessimistic estimates of durations are made for each activity in the project. These estimates are converted into a mean duration and a variance, using the following formulae.

(a) Mean $\mu = \dfrac{a + 4m + b}{6}$

where a = optimistic estimate of activity duration
m = most likely estimate of activity duration
b = pessimistic estimate of activity duration

(b) Variance $\sigma^2 = \dfrac{1}{36}(b-a)^2$

The standard deviation, σ, is $\dfrac{1}{6}(b-a)$.

Once the mean duration and the standard deviation of durations have been calculated for each activity, we can:

(a) find the critical path using the mean activity durations;

(b) estimate the standard deviation of the expected total project time.

Variations in activity times are usually assumed to be normally distributed. This is a big assumption: it makes the mathematics easy, but in many cases it may be false, so the results of PERT must be treated with caution.

NOTES

EXAMPLE: PERT

A project consists of four activities.

Activity	*Preceding activity*	*Time to complete* Optimistic (a) Days	Most likely (m) Days	Pessimistic (b) Days
A	–	5	10	15
B	A	16	18	26
C	–	15	20	31
D	–	8	18	28

Analyse the project using PERT.

Solution

The mean duration for each activity is calculated by the formula $\frac{a + 4m + b}{6}$

Activity	*a + 4m + b*	*Divided by 6* *Days*
A	5 + 40 + 15 = 60	10
B	16 + 72 + 26 = 114	19
C	15 + 80 + 31 = 126	21
D	8 + 72 + 28 = 108	18

The standard deviation of durations for each activity is calculated by the formula $\frac{b - a}{6}$

Activity	*a + 4m + b*	*Divided by 6* *Days*
A	15 – 5 = 10	1.67
B	26 – 16 = 10	1.67
C	31 – 15 = 16	2.67
D	28 – 8 = 20	3.33

The network can be drawn using the mean durations.

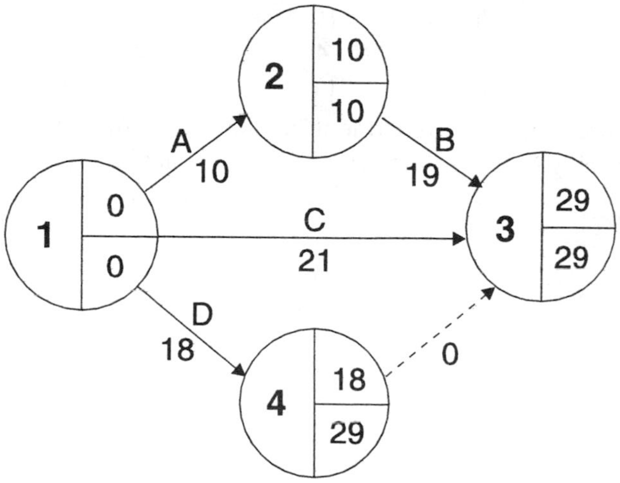

NOTES

EXAMPLE *continued*

If we now wish to calculate the probability that the total project time will exceed, say, 31 days, the procedure is as follows.

(a) We add the *variances* of the uncertain activities in a path. We can do this provided the activity durations are independent.

Variance of activity A's time = 1.67^2	2.78
Variance of activity B's time = 1.67^2	2.78
Combined variance of path AB	5.56

The standard deviation of the durations of path AB is $\sqrt{5.56} = 2.36$ days.

(b) (i) The probability that the duration of AB will remain within 31 days is the probability that it will be not more than $(31 - 29)/2.36 = 0.85$ standard deviations above the mean.

From normal distribution tables, this is $0.5 + 0.3023 = 0.8023$.

(ii) The probability that the duration of C will be within 31 days is the probability that it will be not more than $(31 - 21)/2.67 = 3.75$ standard deviations above the mean, which is very nearly 1.

(iii) The probability that the duration of D will be within 31 days is the probability that it will be not more than $(31 - 18)/3.33 = 3.9$ standard deviations above the mean, which is very nearly 1.

(c) The probability of exceeding 31 days is therefore the same as the probability that path AB will take more than this time, which is $1 - 0.8023 = 0.1977$.

Activity 7

A path through a network comprises four activities, with the following estimated durations.

	Duration in days		
Activity	*Optimistic*	*Most likely*	*Pessimistic*
	(a)	(m)	(b)
A	3	7	11
B	2	5	10
C	4	4	4
D	5	6	11

All the activity durations are independent of each other. Applying the PERT formulae, what is the probability that the duration of the path will exceed 25 days?

NOTES

4 GANTT CHARTS

Definition

Gantt charts are line diagrams, with lines representing both time and activities. They can be used to estimate the amount of resources required for a project. Where activities are in a continuous 'chain', with one activity able to follow immediately after the other, these can be drawn as a continuous line on the chart.

EXAMPLE: GANTT CHARTS

Flotto Limited is about to undertake a project about which the following data is available.

Activity	*Must be preceded by activity*	*Duration Days*	*Men required for the job*
A	–	3	6
B	–	5	3
C	B	2	4
D	A	1	4
E	A	6	5
F	D	3	6
G	C,E	3	3

There is a labour force of nine men available, and each man is paid a fixed wage regardless of whether or not he is actively working on any day. Every man is capable of working on any of the seven activities. If extra labour is required during any day, men can be hired on a daily basis at the rate of £120 per day. If the project is to finish in the minimum time what extra payments must be made for hired labour?

Solution

Draw the network to establish the duration of the project and the critical path. Then draw a Gantt chart, using the critical path as a basis, assuming that jobs start at the earliest possible time. Float times on chains of activities should be shown by a dotted line.

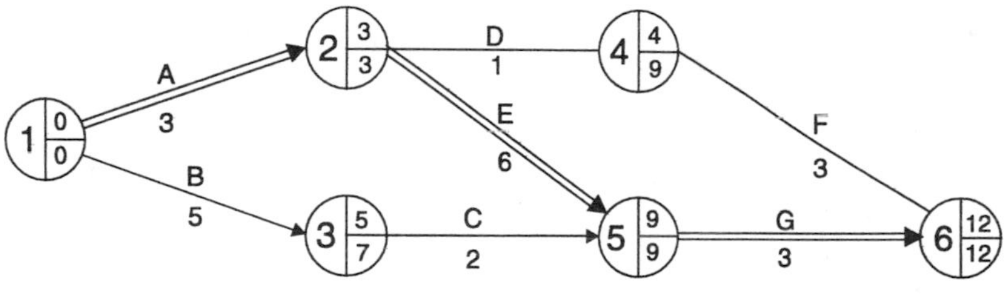

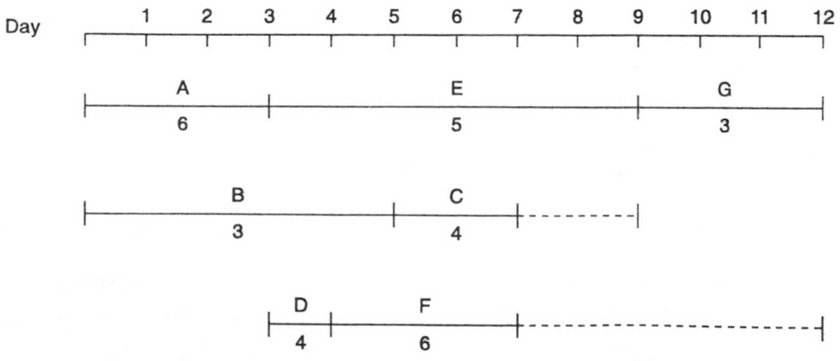

NOTES

EXAMPLE *continued*

It can be seen that if all activities start at their earliest times, as many as 15 men will be required on any one day (days 6–7) whereas on other days there would be idle capacity (days 8–12). The problem can be reduced, or removed, by using up float time on non-critical activities. Suppose we deferred the start of activities D and F until the latest possible day. This would be the end of day 8/start of day 9 – leaving four days to complete the activities by the end of day 12.

The Gantt chart would be redrawn as follows.

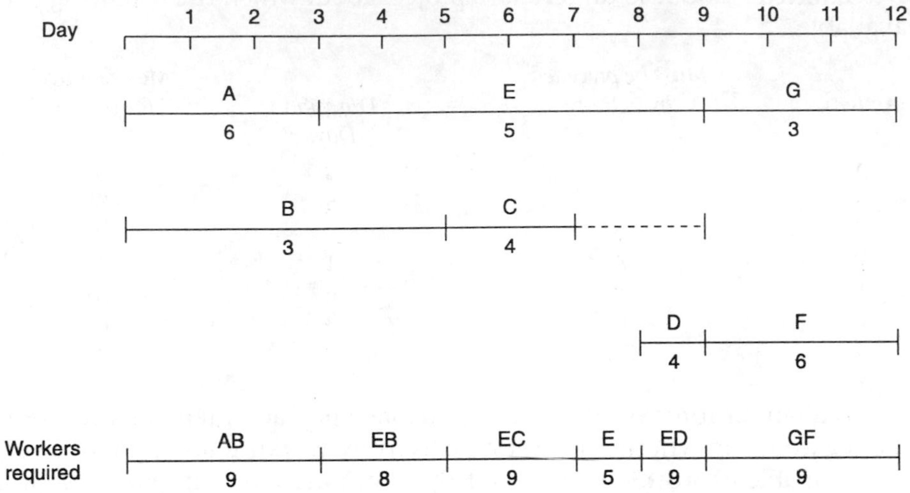

The project can be completed in the minimum time without hiring any additional labour.

Gantt charts used for control

4.1 Gantt charts can also be used very conveniently to show the progress of a project. Consider the following chart which shows progress on a project at day 10.

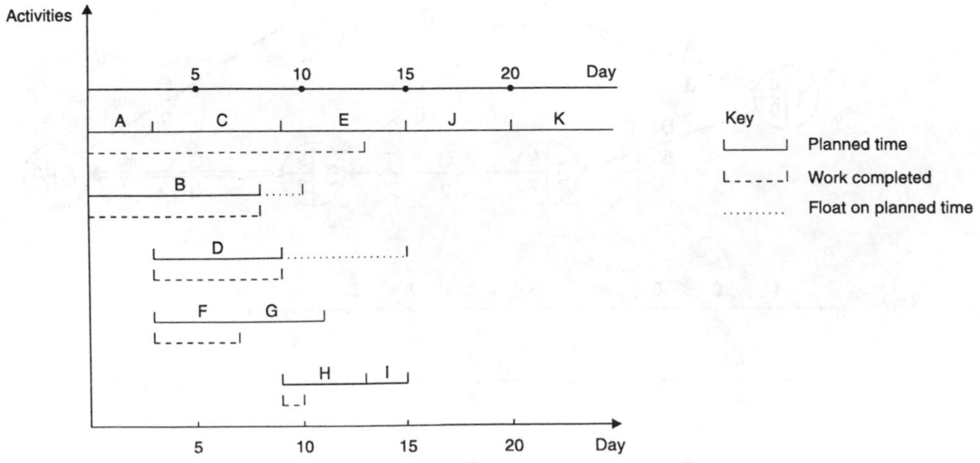

Figure 14.12 A Gantt chart

This chart shows that activities A, B, C and D have been completed; that work on the critical path is slightly ahead of schedule (equivalent to the end of the 13th day); that work on activity H is absolutely on schedule, but that work on F and G is well behind.

NOTES

Activity 8

Thurnon plc are to initiate a project to study the feasibility of a new product. The end result of the feasibility project will be a report recommending the action to be taken for the new product. The activities to be carried out to complete the feasibility project are given below.

Activity	*Description*	*Immediate predecessors*	*Expected time Weeks*	*Number of staff required*
A:	preliminary design	–	5	3
B:	market research	–	3	2
C:	obtain engineering quotes	A	2	2
D:	construct prototype	A	5	5
E:	prepare marketing material	A	3	3
F:	costing	C	2	2
G:	product testing	D	4	5
H:	pilot survey	B, E	6	4
I:	pricing estimates	H	2	1
J:	final report	F, G, I	6	2

(a) Draw a network for the scheme of activities set out above. Determine the critical path and the shortest duration of the project.

(b) Assuming the project starts at time zero and that each activity commences at the earliest start date, construct a chart showing the number of staff required at any one time for this project.

Chapter roundup

- A network represents a project by breaking it down into activities and showing their interdependence.
- Activities are represented by arrows, which are drawn between nodes which represent events. Dummy activities may be needed. Any sequence of activities from the start to the end of a network is a path through the network.
- The path with the greatest duration is the critical path. Any delay on this path will delay the project as a whole.
- The earliest event time for an event is the earliest time that activities starting at that event can start. The latest event time is the latest time by which all activities leading into that event must be completed if the whole project is to be completed in the minimum time.
- For events on the critical path, the earliest and latest event times are the same. Activities on the critical path have zero float: an activity's float is the latest event time of the event at its end minus the earliest event time of the event at its start minus its duration.
- If activity durations are uncertain, the PERT formulae can be used to estimate mean durations and variances of durations. The variances of the durations of activities on the critical path can then be added, and the probability that the duration of the critical path will exceed any given value can be computed.
- Gantt charts can be used to estimate the amount of resources required for a project.

NOTES

Quick quiz

1 When is a dummy activity necessary in a network?
2 What is the critical path?
3 What is an activity's float?
4 What are the formulae used in PERT to estimate the mean and the standard deviation of an activity's duration?
5 Where we have a chain of activities with uncertain durations, can we add the standard deviations of their durations?

Answers to activities

1 Yes, E and H could be carried on simultaneously. Indeed, that might be the most sensible thing to do. If E took five days and F only took one day, H could be started while E was still in progress.

2 There are four paths, as follows.

ABEGIL
ABFHIL
ACJL
ADKL

3

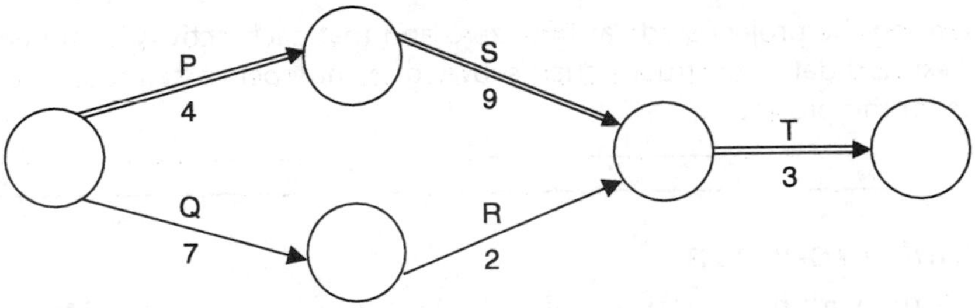

The paths are PST (4 + 9 + 3 = 16 days) and QRT (7 + 2 + 3 = 12 days). The minimum overall duration is 16 days. The critical path is PST.

4 The only earliest event times affected would be those for event 4 (revised to week 9) and for event 7 (revised to week 13).

5

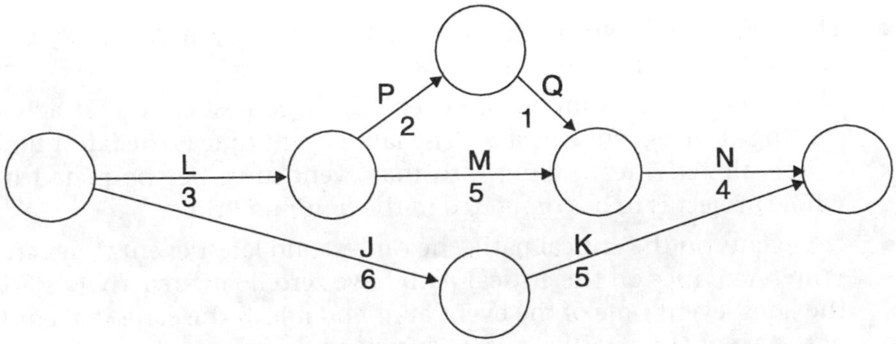

The critical path is LMN, with a duration of 12 weeks. The earliest event time for the event at the end of activity P is 3 + 2 = 5 weeks. The latest event time is 12 – 4 – 1 = 7 weeks.

NOTES

6 Float for activity D = 8 – 4 – 1 = 3 weeks.

Float for activity G = 12 – 7 – 4 = 1 week.

7

Activity	*Mean duration Days*	*Variance*
A	7.000	1.778
B	5.333	1.778
C	4.000	0.000
D	6.667	1.000
	23.000	4.556

The probability that the duration of the path will exceed 30 days is the probability that the duration will be more than $(25 - 23)/\sqrt{4.556} = 0.94$ standard deviations above the mean.

From normal distribution tables, this probability is 0.5 – 0.3264 = 0.1736.

8 (a)

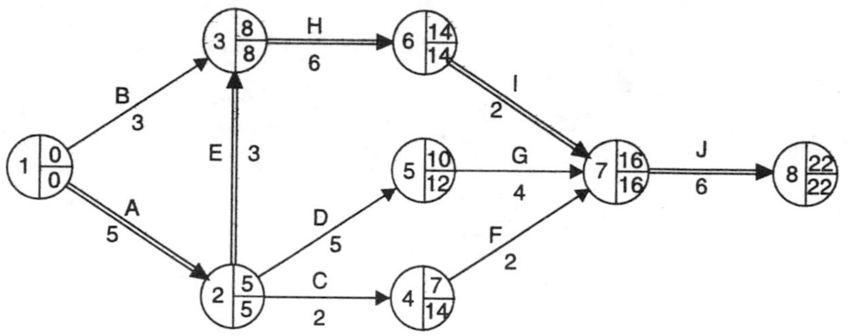

The critical path is AEHIJ, and the minimum total duration is 22 weeks.

(b) To construct a Gantt chart we need to list all possible paths through the network.

A E H I J

A D G J

A C F J

B H I J

Then using the critical path as the basis, we can construct the Gantt chart as follows.

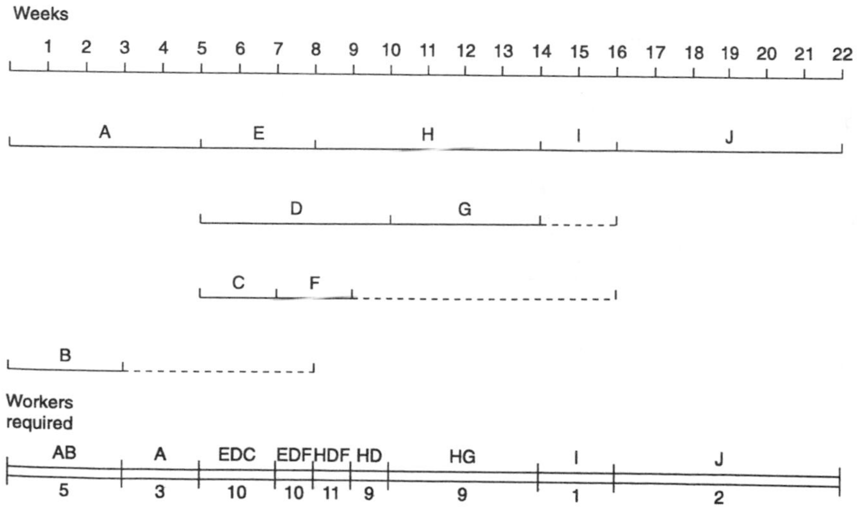

NOTES

Further question practice

Now try the following practice questions at the end of this text.

Multiple choice questions	**93–96**
Exam style question	**14**

Chapter 15

INTEREST AND DISCOUNTING

Introduction

The previous chapters introduced a variety of quantitative methods relevant to business analysis. This chapter extends the use of mathematics and looks at aspects of financial analysis typically undertaken in a business organisation.

In general, financial mathematics deals with problems of investing money, or capital. If a company (or an individual investor) puts some capital into an investment, a financial return will be expected.

Investors may wish to know the following.

- What return will be obtained by investing £x now for a given period, say n years?
- Do the returns over an investment's life make that investment worthwhile?

The two major techniques of financial mathematics are compounding and discounting. Compounding can be used to help provide an answer to the first question above and others like it. The second question (and, of course, others like it) can be answered by employing discounting. These techniques are very closely related to each other. This chapter will begin by describing compounding and will then introduce discounting.

Discounting is the revenue of compounding. The major application of discounting in business is in the evaluation of capital expenditure projects, to decide whether they offer a satisfactory return to the investor. We will be looking at two methods of using discounting to appraise capital expenditure projects, the net present value (NPV) method and the internal rate of return (IRR) method.

Your objectives

After completing this chapter, you should:

(a) understand the concept of simple interest and be able to perform simple interest calculations;

(b) understand the concept of compound interest;

(c) be able to perform compounding calculations;

(d) be aware of the difference between effective and nominal rates of interest and be able to calculate effective rates;

(e) understand the concept of discounting;

(f) understand the concept of present value;

(g) be able to use discount tables;

(h) understand the concept of and be able to calculate net present values;

(i) understand the concept of the internal rate of return and be able to calculate it using interpolation;

(j) understand the concept of annuities and be able to use annuity tables and calculate the present value of an annuity and a required annuity;

(k) understand the concept of perpetuities and be able to calculate the present value of a perpetuity.

1 SIMPLE INTEREST

Definition

Interest is the amount of money which an investment earns over time. *Simple interest* is interest which is earned in equal amounts every year (or month) and which is a given proportion of the original investment (the principal).

1.1 If a sum of money is invested for a period of time, then the amount of simple interest which accrues is equal to the number of periods × the interest rate × the amount invested.

$S_n = P + nrP$

where P = the original sum invested

r = the interest rate (expressed as a proportion, so 10% = 0.1)

n = the number of periods (normally years)

S_n = the terminal value, which is the sum invested after n periods, consisting of the original capital (P) plus interest earned.

EXAMPLE: SIMPLE INTEREST

What is the terminal value after five years if an investor invests £1,000 at 10% simple interest per annum?

Solution

S_n = £1,000 + (5 × 0.1 × £1,000)

= £1,500

1.2 If , for example, the sum of money is invested for 3 months and the interest rate is a rate per annum, then $n = {}^3/_{12} = {}^1/_4$. If the investment period is 197 days and the rate is an annual rate, then $n = {}^{197}/_{365}$.

2 COMPOUND INTEREST

2.1 Interest is normally calculated by means of compounding.

Definition

If a sum of money, the principal, is invested at a fixed rate of interest such that the interest is added to the principal and no withdrawals are made, then the amount invested will grow by an increasing number of pounds in each successive time period, because interest earned in earlier periods will itself earn interest in later periods. This is known as *compounding*.

2.2 Suppose, for example, that £2,000 is invested to earn 10% interest. After one year, the original principal plus interest will amount to £2,200.

	£
Original investment	2,000
Interest in the first year (10%)	200
Total investment at the end of one year	2,200

NOTES

After two years the total investment will be £2,420.

	£
Investment at end of one year	2,200
Interest in the second year (10%)	220
Total investment at the end of two years	2,420

The second year interest of £220 represents 10% of the original investment, and 10% of the interest earned in the first year.

Similarly, after three years, the total investment will be £2,662.

	£
Investment at the end of two years	2,420
Interest in the third year (10%)	242
Total investment at the end of three years	2,662

2.3 The basic formula for compound interest is $S_n = P(1 + r)^n$

where P = the original sum invested

r = the interest rate, expressed as a proportion (so 5% = 0.05)

n = the number of periods

S_n = the sum invested after n periods.

2.4 In the previous example, £2,000 invested at 10% per annum for three years would increase in value to

$$\begin{aligned} & £2{,}000 \times 1.10^3 \\ = \; & £2{,}000 \times 1.331 \\ = \; & £2{,}662. \end{aligned}$$

The interest earned over three years is £662.

Activity 1

(a) What would be the total value of £5,000 invested now:

(i) after three years, if the interest rate is 20% per annum;

(ii) after four years, if the interest rate is 15% per annum;

(iii) after three years, if the interest rate is 6% per annum?

(b) At what annual rate of compound interest will £2,000 grow to £2,721 after four years?

Inflation

2.5 The same compounding formula can be used to predict future prices after allowing for inflation. For example, if we wish to predict the salary of an employee in five years time, given that he earns £8,000 now and wage inflation is expected to be 10% per annum, the formula would be applied as follows.

$$\begin{aligned} S_n &= P(1 + r)^n \\ &= £8{,}000 \times 1.10^5 \\ &= £12{,}884.08 \\ \text{say,} \; & £12{,}900. \end{aligned}$$

Withdrawals of capital or interest

2.6 If an investor takes money out of an investment, it will cease to earn interest. Thus, if an investor puts £3,000 into a bank deposit account which pays interest at 8% per annum, and makes no withdrawals except at the end of year 2, when he takes out £1,000, what would be the balance in his account after four years?

NOTES

	£
Original investment	3,000.00
Interest in year 1 (8%)	240.00
Investment at end of year 1	3,240.00
Interest in year 2 (8%)	259.20
Investment at end of year 2	3,499.20
Less withdrawal	1,000.00
Net investment at start of year 3	2,499.20
Interest in year 3 (8%)	199.94
Investment at end of year 3	2,699.14
Interest in year 4 (8%)	215.93
Investment at end of year 4	2,915.07

2.7 A quicker approach would be as follows.

	£
£3,000 invested for 2 years at 8% would increase in value to	
£3,000 × 1.08^2 =	3,499.20
Less withdrawal	1,000.00
	2,499.20

£2,499.20 invested for a further two years at 8% would increase in value to £2,499.20 × 1.08^2 = £2,915.07

Changes in the rate of interest

2.8 If the rate of interest changes during the period of an investment, the compounding formula must be amended slightly, as follows.

$$S_n = P(1 + r_1)^x (1 + r_2)^{n-x}$$

where r_1 = the initial rate of interest

x = the number of years in which the interest rate r_1 applies

r_2 = the next rate of interest

$n - x$ = the (balancing) number of years in which the interest rate r_2 applies.

Activity 2

(a) If £8,000 is invested now, to earn 10% interest for three years and 8% thereafter, what would be the size of the total investment at the end of five years?

(b) An investor puts £10,000 into an investment for ten years. The annual rate of interest earned is 15% for the first four years, 12% for the next four years and 9% for the final two years. How much will the investment be worth at the end of ten years?

(c) An item of equipment costs £6,000 now. The annual rates of inflation over the next four years are expected to be 16%, 20%, 15% and 10%. How much would the equipment cost after four years?

3 EFFECTIVE AND NOMINAL RATES OF INTEREST

Effective annual rate of interest

3.1 In the previous examples, interest has been calculated annually, but this need not be the case. Interest may be compounded daily, weekly, monthly or quarterly, and an effective annual rate of interest calculated.

Definition

The *effective annual rate of interest* is the equivalent annual rate of interest when interest is compounded at shorter intervals.

The effective annual rate = $[(1+r)^{\frac{12}{n}} - 1]$ or $[(1+r)^{\frac{365}{x}} - 1]$

where r is the rate of interest for each time period
n is the number of months in the time period
x is the number of days in the time period.

EXAMPLE: THE EFFECTIVE ANNUAL RATE OF INTEREST

Calculate the effective annual rate of interest of:

(a) 1.5% per month, compound;
(b) 4.5% per quarter, compound;
(c) 9% per half year, compound.

Solution

(a) $(1.015)^{12} - 1$ = 0.1956 = 19.56%
(b) $(1.045)^{4} - 1$ = 0.1925 = 19.25%
(c) $(1.09)^{2} - 1$ = 0.1881 = 18.81%

Nominal rates of interest and the annual percentage rate

Definition

A *nominal rate of interest* is an interest rate expressed as a per annum figure when the interest is compounded over periods of less than one year.

3.2 Given a nominal rate, it is possible to work out an effective rate. It is this effective rate (shortened to one decimal place) which is quoted in advertisements as the annual percentage rate (APR), sometimes called the *compound annual rate* (CAR).

Depending on whether the compounding is done daily, weekly, monthly, quarterly or six monthly, the APR will vary by differing amounts from the nominal rate.

EXAMPLE: NOMINAL AND EFFECTIVE RATES OF INTEREST

A building society may offer investors 10% per annum interest payable half-yearly. If the 10% is a nominal rate of interest, the building society would in fact pay 5% every six months, compounded so that the effective annual rate of interest would be

$[(1.05)^{2} - 1]$ = 0.1025 = 10.25% per annum.

Similarly, if a bank offers depositors a nominal 12% per annum, with interest payable quarterly, the effective rate of interest would be 3% compound every three months, which is

$[(1.03)^{4} - 1]$ = 0.1255 = 12.55% per annum.

Activity 3

Calculate the effective annual rate of interest of:

(a) 15% nominal per annum compounded quarterly;

(b) 24% nominal per annum compounded monthly.

4 THE CONCEPT OF DISCOUNTING

The basic principles of discounting

4.1 The basic principle of compounding is that if we invest £P now for n years at r% interest per annum, we should obtain £P $(1 + r)^n$ in n years time.

4.2 Thus if we invest £10,000 now for four years at 10% interest per annum, we will have a total investment worth £10,000 × 1.10^4 = £14,641 at the end of four years (that is, at year 4 if it is now year 0).

4.3 Discounting is the reverse of compounding.

Definition

Discounting is an application of financial mathematics. If we wish to have £S in n years' time, we need to invest a certain sum *now* (year 0) at an interest rate of r% in order to obtain the required sum of money in the future.

4.4 For example, if we wish to have £14,641 in four years time, how much money would we need to invest now at 10% interest per annum? This is the reverse of the situation described in Paragraph 4.2.

Let P be the amount of money invested now.

$$£14{,}641 = P \times 1.10^4$$

$$P = £14{,}641 \times \frac{1}{1.10^4} = £10{,}000$$

4.5 £10,000 now, with the capacity to earn a return of 10% per annum, is the equivalent in value of £14,641 after four years. We can therefore say that £10,000 is the present value of £14,641 at year 4, at an interest rate of 10%.

Present value

Definition

The term *present value* simply means the amount of money which must be invested now for n years at an interest rate of r%, to earn a given future sum of money at the time it will be due.

The formula for discounting

4.6 The discounting formula is

$$P = S_n \times \frac{1}{(1+r)^n}$$

where S_n is the sum to be received after n time periods
P is the present value of that sum
r is the rate of return, expressed as a proportion
n is the number of time periods (usually years).

The rate r is sometimes called a cost of capital.

NOTES

EXAMPLE: DISCOUNTING

(a) Calculate the present value of £60,000 at year 6, if a return of 15% per annum is obtainable.

(b) Calculate the present value of £100,000 at year 5, if a return of 6% per annum is obtainable.

(c) Calculate the amount a person needs to invest now at 12% to earn £4,000 at year 2 and £4,000 at year 3.

Solution

(a) PV $= 60{,}000 \times \frac{1}{(1 \cdot 15)^6}$

$= 60{,}000 \times 0.43$

$= £25{,}800$

(b) PV $= 100{,}000 \times \frac{1}{(1 \cdot 06)^5}$

$= 100{,}000 \times 0.75$

$= £75{,}000$

(c) PV $= 4{,}000 \times \left(\frac{1}{(1 \cdot 12)^2} + \frac{1}{(1 \cdot 12)^3}\right)$

$= 4{,}000 \times (0.80 + 0.71)$

$= £6{,}040$

This calculation can be checked as follows.

	£
Year 0	6,040
Interest for the first year (12%)	725
	6,765
Interest for the second year (12%)	812
	7,577
Less withdrawal	(4,000)
	3,577
Interest for the third year (12%)	429
	4,006
Less withdrawal	(4,000)
Rounding error	6

Activity 4

What is the present value of £16,000 received in year 12 when r = 7%?

Capital expenditure appraisal

4.7 Discounted cash flow techniques can be used to evaluate capital expenditure proposals (investments).

Definition

Discounted cash flow (DCF) involves the application of discounting arithmetic to the estimated future cash flows (receipts and expenditures) from a project in order to decide whether the project is expected to earn a satisfactory rate of return.

NOTES

4.8 There are two methods of using DCF techniques.

(a) The net present value (NPV) method

(b) The internal rate of return (IRR) method

5 THE NET PRESENT VALUE (NPV) METHOD

Definition

The *net present value (NPV) method* of capital expenditure appraisal works out the present values of all items of income and expenditure related to an investment at a given rate of return, and then works out a net total. If it is positive, the investment is considered to be acceptable. If it is negative, the investment is considered to be unacceptable.

5.1 Let's look at an example.

EXAMPLE: THE NET PRESENT VALUE OF A PROJECT

Spender Fortune Ltd is considering whether to spend £5,000 on an item of equipment. The 'cash profits', the excess of income over cash expenditure, from the project would be £3,000 in the first year and £4,000 in the second year.

The company will not invest in any project unless it offers a return in excess of 15% per annum.

Required

Assess whether the investment is worthwhile, or 'viable'.

Solution

In this example, an outlay of £5,000 now promises a return of £3,000 *during* the first year and £4,000 *during* the second year. It is a convention in DCF, however, that cash flows spread over a year are assumed to occur *at the end of the year*, so that the cash flows of the project are as follows.

	£
Year 0 (now)	(5,000)
Year 1 (at the end of the year)	3,000
Year 2 (at the end of the year)	4,000

The NPV method takes the following approach.

(a) The project offers £3,000 at year 1 and £4,000 at year 2, for an outlay of £5,000 now.

(b) The company might invest elsewhere to earn a return of 15% per annum.

(c) If the company did invest at exactly 15% per annum, how much would it need to invest now, at 15%, to earn £3,000 at the end of year 1 plus £4,000 at the end of year 2?

(d) Is it cheaper to invest £5,000 in the project, or to invest elsewhere at 15%, in order to obtain these future cash flows?

If the company did invest elsewhere at 15% per annum, the amount required to earn £3,000 in year 1 and £4,000 in year 2 would be as follows.

NOTES

EXAMPLE *continued*

Year	*Cash flow* £	*Discount factor* 15%	*Present value* £
1	3,000	$\frac{1}{1.15} = 0.87$	2,610
2	4,000	$\frac{1}{(1.15)^2} = 0.76$	3,040
			5,650

The choice is to invest £5,000 in the project, or £5,650 elsewhere at 15%, in order to obtain these future cash flows. We can therefore reach the following conclusion.

(a) It is cheaper to invest in the project, by £650.

(b) The project offers a return of over 15% per annum.

The net present value is the difference between the present value of cash inflows from the project (£5,650) and the present value of future cash outflows (in this example, $£5,000 \times 1/1.15^0 = £5,000$).

An NPV statement could be drawn up as follows.

Year	*Cash flow* £	*Discount factor* 15%	*Present value* £
0	(5,000)	1.000	(5,000)
1	3,000	$\frac{1}{1.15} = 0.87$	2,610
2	4,000	$\frac{1}{(1.15)^2} = 0.76$	3,040
		Net present value	+650

The project has a positive NPV, so it is acceptable.

Activity 5

A company is wondering whether to spend £18,000 on an item of equipment, in order to obtain cash profits as follows.

Year	£
1	6,000
2	8,000
3	5,000
4	1,000

The company requires a return of 10% per annum.

Required

Use the NPV method to assess whether the project is viable.

NOTES

Discount tables

5.2 Assuming that money earns, say, 10% per annum:

(a) the PV (present value) of £1 at year 1 is £1 × $\frac{1}{1.10}$ = £1 × 0.91;

(b) similarly, the PV of £1 at year 2 is £1 × $\frac{1}{(1.10)^2}$ = £1 × 0.83;

(c) the PV of £1 at year 3 is £1 × $\frac{1}{(1.10)^3}$ = £1 × 0.75.

Discount tables show the value of $1/(1 + r)^n$ for different values of r and n. The 10% discount factors of 0.91, 0.83 and 0.75 are shown in the discount tables at the front of this Study Guide in the column for 10%. (You will be given discount tables in your examination.)

EXAMPLE: VIABLE PROJECT

Daisy Ltd is considering whether to make an investment costing £28,000 which would earn £8,000 cash per annum for five years. The company expects to make a return of at least 11% per annum.

Required

Assess whether the project is viable.

Solution

Year	*Cash flow* £	*Discount factor* *11%*	*Present value* £
0	(28,000)	1.00	(28,000)
1	8,000	0.90	7,200
2	8,000	0.81	6,480
3	8,000	0.73	5,840
4	8,000	0.66	5,280
5	8,000	0.59	4,720
		NPV	1,520

The NPV is positive, therefore the project is viable because it earns more than 11% per annum.

Project comparison

5.3 The NPV method can also be used to compare two or more investment options. For example, suppose that Daisy Ltd can choose between the investment outlined in the example above *or* a second investment, which also costs £28,000 but which would earn £6,500 in the first year, £7,500 in the second, £8,500 in the third, £9,500 in the fourth and £10,500 in the fifth. Which one should Daisy Ltd choose?

5.4 The decision rule is to choose the option with the highest NPV. We therefore need to calculate the NPV of the second option.

Year	*Cash flow* £	*Discount factor* 11%	*Present value* £
0	(28,000)	1.00	(28,000)
1	6,500	0.90	5,850
2	7,500	0.81	6,075
3	8,500	0.73	6,205
4	9,500	0.66	6,270
5	10,500	0.59	6,195
			NPV = 2,595

Daisy Ltd should therefore invest in the second option since it has the higher NPV.

Expected values and discounting

5.5 Future cash flows cannot be predicted with complete accuracy. To take account of this uncertainty an *expected net present value* can be calculated which is a weighted average net present value based on the probabilities of different sets of circumstances occurring. Let us have a look at an example.

EXAMPLE: EXPECTED NET PRESENT VALUE

An organisation with a cost of capital of 5% is contemplating investing £340,000 in a project which has a 25% chance of being a big success and producing cash inflows of £210,000 after one and two years. There is, however, a 75% chance of the project not being quite so successful, in which case the cash inflows will be £162,000 after one year and £174,000 after two years.

Required

Calculate an ENPV and hence advise the organisation.

Solution

Year	*Discount factor* 5%	*Success* *Cash flow* £'000	*Success* *PV* £'000	*Failure* *Cash flow* £'000	*Failure* *PV* £'000
0	1.00	(340)	(340.0)	(340)	(340.00)
1	0.95	210	199.5	162	153.90
2	0.91	210	191.1	174	158.34
			50.6		(27.76)

ENPV = (25% × 50.6) + (75% × –27.76) = –8.17

The ENPV is – £8,170 and hence the organisation should not invest in the project.

6 THE INTERNAL RATE OF RETURN (IRR) METHOD

6.1 The internal rate of return (IRR) method of evaluating investments is an alternative to the NPV method.

6.2 The NPV method of discounted cash flow determines whether an investment earns a positive or a negative NPV when discounted at a given rate of interest. If the NPV is zero (that is, the present values of costs and benefits are equal) the return from the project would be exactly the rate used for discounting.

NOTES

Definitions

The *IRR method of discounted cash flow* is to determine the rate of interest (the internal rate of return) at which the NPV is 0. The *internal rate of return* is therefore the rate of return on an investment.

EXAMPLE: THE IRR METHOD OVER ONE YEAR

If £500 is invested today and generates £600 in one year's time, the internal rate of return (r) can be calculated as follows.

$$\text{PV of cost} = \text{PV of benefits}$$

$$500 = \frac{600}{(1+r)}$$

$$500\,(1+r) = 600$$

$$1+r = \frac{600}{500} = 1.2$$

$$r = 0.2 = 20\%$$

EXAMPLE: THE IRR METHOD OVER TWO YEARS

If £1,000 is invested today and generates £700 in the first year and £600 in the second year the internal rate of return can be calculated as follows.

$$\text{PV of cost} = \text{PV of benefits}$$

$$1{,}000 = \frac{700}{(1+r)} + \frac{600}{(1+r)^2}$$

Multiply both sides by $(1 + r)^2$

$$1{,}000\,(1+r)^2 = 700(1+r) + 600$$

$$1{,}000 + 2{,}000r + 1{,}000r^2 = 700 + 700r + 600$$

$$1{,}000r^2 + 1{,}300r - 300 = 0$$

$$10r^2 + 13r - 3 = 0$$

$$r = \frac{-13 \pm \sqrt{[169 - (4 \times 10 \times (-3))]}}{20}$$

$$= \frac{-13-17}{20} \text{ or } \frac{-13+17}{20}$$

$$= -1.5 \quad \text{or} \quad +0.2$$

$$= -150\% \quad \text{or} \quad 20\%$$

Since high negative returns are not a practical proposition, r = 20%.

6.3 The IRR method will indicate that a project is viable if the IRR exceeds the minimum acceptable rate of return. Thus if the company expects a minimum return of, say, 15%, a project would be viable if its IRR is more than 15%.

6.4 The examples so far used to illustrate the IRR method have been for one or two year projects. The arithmetic is more complicated for investments and cash flows extending over a longer period of time. A technique known as the interpolation method can be used to calculate an approximate IRR.

EXAMPLE: INTERPOLATION

A project costing £800 in year 0 is expected to earn £400 in year 1, £300 in year 2 and £200 in year 3.

Required

Calculate the internal rate of return.

Solution

The IRR is calculated by first of all finding the NPV at each of two interest rates. Ideally, one interest rate should give a small positive NPV and the other a small negative NPV. The IRR would then be somewhere between these two interest rates: above the rate where the NPV is positive, but below the rate where the NPV is negative.

A very rough guideline for estimating at what interest rate the NPV might be close to zero, is to take

$$\tfrac{2}{3} \times \left(\frac{\text{profit}}{\text{cost of the project}}\right)$$

In our example, the total profit over three years is £(400 + 300 + 200 – 800) = £100

$$\tfrac{2}{3} \times \frac{100}{800} = 0.08 \text{ approx.}$$

A starting point is to try 8%.

(a) Try 8%

Year	*Cash flow*	*Discount factor*	*Present value*
	£	8%	£
0	(800)	1.00	(800)
1	400	0.93	372
2	300	0.86	258
3	200	0.79	158
		NPV	(12)

The NPV is negative, therefore the project fails to earn 8% and the IRR must be less than 8%.

(b) Try 6%

Year	*Cash flow*	*Discount factor*	*Present value*
	£	6%	£
0	(800)	1.00	(800)
1	400	0.94	376
2	300	0.89	267
3	200	0.84	168
		NPV	11

The NPV is positive, therefore the project earns more than 6% and less than 8%.

The IRR is now calculated by interpolation. The result will not be exact, but it will be a close approximation. Interpolation assumes that the NPV falls in a straight line from +11 at 6% to –12 at 8%.

NOTES

EXAMPLE *continued*

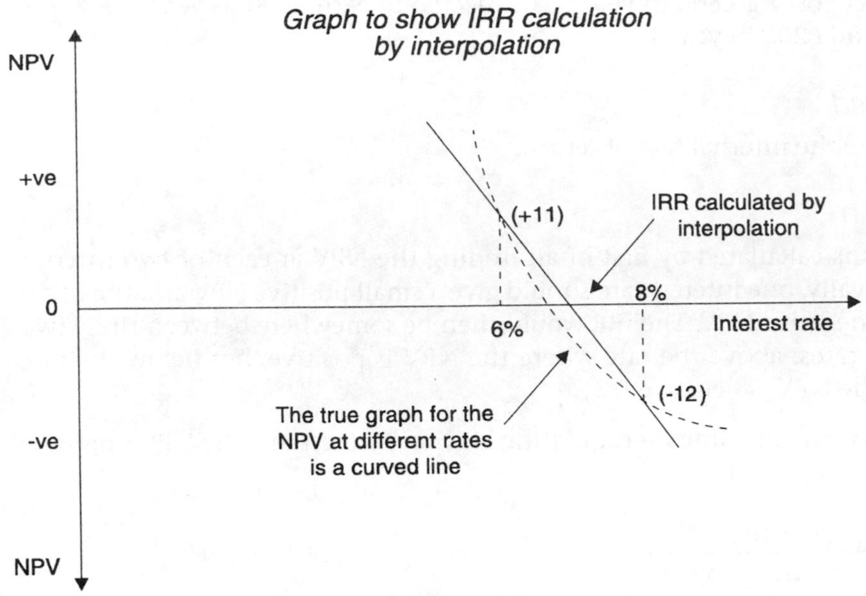

The IRR, where the NPV is zero, can be calculated as:

$$a\% + [\frac{A}{A-B} \times (b-a)]\% \text{ where}$$

a is one interest rate

b is the other interest rate

A is the NPV at rate a

B is the NPV at rate b

$$\text{IRR} = 6\% + [\frac{11}{(11+12)} \times (8-6)]\%$$

$$= (6 + 0.96)\%$$

$$= 6.96\% \text{ (approx)}$$

The answer is only an approximation because the NPV falls in a slightly curved line and not a straight line between +11 and –12. Provided that NPVs close to zero are used, the linear assumption used in the interpolation method is nevertheless fairly accurate.

Note that the formula will still work if A and B are both positive, or both negative, and even if a and b are a long way from the true IRR, but the results will be less accurate.

7 ANNUITIES

Definition

An *annuity* is a constant sum of money each year for a given number of years.

7.1 In the example following paragraph 5.2, there was a constant annual cash flow (an annuity) for five years, years 1-5. The arithmetic in the solution could have been *simplified* as follows.

	8,000 × 0.90		
plus	8,000 × 0.81		
plus	8,000 × 0.73		
plus	8,000 × 0.66		
plus	8,000 × 0.59		£
equals	8,000 × 3.69	=	29,520
Less PV of costs			28,000
NPV			1,520

Annuity tables

7.2 To calculate the present value of a constant annual cash flow, or annuity, we can multiply the annual cash flows by the sum of the discount factors for the relevant years. These total factors are known as *cumulative present value factors* or *annuity factors*. There are tables for annuity factors, which are also shown at the start of this text. (For example, the cumulative present value factor of £1 per annum for five years at 11% per annum is in the column for 11% and the year 5 row, and is 3.70. The figure we found above was 3.69, and the difference of 0.01 is due to rounding differences building up in our computation.)

EXAMPLE: NET PRESENT VALUE

(a) The present value of £1,000 earned each year from years 1 to 10 when the required return on investment is 11% per annum is £1,000 × 5.89 = £5,890.

(b) The present value (PV) of £100 earned each year from years 3 to 6 when the required return is 5% per annum is found as follows.

PV of £1 per annum for years 1 – 6 at 5%	5.08
Less PV of £1 per annum for years 1 – 2 at 5%	1.86
PV of £1 per annum for years 3 – 6 at 5%	3.22

£100 × 3.22 = £322

(c) Hannah U Witty Ltd is considering a project which would cost £14,000 now and earn £3,000 per annum in years 1 – 4 and £2,000 per annum in years 5 – 10. The cost of capital is 12%. Is the project worthwhile?

PV of £1 per annum at 12%, years 1 – 10	5.65
Less PV of £1 per annum at 12%, years 1 – 4	3.04
PV of £1 per annum at 12%, years 5 – 10	2.61

Years	*Cash flow*	*Discount factor*	*Present value*
	£	*12%*	*£*
0	(14,000)	1.00	(14,000)
1 – 4	3,000	3.04	9,120
5 – 10	2,000	2.61	5,220
		Net present value	+ 340

The project has a positive NPV and is therefore worthwhile.

The formula for the present value of an annuity

7.3 You may need to use a formula to calculate the present value of an annuity. The present value of an annuity of £a starting a year from now with an interest rate of r, is as follows.

NOTES

$$PV = \frac{1}{1+r} + \frac{1}{(1+r)^2} + \frac{1}{(1+r)^3} + \ldots + \frac{1}{(1+r)^n}$$

This equals

$$\frac{a\left[1-\left(\frac{1}{1+r}\right)^n\right]}{r}$$

EXAMPLE: THE ANNUITY FORMULATION

What is the present value of £4,000 per annum for years 1 to 4, at a discount rate of 10% per annum?

Solution

$$PV = \frac{£4{,}000 \times \left(1-\left(\frac{1}{1.10}\right)^4\right)}{0.1}$$

$$= \frac{£4{,}000 \times (1-0.6830)}{0.1}$$

$$= £12{,}680$$

This can be checked from the annuity tables:

the PV for years 1 to 4 is £4,000 × 3.17 = £12,680.

Activity 6

What is the present value of £6,000 per annum for four years, years 1 to 4, at a discount rate of 7% per annum? Use the formula and not tables.

Calculating a required annuity

7.4 If PV (or P, for simplicity) $= \frac{a\left(1-\left(\frac{1}{1+r}\right)^n\right)}{r}$

then $a = \frac{Pr}{\left[1-\left(\frac{1}{1+r}\right)^n\right]}$

This enables us to calculate the annuity required to yield a given rate of return (r) on a given investment (P).

NOTES

EXAMPLE: LOAN REPAYMENTS

A building society grants a £30,000 mortgage at 7% per annum. The borrower is to repay the loan in 10 annual instalments. How much must he pay each year?

Solution

$$a = \frac{30{,}000 \times 0.07}{1 - 1/1.07^{10}}$$

$$= \frac{2{,}100}{1 - 0.5083}$$

$$= \frac{2{,}100}{0.4917} = £4{,}271 \text{ per annum}$$

The use of annuity tables to calculate a required annuity

7.5 Just as the formula can be used to calculate an annuity, so too can the tables. Since the present value of an annuity is PV = a × annuity factor from the tables, we have

$$a = \frac{PV}{\text{annuity factor}}$$

In the previous example, the annual repayment on the mortgage would be

$$\frac{£30{,}000}{\text{PV factor of £1 per annum at 7\% for 10 years}}$$

$$= \frac{£30{,}000}{7.02}$$

= £4,274 (a rounding error of £3 arises)

Perpetuities

Definition

A *perpetuity* is an annuity which lasts for ever, instead of stopping after n years.

7.6 The present value of a perpetuity, a, is PV = a/r where r is the cost of capital as a proportion. The discount factor is therefore calculated as 1/r.

EXAMPLE: A PERPETUITY

Evermore Ltd is considering a project which would cost £50,000 now and yield £9,000 per annum every year in perpetuity, starting a year from now. The cost of capital is 15%. Is the project worthwhile?

Solution

Year	*Cash flow*	*Discount factor*	*Present value*
	£	*15%*	*£*
0	(50,000)	1.00	(50,000)
1 onwards	9,000	1/0.15	60,000
		NPV	10,000

The project is worthwhile because it has a positive net present value when discounted at 15%.

The timing of cash flows

7.7 Note that both annuity tables and our formulae assume that the first payment or receipt is a year from now. Always check when the first payment falls.

For example, if there are five equal payments starting now, and the interest rate is 8%, we should use a factor of 1 (for today's payment) + 3.31 (for the other four payments) = 4.31.

Activity 7

A loan of £250,000 is repayable in 15 equal annual instalments, starting a year from now. The interest rate is 8%. Find the annual repayment, without using annuity tables.

Chapter roundup

- Simple interest is interest which is earned in equal amounts every year (or month) and which is a given proportion of the principal. The simple interest formula is $S_n = P + nrP$.
- Compounding means that, as interest is earned, it is added to the original investment and starts to earn interest itself. The basic formula for compound interest is $S_n = P(1+r)^n$.
- If the rate of interest changes during the period of an investment, the compounding formula must be amended slightly to $S_n = P(1+r_1)^x (1 + r_2)^{n-x}$.
- An effective annual rate of interest is the corresponding annual rate when interest is compounded at intervals shorter than a year.
- A nominal rate of interest is an interest rate expressed as a per annum figure, although the interest is compounded over a period of less than one year. The corresponding effective rate of interest shortened to one decimal place is the annual percentage rate (APR).
- Discounting is the reverse of compounding. The discounting formula is $P = S_n \times 1/(1+r)^n$.
- The concept of present value can be thought of in two ways.

  It is the value today of an amount to be received some time in the future.

  It is the amount which would have to be invested today to produce a given amount at some future date.
- Discounted cash flow techniques can be used to evaluate capital expenditure projects. There are two methods: the NPV method and the IRR method.
- The NPV method works out the present values of all items of income and expenditure related to an investment at a given rate of return, and then works out a net total. If it is positive, the investment is considered to be acceptable. If it is negative, the investment is considered to be unacceptable.
- The IRR method is to determine the rate of interest (the IRR) at which the NPV is 0. Interpolation, using the following formula, is often necessary. The project is viable if the IRR exceeds the minimum acceptable return.

  $$\text{IRR} = a\% + \left[\frac{A}{A-B} \times (b-a)\right]\%$$
- An annuity is a constant sum of money each year for a given number of years.

Chapter roundup *continued*

- A formula can be used to calculate the present value of an annuity but tables provide annuity/present value factors.
- A required annuity can be calculated using a formula or tables.
- A perpetuity is an annuity that lasts for ever. The present value of a perpetuity is a/r.
- Ensure that you are aware of all the points above and can use the formulae correctly.

Quick quiz

1 If a sum P is invested earning a simple annual interest rate of r, how much will the investor have after n years?

2 If a sum P is invested earning a compound annual interest rate of r, how much will the investor have after n years?

3 How should withdrawals of money be dealt with in compound interest calculations?

4 How should changes in the rate of interest be dealt with in compound interest calculations?

5 What is meant by an effective annual rate of interest?

6 What is the meaning of the term 'present value'?

7 What is the present value of a sum of money S_n in n years time, given an interest rate of r?

8 What are the two usual methods of capital expenditure appraisal using DCF techniques?

9 What is the internal rate of return of an investment?

10 How would you determine the internal rate of return of a series of cash flows using interpolation?

Answers to activities

1 (a) (i) $£5,000 \times 1.20^3 = £8,640$

(ii) $£5,000 \times 1.15^4 = £8,745.03$

(iii) $£5,000 \times 1.06^3 = £5,955.08$

(b) $2,721 = 2,000 \times (1 + r)^4$

$(1 + r)^4 = 2,721/2,000 = 1.3605$

$1 + r = \sqrt[4]{1.3605} = 1.08$

$r = 0.08 = 8\%$

2 (a) $£8,000 \times 1.10^3 \times 1.08^2 = £12,419.83$

(b) $£10,000 \times 1.15^4 \times 1.12^4 \times 1.09^2 = £32,697.64$

(c) $£6,000 \times 1.16 \times 1.20 \times 1.15 \times 1.10 = £10,565.28$

NOTES

3 (a) 15% per annum (nominal rate) is 3.75% per quarter. The effective annual rate of interest is

$[1.0375^4 - 1] = 0.1587 = 15.87\%$

(b) 24% per annum (nominal rate) is 2% per month. The effective annual rate of interest is

$[1.02^{12} - 1] = 0.2682 = 26.82\%$

4 $PV = £16{,}000 \times \dfrac{1}{1.07^{12}} = £16{,}000 \times 0.44 = £7{,}040$

5

	Cash flow	*Discount factor*	*Present value*
	£	10%	£
0	(18,000)	1.00	(18,000)
1	6,000	$\frac{1}{1.10} = 0.91$	5,460
2	8,000	$\frac{1}{1.10^2} = 0.83$	6,640
3	5,000	$\frac{1}{1.10^3} = 0.75$	3,750
4	1,000	$\frac{1}{1.10^4} = 0.68$	680
		Net present value	(1,470)

The NPV is negative. We can therefore draw the following calculations.

(a) It is cheaper to invest elsewhere at 10% than to invest in the project.

(b) The project would earn a return of less than 10%.

(c) The project is not viable.

6

$$PV = \frac{£6{,}000 \times \left(1 - \left(\frac{1}{1.07}\right)^4\right)}{0.07} = £20{,}323$$

7 $\text{Annual repayment} = \dfrac{£250{,}000 \times 0.08}{1 - 1/1.08^{15}} = £29{,}207$

Further question practice

Now try the following practice questions at the end of this text.

Multiple choice questions	**97–107**
Exam style question	**15**

GLOSSARY

Additive model A model for time series analysis which assumes that the components of the series are independent of each other, an increasing trend not affecting the seasonal variations, for example.

Annuity A constant sum of money each year for a given number of years.

Arithmetic mean Calculated from the sum of values of items divided by the number of items. The arithmetic mean of a variable x is shown as $\overline{x}$ ('x bar').

Attribute Something an object has either got or not got.

Bar chart A method of presenting data in which quantities are shown in the form of bars on a chart, the length of the bars being proportional to the quantities.

Base weighted index See Laspeyre indices.

Binomial distribution A probability distribution used to answer questions like: what is the probability that six new cars in a batch of 100 will be faulty, given that three percent of all new cars are faulty? The binomial distribution applies where there are two possible outcomes, each with a constant probability. It follows that the outcome of one event has no effect on the outcomes of other events: the events are independent. The binomial distribution is for discrete variables.

Breakeven point The point at which neither profit nor loss occurs.

Census A survey in which all of the population is examined.

Central limit theorem The statistical rule that the sampling distribution of sample means is normally distributed, even though the distribution of the parent population is unknown, if the sample size is large enough (>30).

Chi-squared distribution A distribution used to test a sample of items in order to decide whether the items in the sample are distributed according to a preconceived or expected distribution pattern.

Coefficient of correlation Measures the degree of correlation between two variables.

Coefficient of determination The square of the correlation coefficient, r^2. This measures the proportion of the total variation in the value of one variable that can be explained by variations in the value of the other variable.

Combination A set of items, selected from a larger collection of items, regardless of the order in which they are selected.

Compounding An application of financial mathematics. If £X is invested now for n years at r% interest per annum, we should obtain £X $(1 + r)^n$ in n years time.

Contribution The difference between sales value and the marginal cost of sales.

Correlation Variables are said to be correlated when the value of one variable is related to the value of another.

Critical path In network analysis, the longest sequence of consecutive activities through the network.

Cube root The value which, when multiplied by itself twice, equals the original number.

Cumulative frequency distribution Can be used to show the total number of times that a value above or below a certain amount occurs.

Data A scientific term for facts, figures, information and measurements.

Deseasonalisation The process of removing seasonal variations from data to leave figures indicating the trend.

Decimals A way of showing parts of a whole.

Differentiation Measures the rate of change in one variable resulting from a change in another variable at a particular point.

Discounted cash flow The application of discounting arithmetic to the estimated future cash flows from a project in order to decide whether the project is expected to earn a satisfactory return.

Discounting An application of financial mathematics. If we wish to have £S in n years' time, we need to invest a certain sum *now* (year 0) at an interest rate of r% in order to obtain the required sum of money in the future. If X is the sum invested now, $X = S \times 1/(1 + r)^n$.

Dual price The amount by which the value of total contribution will go up (or down) if one unit more (or less) of a scarce resource is made available.

Dummy activity Used in network analysis when two activities could start at the same time and finish at the same time too. It is represented by a broken arrowed line.

Effective annual rate of interest The equivalent annual rate of interest when interest is calculated at intervals shorter than annually.

Equation An expression of the relationship between variables.

Expected value A weighted average value, based on probabilities.

Feasible area The area on a graph of a linear programming problem within which all the inequalities are satisfied.

Fractions A way of showing parts of a whole.

Frequency The number of times each value occurs .

Frequency distribution (or **frequency table**) Records the number of times each value occurs.

Gantt charts A line diagram, with lines representing both time and activities. It can be used to estimate the amount of resources required for a project. Where activities are in a continuous 'chain' of one able to follow immediately after the other, these can be drawn as a continuous line on the chart.

Geometric progression A sequence of numbers in which there is a common or constant ratio between adjacent terms.

Histogram A data presentation method for (usually) grouped data of a continuous variable. Visually similar to a bar chart but frequencies are represented by areas covered by the bar rather than by their height.

Historigram A graph of a time series.

Hypothesis testing The process of establishing the significance of results of sample data for beliefs (hypotheses) about a population.

Identity matrix (I) A square matrix which behaves like the number 1 in multiplication.

Index A measure, over time, of the average changes in the values (prices or quantities) of a group of items. An index comprises a series of index numbers.

Index relative (or **relative**) The name given to an index number which measures the change in a single distinct commodity.

Integer A whole number, either positive or negative.

Intercept The point at which a straight line crosses the y axis.

Interest The amount of money which an investment earns over time.

Internal rate of return The rate of return at which the net present value of an investment is zero.

Inter-quartile range The difference between the values of the upper and lower quartiles, hence showing the range of values of the middle half of the population.

Laspeyre indices Indices that use weights from the base period and are therefore sometimes called base weighted indices.

Linear equation An equation of the form y = a + bx.

Linear programming A technique for solving problems of profit maximisation (or cost minimisation) and resource allocation. The word 'programming' is simply used to denote a series of events. The various aspects of the problem are expressed as linear equations.

Linear regression analysis (least squares method) A technique for estimating the equation of a line of best fit.

Logarithm The power to which 10 must be raised to equal a given number.

Marginal cost The additional costs from producing one extra unit.

Marginal revenue The additional revenue from selling one extra unit.

Margin of safety The difference between budgeted sales volume (or revenue) and actual sales volume (or revenue) as a percentage of budgeted sales volume (or revenue).

Matrix (plural **matrices**) An array or table of numbers or variables.

Maximum turning point A turning point at which the second differential is less than zero.

Mean deviation A measure of the average amount by which the values in a distribution differ from the arithmetic mean.

Median The value of the middle member of a distribution once all of the items have been arranged in order of magnitude.

Minimum turning point A turning point at which the second differential is more than zero.

Mode An average which indicates the most frequently occurring value.

Moving averages Consecutive averages of the results of a fixed number of periods.

Multiplicative model A model for time series analysis which expresses each actual figure as a proportion of the trend.

Negative correlation Low values of one variable are associated with high values of the other, and high values of one variable with low values of the other.

Net present value method A capital expenditure appraisal method which works out the present value of all items of income and expenditure related to an investment at a given rate of return and then works out a net total. If the total is positive the investment is acceptable but if negative it is not.

Network analysis A technique basically concerned with the deployment of available resources for the completion of a complex task.

Nominal rate of interest A rate of interest expressed as a per annum figure when the interest is compounded over periods of less than one year.

Non-linear equations Equations in which one variable varies with the nth power of another, where n > 1.

Normal distribution A probability distribution most often applied to continuous variables.

Null matrix A matrix in which every element is 0.

Objective function The mathematical expression of the aim of a linear programming exercise.

Ogive Used to show the cumulative number of items with a value less than or equal to, or alternatively greater than or equal to, a certain amount.

Paasche indices Use current time period weights; in other words the weights are changed every time period.

Pearsonian correlation coefficient See coefficient of correlation.

Percentage Indicates the relative size or proportion of an item.

Permutation A set of items, selected from a larger group of items, in which the order of selection or arrangement is significant.

Perpetuity An annuity which lasts for ever, instead of stopping after n years.

Pie chart Shows pictorially the relative sizes of the component elements of a total.

Point of inflexion The point on a graph at which both the first derivative and the second derivative of the function equal zero.

Poisson distribution A probability distribution used to answer questions like: what is the probability of receiving 5 letters tomorrow, given that on average 2 letters a day are received? The Poisson distribution applies where events occur randomly within an interval, for example defects in a 100m length of rope, or telephone sales orders received in an hour. It can also be used as an approximation to the binomial distribution, when n is large (say ten or more) and p is small (say 0.1 or less). The Poisson distribution is for discrete variables.

Positive correlation Low values of one variable are associated with low values of the other, and high values of one variable are associated with high values of the other.

Present value The amount of money which must be invested now for n years at an interest rate of r%, to earn a given future sum of money at the time it will be due.

Price index Measures the change in the money value of a group of items over time.

Primary data Data collected especially for the purpose of whatever survey is being conducted.

Probability A measure of likelihood which can be stated as a percentage, a ratio, or more usually as a number between 0 and 1.

Probability distribution An analysis of the proportion of times each particular value occurs in a set of items.

Product moment correlation coefficient See coefficient of correlation.

Project evaluation and review technique (PERT) A form of network analysis that takes account of uncertainty.

Proportional model See multiplicative model.

Quadratic equations A type of non-linear equation in which one variable varies with the square (or second power) of the other variable.

Quantiles A collective term for quartiles, deciles and percentiles, and any other similar dividing points for analysing a frequency distribution.

Quantity index (also called a **volume index**) Measures the change in the non-monetary values of a group of items over time.

Random sample A sample selected in such a way that every item in the population has an equal chance of being included.

Range The difference between the highest observation and the lowest observation.

Raw data Primary data which have not been processed at all, but are still just (for example) a list of numbers.

Reciprocal The reciprocal of a number is 1 divided by that number.

Residual The difference between the actual results and the results which would have been predicted (for a past period for which we already have data) by the trend line adjusted for the average seasonal variation.

Sampling Involves selecting a sample of items from a population.

Sampling distribution of a mean A frequency distribution of the mean of a large number of samples.

Sampling frame A numbered list of all the items in the population.

Scattergraph method Involves plotting pairs of data for two related variables on a graph to produce a scattergraph, and then to use judgement to draw what seems to be a line of best fit through the data.

Seasonal variations Short-term fluctuations in recorded values, due to different circumstances which affect results at different times of the year, on different days of the week and so on.

Secondary data Data which have already been collected elsewhere, for some other purpose, but which can be used or adapted for the survey being conducted.

Second derivative/differential of a function The derivative of dy/dx.

Semi-logarithmic graph This has a normal horizontal axis against which time is plotted but, on the vertical axis, equal intervals represent equal proportional changes in the variable. For example, the distance on the axis between y = 10 and y = 30 is the same as the distance between y = 30 and y = 90 (both represent a three-fold increase).

Sensitivity analysis Involves changing significant variables in order to determine the effect of these changes on the planned outcome.

Shadow price See dual price.

Simple interest Interest which is earned in equal amounts every year (or month) and which is a given proportion of the original investment (the principal).

Simplex technique A linear programming technique which tests a number of feasible solutions to a problem until the optimal solution is found. The technique is a repetitive step-by-step process and therefore an ideal computer application. If the manual process is used, however, this is done in the form of a tableau (or 'table' or 'matrix') of figures.

Simultaneous equations Two or more equations which are satisfied by the same variable values.

Skewness The asymmetry of a frequency distribution curve.

Slack variable The amount of a constraining resource or item that is unused.

Spearman's rank correlation coefficient Measures the correlation between the order or rank of two variables.

Square root A value which, when multiplied by itself, equals the original number.

Standard deviation Square root of the variance.

Standard error of the mean The standard deviation of a sampling distribution of the mean.

Table A matrix of data in rows and columns, with the rows and columns having titles.

t distribution The distribution of small sample means.

Time series A series of figures or values recorded over time.

Trend The underlying long-term movement over time in the values of the data recorded.

Turning point A 'flip over' point on the graph of a function which occurs when dy/dx (in other words, the gradient of the curve) is zero.

Unit matrix See identity matrix.

Variable Something which can be measured. Variables may be classified as discrete (can only take a finite or countable number of values within a given range) or continuous (may take on any value).

Variance Average of the squared mean deviation for each value in a distribution.

Vector A table of numbers or variables which has just one row or column.

Z chart A form of time series chart.

MULTIPLE CHOICE QUESTIONS

Chapter 1

1 The term x^{-1} equals

A $-x$

B $^1/_x$

C x^2

D $x - 1$

A B C D

2 A coat which was priced at £45.99 last year is now £53.99.

What is the percentage increase in price to two decimal places?

A 17.39%

B 17.40%

C 19.78%

D 20.09%

A B C D

3 The graph of Y = 2X is shown by which of the following lines?

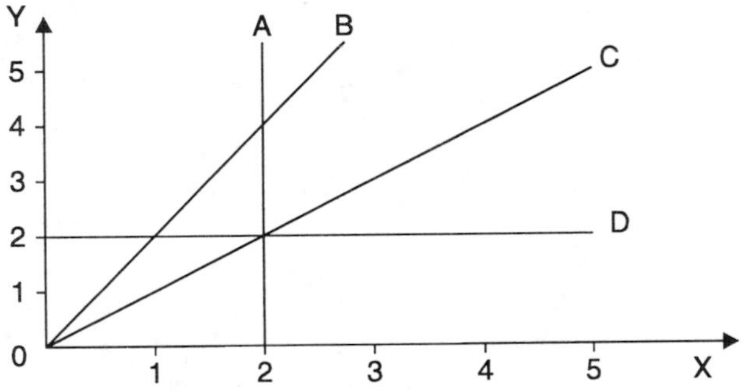

A B C D

4 A square-ended rectangular box has a volume of 1,458 cm^3. The length of the box is twice that of one side of the square end.

One side of the square end therefore measures

A 6 cm

B 9 cm

C 18 cm

D 24 cm

A B C D

5 A store sells oranges either for 39p per kg, or in bulk at £7 per 22 kg bag. The percentage saving (per kg) from buying a 22 kg bag is closest to

A 7.2%

B 16.0%

C 18.4%

D 20.0%

A B C D

NOTES

6 If price per unit is estimated to within ± 20% and the quantity of units supplied to within ± 10%, then the *maximum* possible error in revenue is

A 10%

B 20%

C 28%

D 32%

A B C D

7 If P is measured to within ± 10%, Q to within ± 20% and R to within ± 30%, then $\frac{PQ}{R}$ will be subject to a *maximum error* closest to:

A 10%

B 30%

C 50%

D 90%

A B C D

8 P, Q and R all had birthdays yesterday. P's age is 2 less than the sum of Q's age and R's age. Q's age is 3 less than half the sum of P's age and R's age. R's age is 5 less than half of P's age. How old is Q?

A 30 years

B 32 years

C 34 years

D 36 years

A B C D

9 $ax^2 - 3x + 20$ equals zero when x is –4 or +2.5. The value of a is

A –2

B –1.5

C 1

D 1.5

A B C D

10 There are two quantities, X and Y. X = –1 and Y = –2. Therefore

A $2X^2 > Y^2 < 0$

B $2X^2 < Y^2 < 0$

C $2X^2 < Y^2 > 0$

D $2X^2 > Y^2 > 0$

A B C D

NOTES

Chapter 2

11 A management accountant is checking invoices for errors. Every invoice has a serial number, the first being 3001. She has decided to sample 1 in 5 invoices. After selecting a random number from 1 to 5 (which turned out to be 5) she will then check invoices numbered 3005, 3010, 3015, 3020, etc. The sampling method is termed

A simple random

B stratified

C clustered

D systematic

A B C D

12 As part of a quality control exercise, an accountant selects two of her company's ten sales regions, and then 1 in 5 customers within each region. In each case the sampling is carried out with probability proportional to size. The type of sample selected is termed

A cluster

B quota

C random

D stratified

A B C D

13 In assessing the penetration of the home computer market, which is likely to provide the most accurate sample of the UK's 25 million households? (In each case the final selection of units is random.)

A A single-stage cluster sample, with 10 clusters of 200 households

B A single-stage cluster sample, with 200 clusters of 10 households

C A simple random sample of 2,000 households

D A stratified random sample of 2,000 households

A B C D

14 Which of the following definitions best describes qualitative data?

A They are data which are collected specifically for the current purpose.

B They are a mass of data which have been reduced to manageable proportions by classifying and summarising them.

C They are data which cannot be measured but reflect some quality of what is being observed.

D They are data which can take on only certain definite and separate values.

A B C D

NOTES

15 Which of the following is/are required for an accountant to select a stratified random sample of invoices?

I Each invoice must be given an equal chance of being picked.

II A record of all invoices is necessary.

III The number of invoices in each stratum must be known.

A I only

B II only

C III only

D II and III only

A B C D

Chapter 3

16 In a pie-diagram representing a total of £550,000 operating costs, the segment for wages is represented by 89°.

The amount of wages is approximately

A £6,180

B £135,972

C £137,556

D £489,500

A B C D

17 In a histogram in which one class interval is one and a half times as wide as the remaining classes, the height to be plotted in relation to the frequency for that class is

A × 0.67

B × 0.75

C × 1.00

D × 1.50

A B C D

18 A component bar chart showed the numbers of employees at each grade in a company on 31 December each year. The data were as follows.

	Number of employees	
Grade	*19X5*	*19X6*
1	20	25
2	57	65
3	180	220
4	1,200	1,450
5	663	670
	2,120	2,430

NOTES

The bar for 19X5 was 10.6 cm high. How high was the segment for grade 4 exployees for 19X6?

A 7.23 cm

B 7.24 cm

C 7.25 cm

D 7.26 cm

A B C D

19 In a histogram, one class is three-quarters of the width of the remaining classes.

If the score in that class is 21, the correct height to plot on the histogram is

A 15.75

B 21

C 28

D 42

A B C D

20 You have just calculated for the last two six-monthly periods, the running costs of a factory, broken down into five categories. You are using a computer package which can produce Z charts, pie-charts, time series graphs, Gantt charts and scatter diagrams, amongst others. The graphics to illustrate best the relative sizes of the cost categories in this situation will be

A Z charts

B Pie-charts

C Time series graphs

D Bar charts

A B C D

21 A data presentation format drawn in such a way that the number of items in each class is represented by the area of the bar is called

A an ogive

B a histogram

C a bar chart

D a table

A B C D

NOTES

Chapter 4

22 The price index for a commodity in the current year is 135 (base year = 100). The current price for the commodity is £55.35 per kg.

What was the price per kg in the base year?

A £35

B £41

C £74.72

D £100

A B C D

23 An index-linked pension of £10,000 a year became payable on 1 January 1992. Details of the index of Retail Prices are shown below.

Index of Retail Prices each January (January 1987 = 100)

1987	1991	1992	1993	1994
100	130.2	135.6	137.9	142.0

(Source: *Monthly Digest of Statistics*, February 1994)

The annual pension payable from 1 January 1994 is closest to

A £10,297

B £10,472

C £10,906

D £13,560

A B C D

24 An inflation index and index numbers of a company's sales (£) for the last year are given below.

Quarter	*1*	*2*	*3*	*4*
Sales (£) index	109	120	132	145
Inflation index	110	110	110	110

'Real' sales, ie adjusted for inflation, are

A approximately constant and keeping up with inflation

B growing steadily and not keeping up with inflation

C growing steadily and keeping ahead of inflation

D falling steadily and keeping up with inflation

A B C D

NOTES

25 A Laspeyre price index is to be constructed for two commodities. The first one cost £8 per kg in the base year, when 3 kg were used. The second one cost £5 per kg in the base year, when 4 kg were used. In the current year, the corresponding figures are £20 and 5 kg for the first commodity, and £25 and 3 kg for the second. What is the current year index number?

A 318

B 346

C 364

D 393

A B C D

26 A business buys two components, the A and the B. In 19X1 each A cost £5, each B cost £8 and the numbers of each used were 2,000 of A and 3,000 of B. By 19X5 the prices were £6 and £10 and the numbers used 2,200 and 2,500. A Paasche price index for 19X5 based on 19X1 will be

A 120.00

B 122.50

C 123.23

D 123.53

A B C D

Chapter 5

27 Over a period a firm made purchases of £400, £500, £550 and £600 on items, the unit costs of which were £10.00, £12.50, £11.00 and £12.00 respectively.

To the nearest penny, the average price paid per item was

A £11.21

B £11.37

C £11.39

D £12.00

A B C D

28 The following scores are observed for the times taken to complete a task, in minutes.

12, 34, 14, 15, 21, 24, 9, 17, 11, 8

The median score is

A 14.00

B 14.10

C 14.50

D 16.50

A B C D

NOTES

29 Sales for the first five months of the year averaged £8,200 per month.

For the last four months of the year sales averaged £8,500 per month.

If sales for the year totalled £102,000, the average for the sixth, seventh and eighth months must be

A £8,500

B £9,000

C £9,500

D £10,200

A B C D

30 The median of the scores 34, 23, 78, 12, 56, 43, 28, 9, 24 and 87 is

A 31

B 39.4

C 48

D 49.5

A B C D

31 When the mean purchase price of 10 units at 50p, 10 units at 70p, and 20 units at Xp is 80p, the value of X is

A 40p

B 60p

C 80p

D 100p

A B C D

32 The arithmetic mean of the following ten invoice values is £20:

£X, £15, £22, £14, £21, £15, £20, £18, £27, £X.

Therefore £X equals

A £19

B £20

C £24

D £28

A B C D

33 A car travels 20 miles at 30 mph, then 10 miles at 60 mph.

The mean speed for the whole journey of 30 miles is closest to (mph)

A 36

B 40

C 42

D 45

A B C D

NOTES

34 A factory employs staff in four departments for which the average (mean) wage per employee per week is as follows.

Department	*W*	*X*	*Y*	*Z*
Mean wage	£50	£100	£70	£80
Number of employees	20	5	10	5

The average (mean) wage per employee per week in this factory is

A £50

B £65

C £70

D £75

A B C D

35 The average (mean) cost of producing 10 units of X is £1, of producing 20 units of Y is £2 and of producing 30 units of Z is £3. The average (mean) unit cost of producing all items is closest to:

A £2

B £2.25

C £2.33

D £2.50

A B C D

36 Quality control of four independent production processes reveals the length of certain parts (in mm) to be as follows:

Process	*Mean*	*Standard deviation*
W	100	10
X	40	5
Y	80	8
Z	150	12

The process(es) with the largest relative variation, as measured by the coefficient of variation, is/are

A X only

B Z only

C X and Y

D W and Y

A B C D

Chapter 6

37 A sample of 100 companies has been analysed by size and whether they pay invoices promptly. The sample has been cross-tabulated into *large/small* against *fast payers/slow payers*. 60 of the companies are classified as *large* of which 40 are *slow payers*. In total, 30 of all the companies are *fast payers.*

NOTES

The probability that a company chosen at random is a *fast paying small company* is

A 0.10

B 0.20

C 0.30

D 0.40

A B C D

38 Next year, sales may rise, fall or remain the same as this year, with the following respective probabilities: 0.56, 0.23 and 0.21.

The probability of sales remaining the same or falling is

A 0.05

B 0.12

C 0.13

D 0.44

A B C D

39 In a group of 100 CIMA students, 30 are male, 55 are studying for Stage 1 and 6 of the male students are not studying for Stage 1. A student chosen at random is female. What is the probability that she is not studying Stage 1?

A 0.80

B 0.56

C 0.44

D 0.20

A B C D

40 A company is bidding for three contracts which are awarded independently of each other. The board estimates its chances of winning contract X as 50%, of winning contract Y as 1 in 3, and of winning contract Z as 1 in 5. The profits from X, Y and Z are estimated to be £50,000, £90,000 and £100,000 respectively.

The *expected value* to the company of the profits from all three contracts will be closest to (£'000)

A 50

B 75

C 90

D 100

A B C D

NOTES

41 A company recommends its employees to have free influenza vaccinations but only 50% do so. The effectiveness of the vaccine is know to be 90%. The probability of any non-vaccinated employee getting influenza by chance is 0.3. An employee catches influenza. What is the probability that she was vaccinated?

A 0.05

B 0.10

C 0.25

D None of the values

A B C D

42 Three sales representatives – J, K and L – rate their (independent) chances of achieving certain levels of sales as follows.

Possible sales		*£10,000*	*£20,000*	*£30,000*
J	Probability	0.3	0.5	0.2
K	Probability	0.3	0.4	0.3
L	Probability	0.2	0.6	0.2

(For example, J rates her chances of selling £20,000 worth of business as '50–50' and K has a 30% chance of selling £30,000 worth.)

On this evidence, the highest expected sales will be from

A J alone

B K alone

C L alone

D K and L

A B C D

43 The probability of rain tomorrow is 0.3. The probability of rain the day after is 0.6 if it rains tomorrow, but 0.2 if it does not rain tomorrow. What is the probability that it will be dry the day after tomorrow?

A 0.24

B 0.40

C 0.56

D 0.68

A B C D

NOTES

44 Brian Ltd is considering launching a new product. Expected sales volumes (at a selling price of £5 per unit) and expected unit variable costs are as follows.

Sales		*Variable costs per unit*	
Units	*Probability*	*£*	*Probability*
1,000	0.9	1.30	0.55
2,000	0.1	1.50	0.45

Fixed costs are expected to be £3,000. The company produces to order. What is the expected profit?

A £2,400

B £30

C £3,971

D £971

A B C D

Chapter 7

45 Cars arrive randomly at a traffic junction. What statistical distribution represents the arrival rate?

A Poisson

B Binomial

C Normal

D None of these

A B C D

46 Customers arrive at a box office ticket window according to a Poisson distribution with mean 10/hour. What is the probability that nobody arrives in a 6 minute period?

A 0.00004

B 0.3679

C 0.0025

D 0

A B C D

47 A normal distribution has a mean of 55 and a variance of 14.44. The probability of a score of 59 or more is approximately

A 0.15

B 0.35

C 0.50

D 0.65

A B C D

NOTES

48 A normal distribution has a mean of 75 and a variance of 25.

The upper quartile of this distribution is therefore

A 58.25

B 71.65

C 78.35

D 91.75

A B C D

49 A normal distribution has a mean of 150, and a standard deviation of 20. 80% of the distribution is below (approximately)

A 158

B 170

C 161

D 167

A B C D

50 A normal distribution is to be split into four equal areas, two to the right of z = 0 and two to the left of z = 0 (z = 0 at the mean). Using CIMA tables, the |z| value that splits the area in this way is closest to

A 0.10

B 0.19

C 0.33

D 0.67

A B C D

51 An analysis of a machine's output shows that 40% of items manufactured are rejected. A random sample of 100 recently manufactured items was taken. What is the probability that there are more than 45 rejects in the batch?

A 0.1562

B 0.1788

C 0.1314

D 0.4

A B C D

52 If n, p and q are the parameters of the binomial distribution, the normal approximation to this distribution can be used when certain conditions apply. Which option fully defines these required conditions?

A n large, p small

B n large

C p small

D n large, p approximately 0.5

A B C D

NOTES

53 Three coins are tossed in the air. What is the probability that one and only one of them will fall 'tails'?

A $^3/_8$

B $^1/_8$

C $^1/_3$

D $^1/_2$

A B C D

54 A random variable follows a Poisson distribution with mean 4. What is the standard deviation?

A 4

B 2

C 16

D 8

A B C D

Chapter 8

55 A sample has a mean value of £500 and a standard deviation of £30.61. The 95% confidence interval is £496 to £504.

The number in the sample (to the nearest whole number) is

A 215

B 220

C 224

D 225

A B C D

56 A sample size 100 has a mean of 120.87 and a variance of 81. The 95% upper confidence limit of the population mean is therefore

A 122.634

B 123.162

C 127.823

D 136.746

A B C D

57 The 95% confidence interval for a population mean is £174 ± £4.90 based on a normal distribution.

If the sample size is 36, the size of the sample standard deviation is

A £10

B £15

C £20

D £25

A B C D

58 As part of a quality control system, a simple random sample of 100 units was taken from a large batch of production, and tested. Ten units were found to be faulty. Therefore, 95% confidence limits for the true fault rate in the whole batch will be closest to 10% plus or minus

A 1%

B 2%

C 3%

D 6%

A B C D

59 In a report, it is stated that *'The standard error of the sample percentage is 5%'*. This means that

A the true population value will fall within ± 5% of the sample value

B the bias in the sample is ± 5%

C 95% of the sample values fall within ±5% of the true value

D none of the options above is true

A B C D

60 An accountant wishes to know the average (mean) value of a large population of invoices. From past experience it is known that the standard deviation is £10. For the accountant to be at least 90% confident that a sample estimate is within ± £2 of the true average value, the minimum size of the simple random sample must be nearest to:

A 17

B 34

C 68

D 272

A B C D

61 An opinion poll, based on a simple random sample of 2,500 people, finds that 1,000 support Party X and 1,500 support Party Y. The standard error of the percentage supporting either party is closest to

A 0.1%

B 1%

C 2%

D 10%

A B C D

NOTES

62 A manager is trying to tell if machine operators are independent of the proportion of rejected batches. A contingency table drawn containing appropriate information on 200 production batches is as follows.

	Rejects		
	< 10%	*< 15%*	*< 20%*
Machine A	40	40	30
Machine B	60	20	10

How many batches would machine operator A be expected to produce having < 10% rejects if machine operator and proportion of rejected batches were independent?

A 45

B 33

C 22

D 55

A B C D

63 In the above question (Q 62), what is the tabular value of chi squared if the test were performed at the 5% level of significance?

A 12.6

B 11.1

C 5.99

D 3.84

A B C D

64 Two random sample, of sizes n_A and n_B, are taken from two populations. The sample means, estimates of the population variances and the sample sizes are as follows.

	Sample	
	A	*B*
Sample mean	50	55
Estimate of the population variance	25	64
Sample sizes	16	25

What is the pooled estimate of variance?

A 25

B 64

C 49

D 89

A B C D

NOTES

Chapter 9

65 If $\Sigma x = 440$, $\Sigma y = 330$, $\Sigma x^2 = 17{,}986$, $\Sigma y^2 = 10{,}366$, $\Sigma xy = 13{,}467$ and $n = 11$, then the value of r, the coefficient of correlation, to two decimal places, is

A 0.98

B 0.63

C 0.96

D 0.59

A B C D

66 A rank correlation coefficient is being calculated, using the formula

$$R = 1 - \frac{6\Sigma d^2}{n\left(n^2 - 1\right)}$$. If $\Sigma d^2 = 50$ and $n = 10$, R will

(to 2 decimal places) be

A –0.30

B –0.25

C 0.30

D 0.70

A B C D

67 A company's management accountant is analysing the reject rates achieved by 100 factory operatives working in identical conditions. Reject rates, Y%, are found to be related to months of experience, X, by this regression equation: $Y = 20 - 0.25X$. (The correlation coefficient was $r = -0.9$.)

Using the equation, the predicted reject rate for an operative with 12 months' experience is closest to

A 17%

B 19%

C 20%

D 23%

A B C D

68 A company's weekly costs (£C) were plotted against production level (P) for the last 50 weeks and a regression line calculated to be $C = 1{,}000 + 250P$. Which statement about the breakdown of weekly costs is true?

A Fixed costs are £1,000. Variable costs per unit are £5.

B Fixed costs are £250. Variable costs per unit are £4.

C Fixed costs are £250. Variable costs per unit are £1,000.

D Fixed costs are £1,000. Variable costs per unit are £250.

A B C D

NOTES

69 An accountant obtained the costs associated with the manufacture of five batches of identical items. These were as follows.

Batch	*1*	*2*	*3*	*4*	*5*
Batch size	100	200	300	400	500
Total cost	£800	£1,500	£2,500	£3,500	£4,400

What is the value of the gradient of the sample line of linear regression of total cost on batch size?

A 8.0
B 7.5
C 9.2
D 5.0

A B C D

70 In the general equation for a straight line y = a + bx the letter a represents

A the gradient
B the intercept on the x axis
C the intercept on the y axis
D the value of x when y = 0

A B C D

71 A company has weekly fixed costs of £5,000 and variable costs per unit of production of £10. The equation of the straight line relating production (P) to costs (C) is therefore

A C = 5,000P + 10
B P = 5,000 + 10C
C C = 5,000 + 10/P
D C = 5,000 + 10P

A B C D

Chapter 10

72 Over an 18-month period, sales have been found to have an underlying linear trend of y = 7.112 + 3.949x, where y is the number of items sold and x represents the month. Monthly deviations from trend have been calculated and month 19 is expected to be 1.12 times the trend value.

The forecast number of items to be sold in month 19 is approximately

A 91
B 92
C 93
D 94

A B C D

NOTES

73 Based on the last 15 periods the underlying trend of sales is y = 345.12 – 1.35x. If the 16th period has a seasonal factor of –23.62, assuming an additive forecasting model, then the forecast for that period, in whole units, is

A 300

B 343

C 347

D 390

A B C D

74 A product has a constant (flat) trend in its sales, and is subject to quarterly seasonal variations as follows.

Quarter	*Q1*	*Q2`*	*Q3*	*Q4*
Seasonality	+50%	+50%	–50%	–50%

Sales last quarter, Q2, were 240 units.

Assuming a multiplicative model for the time series, predicted unit sales for the next quarter, Q3, will be closest to

A 60

B 80

C 120

D 160

A B C D

75 The long-term trend of a time series, showing demand (y) increasing with time (t) is given by the following equation

y = 25 + 7t

where t = 1 represents 19X1 quarter 1

The additive seasonal components are:

Quarter 1: 25

Quarter 2: –15

Quarter 3: –20

Quarter 4: 10

Ignore cyclical and random effects. What is the forecast for 19X4 quarter 3?

A 46

B 26

C 110

D 130

A B C D

NOTES

76 A centred, 12-month moving average is used to update a company's long-term sales trend. Seasonal variations are calculated as (sales – trend). If the first data point (of past sales) commences at January 19X1, what is the month in which the first seasonal variation can be obtained?

A January
B March
C July
D December

A B C D

77 A time series is shown below:

Year	*19X1*	*19X2*	*19X3*	*19X4*	*19X5*	*19X6*	*19X7*
Annual sales (£'000)	500	625	720	780	900	940	990

If a three point moving average is used, what is the value of the third moving average point?

A 720
B 780
C 800
D 900

A B C D

Chapter 11

Data for questions 78–84

Consider the following scenario.

A company makes two products, the X and the Y. Relevant data are as follows.

	X per unit	*Y per unit*	*Maximum per week*
Contribution	£3	£4	
Labour (hours)	1	2	800
Materials (kg)	2	1	850

78 What is the labour resource?

A 800 hours
B 850 hours
C £3
D £4

A B C D

79 What is the labour constraint?

A $x + 2y \leq 800$
B $x + 2y \geq 800$
C $2x + y \leq 800$
D $2x + y \geq 800$

A B C D

NOTES

80 What is the objective function representing C, the contribution?

A $C = 800x + 850y$

B $C = 3x + 4y$

C $C = x + 2y$

D $C = 2x + y$

A B C D

81 What is the point of intersection of the two equations formed from the two constraints?

A (400,800)

B (250,300)

C (300,250)

D (425,850)

A B C D

82 What is the maximum contribution that can be obtained?

A £1,900

B £1,950

C £4,400

D £4,675

A B C D

83 If the unit contribution of product X change from £3 to £4, how would the product mix change?

A $x = 0, y = 400$

B $x = 425, y = 0$

C $x = 800, y = 0$

D product mix remains unchanged

A B C D

84 If an additional constraint

$x + y < 600$

was added to the problem, how would the product mix be affected?

A The product mix changes to (600,200)

B The product mix changes to (250,350)

C The product mix changes to (600,0)

D The product mix remains unchanged

A B C D

NOTES

85 Clive Ltd makes two products, the Woof and the Bark. Each Woof requires 20 minutes in department 1 whereas each Bark requires 30 minutes. Due to a flu epidemic, however, available labour time in department 1 will be restricted to 250 working hours next week. Which of the following best describes the situation facing Clive Ltd?

A $\frac{1}{3}x + \frac{1}{2}y \leq 250$

B $3x + 2y \leq 250$

C $250x + 250y \leq 600$

D $20x + 30y \leq 250$

A B C D

Chapter 12

86 Demand for a product is given by:

$d = 12p - 3p^2$

where d is the demand and p is the price.

At what price will demand be at a maximum?

A 2

B 12

C 3

D 6

A B C D

87 If $y = 4x^5 - 10x^4 + 20x^2 - 2x^{-2}$, what is the value of $\frac{d^2y}{dx^2}$ at x = 1?

A −12

B 12

C 0

D 40

A B C D

88 If $y = x^3 - 5x^4 + 2x + 3$, what is $\frac{dy}{dx}$ at x = 1?

A −15

B 1

C 10

D 0

A B C D

89 y varies with x according to the relationship $y = 2x^2 - 3x + 20$. The gradient of this curve is zero when x equals

A 0

B −2.5

C −4

D 0.75

A B C D

NOTES

90 What is the second differential of
$y = 4x^2 + 3x^8 - 2x^{-2} + 7x - 15$

A $= 8x + 24x^7 + 4x^{-3} + 7$

B $= 8 + 168x^6 - 12x^{-4}$

C $= 8 + 168x^6 + 12x^{-4}$

D $= 8 + 168x^6 - 12x^4$

A B C D

Chapter 13

91 Milly Ltd produces and sells one product, the selling price of which she has decided to set at £50 per unit. Each unit requires £10 of material and her monthly fixed costs are £5,000. If the only other direct cost is labour, and each unit requires 2.5 hours of direct labour time, what is the maximum hourly rate that the work force can be paid if the company wishes to breakeven at a monthly sales level of 1,000 units?

A £14

B £13

C £12

D £11

A B C D

92 From the sales of 100 units of product x in one particular week £3,300 of revenue was generated. £800 of variable costs were incurred and fixed costs amounted to £500 per week. What is the break-even point?

A 57 units

B 788 units per year

C 1,040 units per year

D 3,250 units per year

A B C D

Chapter 14

93 In a network, what is the critical path?

A The shortest route through the network

B The best decision option

C The longest route through the network

D The worst decision option

A B C D

NOTES

94 If the optimistic duration, likely duration and pessimistic duration are 6, 9 and 18 respectively, what is the mean duration?

A 6

B 9

C 10

D 18

A B C D

95 A project comprises the following activities.

Activity	*Preceded by*	*Duration Days*
J	-	5
K	–	6
L	J	12
M	K	10
N	L, M	5
O	N	4
P	N	6

What is the total duration of the critical path?

A 25 days

B 26 days

C 27 days

D 28 days

A B C D

96 A project comprises the following activities.

Activity	*Preceded by*	*Duration Days*	*Staff required*
T	-	5	8
U	-	3	7
V	T	6	6
W	U	3	4
X	V, W	5	6
Y	X	6	8
Z	V, W	3	8

The numbers of staff stated are required throughout the activities' durations. Once an activity has been started, it cannot be interrupted. The whole project is to be completed in the minumum possible time.

What is the lowest possible figure for the maximum number of staff required simultaneously?

A 13

B 14

C 15

D 16

A B C D

NOTES

Chapter 15

97 The annual rent of a building is £1,200 payable in advance at the beginning of each year. At an interest rate of 14%, the present value of the rental payments is £5,319.60.

The length of the lease is

A 3 years

B 4 years

C 5 years

D 6 years

A B C D

98 A building society adds interest monthly to investors' accounts even though interest rates are expressed in annual terms. The current rate of interest is 6% per annum.

An investor deposits £1,000 on 1 January. How much interest will have been earned by 30 June?

A £30.00

B £30.38

C £60.00

D £61.68

A B C D

99 A one-year investment yields a return of 15%. The cash returned from the investment, including principal and interest, is £2,070. The interest is

A £250

B £270

C £300

D £310.50

A B C D

100 It is estimated that, because of productivity improvements, costs will fall by $2^1/_2$% per annum on a compound basis. If annual costs are now £160,000 then by the end of five years they will have fallen, to the nearest £, to

A £137,450

B £140,000

C £140,975

D £145,590

A B C D

NOTES

101 It is estimated that a particular cost will decline by 5% per annum on a compound basis.

If the cost now is £10,000, by the end of year 4 the cost will be approximately

A £7,500

B £8,000

C £8,145

D £8,500

A B C D

102 A firm has arranged a ten-year lease, at an annual rent of £8,000. The first rental payment has to be paid immediately, and the others are to be paid at the end of each year.

What is the present value of the lease at 12%?

A £50,640

B £51,562

C £45,200

D £49,852

A B C D

103 If a single sum of £12,000 is invested at 8% per annum with interest compounded quarterly, the amount to which the principal will have grown by the end of year three is approximately

A £15,117

B £14,880

C £15,219

D £15,880

A B C D

104 £2,500 was invested exactly three years ago, at a guaranteed rate of compound interest of 8% per annum. Its value now (to the nearest £) is

A £2,916

B £3,100

C £3,149

D £3,401

A B C D

105 Which is worth most, at present values, assuming an annual rate of interest of 8%?

A £1,200 in exactly one year from now

B £1,400 in exactly two years from now

C £1,600 in exactly three years from now

D £1,800 in exactly four years from now

A B C D

NOTES

106 An annual rent of £1,000 is to be received for ten successive years. The first payment is due tomorrow. Assuming the relevant interest rate to be 8%, the present value of this stream of cash flows is closest to

A £6,250

B £6,710

C £7,250

D £7,710

A B C D

107 A bank offers depositors a nominal 4% pa, with interest payable quarterly. What is the effective annual rate of interest?

A 1%

B 4%

C 1.025%

D 4.06%

A B C D

EXAM STYLE QUESTIONS

Chapter 1

1 PRODUCING BATCHES

(a) The total cost of producing a batch of a given product is assumed to follow a quadratic relationship. Batches of 10, 20 and 40 units of the product cost £700, £400 and £1,600 respectively.

(i) Determine the precise form of the relationship.

(ii) Draw a graph of the total cost function for batches of sizes 0 to 50 units.

(iii) From the graph, determine the batch size that minimises total cost.

(b) The product sells for £30 per unit.

(i) Draw, on the same graph as before, the revenue function.

(ii) Find from the graph the range of batch sizes over which the product makes a profit.

(iii) Determine the precise form of the profit function.

Chapter 2

2 100 SQUARE MILES

A local weekly newspaper sells about half a million copies in a week in a region of about 100 square miles. Market research indicates that the readership profile is as follows.

Age	%	*Annual income* £'000	%	*Sex*	%
Under 25	10	Under 10	10	Male	50
25 – 34	15	10 – 15	10	Female	50
35 – 44	20	15 – 20	25		
45 – 54	20	20 – 25	25	Region	%
55 – 64	20	25 – 30	20	Rural	10
65 +	15	Over 30	10	Suburban	30
Total	100	Total	100	Town	60

You are working with a marketing colleague on the design of a sample survey to find out (i) current strengths and weaknesses of the paper and (ii) whether the introduction of colour, leisure and/or business supplements and so on would increase sales and by how much.

Required

(a) Considering the information requirements, recommend a method for collecting the data (such as by post, telephone, personal interviews and so on), giving reasons.

(b) Design and explain a suitable practical sampling scheme that would achieve the objectives.

Do not attempt to write a questionnaire.

NOTES

Chapter 3

3 TELEVISION ADVERTISING

The unit sales of a brand for 19X1 and 19X2 were as follows.

	Jan	*Feb*	*Mar*	*Apr*	*May*	*Jun*	*Jul*	*Aug*	*Sept*	*Oct*	*Nov*	*Dec*
19X1	29	30	30	34	37	39	40	40	40	45	49	52
19X2	54	55	55	55	50	46	43	41	40	40	42	44

The brand has been supported by two weeks of television advertising every March and September. From April 19X2 there has been heavy price-cutting by its competitors.

Required

(a) Calculate the following for 19X2.

(i) Cumulative monthly sales

(ii) Moving annual totals

(b) Plot a Z chart for this period.

(c) Explain what these data show.

Chapter 4

4 PRODUCTION INDUSTRIES INDEX

The data below refer to Average Earnings Index numbers in the UK for different sectors of industry, 1988 = 100, and the Retail Prices Index, 1987 = 100.

Date	*Whole economy*	*Production industries*	*Service industries*	*Retail Prices Index*
1988	100.0	100.0	100.0	107.0
1989				
Feb	104.6	104.9	104.4	111.5
May	107.5	108.1	107.2	115.0
Aug	109.1	109.2	108.7	115.8
Nov	112.8	112.9	112.7	118.5
1990				
Feb	114.0	114.3	113.7	120.2
May	118.5	118.2	118.6	126.2
Aug	120.9	119.7	121.1	128.1
Nov	123.8	123.7	123.0	130.0
1991				
Feb	124.7	125.2	123.8	130.9
May	128.1	129.2	127.1	133.5
Aug	130.8	130.2	130.4	134.1
Nov	130.8	131.8	129.7	135.6

(Source: *Employment Gazette*, January 1992)

Required

(a) Using 1988 = 100 as base throughout, deflate the Production Industries Index and comment briefly on the real (inflation-adjusted) change in its average earnings over the period 1989/91.

(b) A retired person from the Service Industries had an index-linked pension of £5,000 a year, starting in May 1989 and updated each November in line with the average earnings index for that sector. Find the pension rates for November in each of the years 1989, 1990, 1991 and comment on their value in real terms.

Chapter 5

5 AGE STRUCTURE

A firm is comparing the age structure of its workforce in the current year with that of five years ago, as shown in the table below.

Age group (years)	*5 years ago* *Number in group*	*Current year* *Number in group*
25 < 30	2	5
30 < 35	6	10
35 < 40	8	13
40 < 45	13	28
45 < 50	15	21
50 < 55	35	12
55 < 60	12	8
60 < 65	9	3

The mean age and standard deviation of ages five years ago were as follows.

Mean age	49.05 years
Standard deviation	8.45 years

Required

(a) Calculate the mean age and the associated standard deviation for the current year.

(b) Compare the results in (a) with the calculations for five years ago, saying why you think the means and standard deviations may have changed.

Note. You are not expected to conduct statistical tests.

(c) Draw a bar chart that will illustrate the changes in the age structure of the workforce over the five-year period.

Chapter 6

6 PHARMACEUTICAL COMPANY

A pharmaceutical company has developed a new headache treatment which is being field tested on 1,000 volunteers. In a test some volunteers have received the treatment and some a placebo (a harmless neutral substance). The results of the test are as follows.

	Treatment received	*Placebo received*
Some improvement	600	125
No improvement	150	125

Required

(a) Calculate the probability that a volunteer has shown some improvement.

(b) Calculate the conditional probability that the volunteer has shown some improvement given that he or she has received the treatment.

(c) Calculate the conditional probability that the volunteer has received the treatment given that no improvement has been observed.

(d) Calculate the conditional probability that the volunteer has received the placebo, given that some improvement has been observed.

(e) Explain briefly what the evidence in the table suggests to you about the effectiveness of the treatment.

Chapter 7

7 NORMAL DISTRIBUTION

The value of an invoice is known to be normally distributed with mean £48 and standard deviation £5.

(a) What proportion of invoices lie between £40 and £50?

(b) Invoices whose values are greater than £60 require special attention. What proportion of invoices fall in this category?

(c) The accounts manager likes to review the 10% of the invoices which have the lowest values. What is the highest invoice value in this range?

(d) In a particular week, 1,000 invoices were received. What is the expected number having values lying between £45 and £55?

Chapter 7 and Chapter 8

8 NORMAL DISTRIBUTION AND SAMPLING

(a) Applicants for a certain job are given an aptitude test. Past experience shows that the scores from the test are normally distributed with a mean of 60 points and a standard deviation of 12 points. What percentage of candidates would be expected to pass the test, if a minimum score of 75 is required?

(b) To determine the average height of 18-year-old males in a particular town, a simple random sample was taken of 100 18-year-old male inhabitants of the town, and their heights measured. The average height was found to be 1.75 m, with a standard deviation of 10 cm.

Required

Calculate 95% confidence limits for the average height of 18-year-old males in the town in question.

NOTES

Chapter 9

9 FLEET OF VEHICLES

A company has a fleet of vehicles and is trying to predict the annual maintenance costs per vehicle. The following data have been supplied for a sample of vehicles.

Vehicle number	*Age in years*	*Maintenance cost per annum £ x 10*
	(x)	*(y)*
1	2	60
2	8	132
3	6	100
4	8	120
5	10	150
6	4	84
7	4	90
8	2	68
9	6	104
10	10	140

Required

(a) Using the least squares technique, calculate the values of *a* and *b* in the equation $y = a + bx$, to allow managers to predict the likely maintenance cost, knowing the age of the vehicle.

(b) Prepare a table of maintenance costs covering vehicles from 1 to 10 years of age, based on your calculations in (a).

(c) Estimate the maintenance costs of a 12-year-old vehicle and comment on the validity of making such an estimate.

Chapter 10

10 YELESOL ICE CREAM

The sales of Yelesol ice cream for the last twelve quarters have been as follows.

		Sales Thousand units	Moving annual total Thousand units
19X1	Q4	14	–
19X2	Q1	16	–
	Q2	30	100
	Q3	40	104
	Q4	18	104
19X3	Q1	16	108
	Q2	34	112
	Q3	44	108
	Q4	14	108
19X4	Q1	16	112
	Q2	38	120
	Q3	52	–
	Q4		–

Required

(a) Calculate a centred moving average.

(b) Plot a graph of the data and the centred moving average.

(c) Find the average quarterly seasonal variations.

(d) Calculate sales forecasts for the next two quarters.

Chapter 11

11 CRUDE OIL

A chemical company refines crude oil into petrol. The refining process uses two types of crude oil, heavy and light. A mixture of these oils is blended into either super or regular petrol.

In the refining process one gallon (g) of super is made from $^7/_{10}$g of heavy crude and $^1/_2$g of light crude. One gallon of regular is made from $^1/_2$g of heavy crude and $^7/_{10}$g of light crude oil. (There is a refining loss of $^1/_5$g in each case.)

At present, 5,000g of heavy crude and 6,000g of light crude oil are available for refining each day. Market conditions suggest that at least two thirds of the petrol should be super. The company sells super for £1.80 a gallon and regular for £1.65 a gallon, the profit being £0.25 and £0.10 a gallon respectively, and wishes to maximise total profit.

Required

(a) State the objective function and three constraints, one for heavy crude, one for light crude and one for market conditions.

(b) Graph the constraints and shade the feasible region.

(c) Deduce the optimal policy and the profit generated, and comment briefly on your answer.

NOTES

(d) A qualified management accountant has seen your calculations and provided you with a long list of other matters that need to be taken into account, such as competitors' actions, the large number of other by-products from the refining process, the unpredictable actions of suppliers, distribution factors, and so on.

How can these matters be incorporated into the decision?

Chapter 12

12 TOTAL REVENUE AND TOTAL COST

The total revenue (TR) and total cost (TC) functions for a business (for output between 1,000 and 1,300 units per period) are as follows.

$TR = \frac{-x^2}{2} + 1{,}500x$

$TC = 330x + 415{,}000$

(where x is the level of output in units and TR and TC are in pounds £)

Required

(a) Give an expression for total profit

(b) Using differential calculus:

(i) determine the expressions for marginal revenue and marginal profit;

(ii) find the profit-maximising output, and confirm that it is a maximum value.

(c) Draw a graph showing marginal revenue and marginal cost for output between 1,000 and 1,300 units per period, clearly indicating the profit-maximising output.

(d) Following changes to the production process, the business's total cost function becomes $TC = 330x - 1{,}779{,}750$. Given that the total revenue function remains the same, find a revised expression for total profit and hence find the output level(s) at which the business makes neither a profit nor a loss.

Chapter 13

13 BUILDING COMPANY

A building company constructs a standard unit which sells for £30,000. The company's costs can be readily identifiable between fixed and variable costs.

Budgeted data for the coming six months includes the following..

	Sales Units	*Profit £*
January	18	70,000
February	20	100,000
March	30	250,000
April	22	130,000
May	24	160,000
June	16	40,000

You are told that the fixed costs for the six months have been spread evenly over the period under review to arrive at the monthly profit projections.

Required

Prepare a graph for total sales, costs and output for the six months under review that shows the breakeven point in units and revenue, total fixed costs, the variable cost line and the margin of safety for the total budgeted sales.

NOTES

Chapter 14

14 EIGHT ACTIVITIES

The network for a project consisting of eight activities is shown below, together with the time (in days) required to complete each stage.

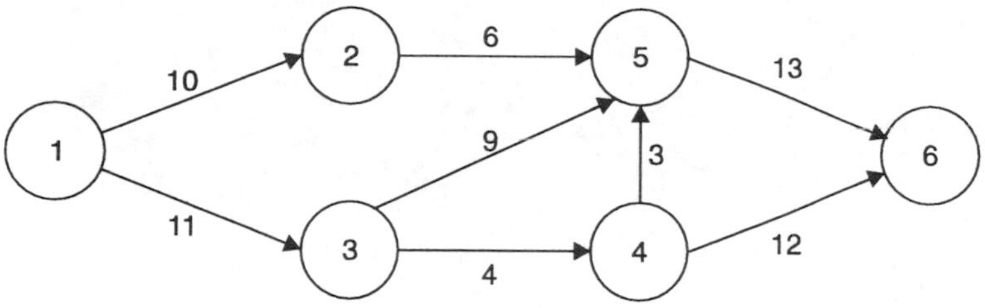

Required

(a) State the four possible paths through the network and the total time required to complete each one.

(b) Deduce the critical path, and state its duration and importance.

(c) Complete the five blank columns in the table below.

(d) Explain briefly the information conveyed by the total float.

Activity	*Time*	*Earliest start*	*Earliest finish*	*Latest start*	*Latest finish*	*Total float*
1-2	10					
1-3	11					
2-5	6					
3-5	9					
3-4	4					
4-5	3					
4-6	12					
5-6	13					

Chapter 15

15 DAISY HOOF LTD

Daisy Hoof Ltd is considering a four-year project to purchase some equipment which would have the following cash flows.

Year	*Cash flow* £
0	(50,000)
1	18,000
2	25,000
3	15,000
4	10,000

The estimated trade-in value of the equipment at the end of year 4, which is £2,000, has not been included in the cash flows above.

The company has a cost of capital of 16%.

NOTES

Required

Calculate the following.

(a) The NPV of the project

(b) The IRR of the project

ANSWERS TO MULTIPLE CHOICE QUESTIONS

1 B x^{-1} equals 1/x by definition.

2 B $\frac{53.99}{45.99} = 1.173951$

The percentage increase is 17.3951% which becomes 17.40% when rounded to two decimal places.

3 B If x = 0, y = 0

If x = 2, y = 2 × 2 = 4

∴ The line goes through (0,0) and (2,4)

∴ It is line B

4 B Let length of box = L cm

Let side of square end = s cm

∴ 2s = L (equation (1))

Volume of box = $(s^2 \times l)cm^3 = 1{,}458\ cm^3$

$\therefore L = \frac{1{,}458}{s^2}$ (equation (2))

Sub (2) into (1) $2s = \frac{1{,}458}{s^2}$

Multiply both sides by s^2 $2s^3 = 1{,}458$

$s^3 = 729$

$s = 9$

5 C 22 kg costs £7.00

∴ 1 kg costs £7.00/22 = £0.3182

$\therefore$ Percentage saving = $\frac{0.39-0.3182}{0.39} = 0.184 = 18.4\%$

6 D Revenue = price × quantity

Revenue will lie between (0.8 × price) × (0.9 × quantity) and (1.2 × price) × (1.1 × quantity) ie between (0.72 × price × quantity) and (1.32 × price × quantity)

∴ Maximum possible error = 32%

7 D To ensure that the error is at a maximum, the numerator needs to be as large as possible and the denominator as small as possible.

Say P = Q = R = 10

P could be measured nine to 11

Q could be measured from eight to 12

R could be measured from seven to 13.

Maximising P and Q and minimising R gives

$\frac{PQ}{R} = \frac{11 \times 12}{7} = 18.86$

Using the actual values of P = Q = R = 10

$\frac{PQ}{R} = \frac{10 \times 10}{10} = 10$

Error $= \frac{18.86 - 10}{10} = \frac{8.86}{10} = 88.6\%$

NOTES

8 B Let the ages of the three people be p, q and r respectively. We then have three simultaneous equations.

$p = q + r - 2$ (1)
$q = 0.5(p + r) - 3$ (2)
$r = 0.5p - 5$ (3)

Substituting 0.5p – 5 (from (3)) for r in equations (1) and (2) gives

$p = q + 0.5p - 5 - 2$ (4)
$q = 0.5\ (p + 0.5p - 5) - 3$ (5)

Simplifying (4) and (5) gives

$0.5p = q - 7$ (6)
$q = 0.75p - 5.5$ (7)

Multiplying (6) by 1.5 gives

$0.75p = 1.5q - 10.5$ (8)

Substituting 1.5q – 10.5 for 0.75p in (7) gives

$q = 1.5q - 10.5 - 5.5$
$q = 1.5q - 16$
$16 = 0.5q$
$32 = q$

9 A By trial and error, the option satisfying the expression is a = –2.

10 C $2X^2 = 2$, $Y^2 = 4$, $2 < 4$, $4 > 0$.

11 D

12 A

13 D Stratified random sampling provides better estimates than simple random or cluster sampling.

(*Tutorial note.* A stratified random sample would unquestionably be the most accurate method but it is not practical when surveying the whole of the UK. It is important to read the question carefully and to see that it is about accuracy and not practicality.)

14 C A describes primary data, B aggregated data and D discrete data.

15 D

16 B 89° is 89/360th of the whole (there being 360° in a circle)

∴ The amount of wages $= 89/360 \times £550{,}000$
$= £135{,}972$

17 A Frequency is indicated by the area covered by the block on a histogram, rather than by the block's height. If the width of the block is one and a half the standard width, we must divide the frequency by one and a half, ie multiply by 0.67 ($1 \div 1.5 = 1/(\frac{3}{2}) = \frac{2}{3} = 0.67$).

18 C If a bar for 2,120 employees (the 19X5 total) was 10.6 cm high, the scale must be

$$\frac{10.6}{2{,}120} = 0.005 \text{ cm per employee}$$

A segment for 1,450 employees (19X6, grade 4) will therefore have a height of $1{,}450 \times 0.005 = 7.25$ cm.

NOTES

19 C If the width of an interval is n times the width of the remaining intervals, then the height of the corresponding histogram rectangle is given by that interval's frequency divided by n. In this case, n is 3⁄4, so the height is 21 ÷ 3⁄4 = $\frac{21 \times 4}{3}$ = 28.

20 B Pie-charts illustrate the way in which one or more totals are broken down into their components.

21 B This is the definition of a histogram.

22 B $100 \times P_1/P_0 = 135$

$P_1 = £55.35$

$$\therefore \frac{100 \times £55.35}{P_0} = 135$$

$$\therefore \frac{100 \times £55.35}{135} = P_0 = £41$$

23 B Payable in 1994 = $£10{,}000 \times \frac{142.0}{135.6} = £10{,}472$

24 A Sales index for a particular quarter multiplied by the inflation index for a particular quarter is approximately equal to the sales index of the following quarter.

25 C The formula for the Laspeyre index is $100 \times \frac{\Sigma Q_0 P_1}{\Sigma Q_0 P_0}$

P_0	Q_0	Q_0P_0	P_1	Q_0P_1
8	3	24	20	60
5	4	20	25	100
		44		160

Laspeyre index = $\frac{160}{44} \times 100 = 364$

26 C Paasche price index number = $100 \times \frac{\Sigma Q_1 P_1}{\Sigma Q_1 P_0}$

	P_0	P_1	Q_1	Q_1P_0	Q_1P_1
A	5	6	2,200	11,000	13,200
B	8	10	2,500	20,000	25,000
				31,000	38,200

Index for 19X5 on 19X1 $= \frac{38{,}200}{31{,}000} \times 100$

$= 123.23$

NOTES

27 C

x	fx		f
£	£		
10.00	400	400 ÷ 10.00 =	40
12.50	500	500 ÷ 12.50 =	40
11.00	550	550 ÷ 11.00 =	50
12.00	600	600 ÷ 12.00 =	50
	2,050		180

$$\therefore \bar{x} = \frac{\Sigma fx}{\Sigma f} = \frac{£2,050}{180} = £11.39$$

28 C In order of magnitude scores are

8 9 11 12 14 15 17 21 24 34

Position of median is $\frac{10+1}{2} = 5^1/_2$ and therefore the median is the average of the 5th and 6th items, that is of 14 and 15. The median is therefore 14.5.

29 B Total sales for first five months = £8,200 × 5 = £41,000

Total sales for last four months = £8,500 × 4 = £34,000

So total sales for remaining 3 months = £(102,000 – 41,000 – 34,000) = £27,000, giving an average of $\frac{£27,000}{3}$ = £9,000

30 A The median is the middle value in order of magnitude.

9 12 23 24 28 34 43 56 78 87

In this case there are two middle values, 28 and 34, and so the median is their average = (28 + 34)/2 = 31.

31 D $80 = \frac{(10\times50)+(10\times70)+(20\times X)}{10+10+20}$

80 × 40 = 500 + 700 + 20X

3,200 – 1,200 = 20X

2,000 = 20X

100 = X

32 C

Total of invoices	=	average × 10
2X + 152	=	200
2X	=	200 – 152 = 48
X	=	£24

33 A To calculate a mean speed we need to know the distance and the time of the journey.

Time = $^{20}/_{30}$ hr + $^{10}/_{60}$ hr = $^5/_6$ hr

∴ Mean speed = 30 miles ÷ $^5/_6$ hr = 36 mph

NOTES

34 B To calculate a mean factory wage we need to determine total wages and total number of employees.

Department	*Mean wage*		*Number of employees*		*Total wage*
	£				£
W	50	×	20	=	1,000
X	100	×	5	=	500
Y	70	×	10	=	700
Z	80	×	5	=	400
			40		2,600

Mean factory wage = £2,600/40 = £65

35 C Arithmetic mean $= \frac{\text{Sum of value of items}}{\text{Number of items}}$

For 10 units, $1 = \frac{\text{Sum of value of items}}{10}$

$10 = \text{Sum of value of items}$

For 20 units, $2 = \frac{\text{Sum of value of items}}{20}$

$40 = \text{Sum of value of items}$

For 30 units, $3 = \frac{\text{Sum of value of items}}{30}$

$90 = \text{Sum of value of items}$

Arithmetic mean of all items $= \frac{\text{Sum of value of all items}}{\text{Number of items}}$

$= \frac{10+40+90}{10+20+30} = \frac{140}{60}$

$=$ £2.33

36 A The coefficients of variation are given by:

W: $\frac{10}{100} \times 100 = 10\%$

X: $\frac{5}{40} \times 100 = 12^1/_2\%$

Y: $\frac{8}{80} \times 100 = 10\%$

Z: $\frac{12}{150} \times 100 = 8\%$

Hence X has the largest coefficient of variation.

37 A

	Large	*Small*	*Total*
Fast payers	20*	10**	30
Slow payers	40	30****	70***
	60	40	100

*60 – 40 ** 30 – 20 *** 100 – 30 **** 70 – 40

P(fast paying small company) = 10/100 = 0.1

NOTES

38 D Probability of A or B occurring = P(A) + P(B), provided A and B cannot both be true, so P(sales remaining the same or falling) = P(same) + P(falling) = 0.21 + 0.23 = 0.44.

39 B Number of female students $= 100 - 30 = 70$

P(not studying for stage 1) $= \frac{100-55}{100} = \frac{45}{100}$

P(female and not studying for stage 1) $= \frac{45-6}{70} = \frac{39}{70}$

$= 0.56$

40 B Expected value = probability × profit

Contract		*Expected value*
		£
X	1/2 × £50,000	25,000
Y	1/3 × £90,000	30,000
Z	1/5 × £100,000	20,000
		75,000

∴ Expected value is closest to £75,000.

41 C Assume all people are exposed to the virus and that there are 1,000 employees.

		Vaccinated		*Non-vaccinated*	*Total*
Get flu	(10% × 500)	50	(30% × 500)	150	200
No flu	(90% × 500)	450	(70% × 500)	350	800
		500		500	1,000

P (vaccinated/catches influenza) = 50/200 = 1/4 = 0.25

42 D The expected sales are given by

J: 10,000 × 0.3 + 20,000 × 0.5 + 30,000 × 0.2 = 19,000

K: 10,000 × 0.3 + 20,000 × 0.4 + 30,000 × 0.3 = 20,000

L: 10,000 × 0.2 + 20,000 × 0.6 + 30,000 × 0.2 = 20,000

43 D P (dry day after tomorrow) = P (dry tomorrow) x P (dry day after tomorrow/dry tomorrow) + P (rain tomorrow) x P (dry day after tomorrow/ rain tomorrow) = (1 – 0.3) × (1 – 0.2) + 0.3 × (1 – 0.6) = 0.7 × 0.8 + 0.3 × 0.4 = 0.56 + 0.12 = 0.68

44 D Expected sales quantity = (1,000 × 0.9) + (2,000 × 0.1) = 1,100

∴ Expected sales revenue = 1,100 × £5 = £5,500

Expected unit cost = (1.30 × 0.55) + (1.50 × 0.45) = £1.39

∴ Expected total variable costs = £1.39 × 1,100 = £1,529

Profit calculation	£
Sales revenue	5,500
Less: variable costs	(1,529)
fixed costs	(3,000)
	971

NOTES

45 A Poisson distribution. Any situation involving random arrivals implies this distribution.

46 B Mean = 10/hour which is equivalent to 1 every 6 mins. The Poisson distribution is

$$P(x) = \frac{m^x e^{-m}}{x!}$$

When x = 0, $P(0) = \frac{1^0 e^{-1}}{0!} = e^{-1} = 0.3679$

47 A $P(\text{score} > 59) = P(z > \frac{59-55}{\sqrt{14.44}}) = P(z > 1.05) = 0.5 - 0.3531 = 0.1469$

= 0.15 approx

48 C 25% of normal frequencies will occur between the mean and the upper quartile. From normal distribution tables, 25% of frequencies lie between the mean and a point 0.67 standard deviations above the mean.

The standard deviation is the square root of the variance and is $\sqrt{25} = 5$ in this case.

The upper quartile is therefore $0.67 \times 5 = 3.35$ above the mean

∴ The upper quartile = 3.35 + 75 = 78.35

49 D 50% of the distribution lies below the mean. We therefore need to find the point x above the mean such that 30% of the distribution falls between the mean and x.

From tables we see that the point x has to be 0.84 standard deviations above the mean.

If $z = 0.84 = \frac{x-\mu}{\sigma}$, then $0.84 = \frac{x-150}{20}$

∴ $20 \times 0.84 = x - 150$

$16.8 + 150 = x$

$166.8 = x$

∴ 80% of the distribution lies below 167 (approximately)

50 D Total area under normal curve = 1

Therefore each of four areas = 0.25

The table shows the area between 0 and the specified value of z so we must find the value 0.25 in the table and the z value that corresponds most closely to it.

z = 0.67

NOTES

51 C Use the normal approximation to the Binomial distribution.

n = 100, p = 0.4 (probability of a reject)

Mean = np = 100 × 0.4 = 40

Standard deviation = $\sqrt{npq} = \sqrt{100 \times 0.4 \times 0.6} = 4.9$

P (number of rejects > 45) (discrete scale)

= P (number of rejects > 45.5) (continuous scale)

$= P(z > \frac{45.5 - 40}{4.9})$

= P(z > 1.12) = 0.5 – 0.3686

= 0.1314

52 D

53 A n = 3, p = $^1/_2$ Binomial distribution conditions apply.

Let x = number of tails

$P(x) = {}^nC_x p^x (1 - p)^{n-x}$

$P(x = 1) = {}^3C_1 (^1/_2)^1 (^1/_2)^2 = \frac{3!}{1!2!} (^1/_2)(^1/_4) = {}^3/_8$

54 B The standard deviation is equal to the square root of the mean = 2.

55 D At the 95% level of confidence, the population mean = $\bar{x}$ ± 1.96se (where $\bar{x}$ is the sample mean)

∴ $\bar{x}$ – 1.96se = 496 and $\bar{x}$ + 1.96se = 504

But $\bar{x}$ = £500

∴ 500 – 1.96 se = 496

500 – 496 = 1.96se

∴ 4/1.96 = se = 2.0408

But se = s/√n

∴ 2.0408 = 30.61/√n

∴ n = $(30.61/2.0408)^2$ = 225

56 A n = 100, $\bar{x}$ = 120.87, s = √81 = 9

∴ 95% upper confidence limit = 120.87 + 1.96 (9/√100)

= 120.87 + 1.764 = 122.634

57 B The 95% confidence interval is given by mean ± 1.96 × standard error

£4.90 = 1.96 × standard error

∴ Standard error = £4.90/1.96 = £2.50

Standard error = $s/\sqrt{n}$

∴ £2.50 × 6 = s = £15

NOTES

58 D The probability of picking a faulty unit = 10/100 = 0.1.

We are to consider 'proportions' and so we use the sampling distribution of sample proportions.

Standard error proportion $= \sqrt{\frac{pq}{n}} = \sqrt{\frac{0.1 \times 0.9}{100}}$

$= \sqrt{0.0009}$

$= 0.03$

95% confidence limits $= p \pm 1.96 \times$ standard error proportion

$= 0.1 \pm 1.96 \times 0.03$

$= 0.1 \pm 0.0588$

$\approx 10\% \pm 6\%$

59 D 'The standard error of the sample percentage is 5%' means that the sampling distribution has a standard deviation of 5%.

60 C The confidence interval is given by $1.645 \times 10/\sqrt{n}$

But the confidence interval =2

$\therefore 2 \quad = 1.645 \times 10/\sqrt{n}$

$\therefore \sqrt{n} \quad = 1.645 \times 5$

$\therefore n \quad = 67.65 \approx 68$

61 B The proportion supporting X = 1,000/2,500 = 2/5 = P

The proportion supporting Y = 1 – p = 3/5

The standard error $= \sqrt{\frac{p(1-p)}{n}} = \sqrt{\frac{2/5 \times 3/5}{2,500}} = 0.0098$

= 0.98%

= 1% (to 1 sig fig)

62 D Expected frequency $= \frac{\text{Row total} \times \text{Column total}}{\text{Overall total}}$

$= \frac{110 \times 100}{200}$

$= 55$

63 C There are (rows – 1) (columns – 1) degrees of freedom. In this case, number of degrees of freedom is (2 – 1)(3 – 1) = 1 × 2 = 2

Level of significance = 5%

Hence $\chi^2 = 5.99$

64 C The pooled estimate of variance is given by $\hat{\sigma}^2$ where

$$\hat{\sigma}^2 = \frac{(n_{A-1})\hat{\sigma}_A^{\ 2} + (n_{B-1})\hat{\sigma}_B^{\ 2}}{n_A + n_B - 2}$$

$$= \frac{(16-1)25 + (25-1)64}{16+25-2}$$

$$= \frac{375 + 1,536}{39} = \frac{1,911}{39}$$

$$= 49$$

NOTES

65 B $r = \dfrac{n\Sigma xy - \Sigma x\Sigma y}{\sqrt{(n\Sigma x^2 - (\Sigma x)^2)(n\Sigma y^2 - (\Sigma y)^2)}}$

$= \dfrac{(11 \times 13{,}467) - (440 \times 330)}{\sqrt{((11 \times 17{,}986) - (440)^2)((11 \times 10{,}366) - (330^2))}}$

$= \dfrac{2{,}937}{\sqrt{(4{,}246 \times 5{,}126)}} = 0.63$

66 D $R = 1 - \dfrac{6\Sigma d^2}{n(n^2 - 1)}$

$R = 1 - \dfrac{6 \times 50}{10 \times 99} = 0.70$

67 A $Y = 20 - 0.25X$

$X = 12$

$\therefore Y = 20 - 0.25(12) = 17\%$

68 D

69 C In the table below, x is in 100's of units and y is in £'00's.

x	*y*	*x*²	*xy*
1	8	1	8
2	15	4	30
3	25	9	75
4	35	16	140
5	44	25	220
15	127	55	473

ie $\Sigma x = 15$, $\Sigma y = 127$, $\Sigma x^2 = 55$, $\Sigma xy = 473$, $n = 5$

The sample equation is y = a + bx, where b is the gradient (required in question)

$b = \dfrac{n\Sigma xy - \Sigma x\Sigma y}{n\Sigma x^2 - (\Sigma x)^2} = \dfrac{5 \times 473 - 15 \times 127}{5 \times 55 - (15)^2}$

$= \dfrac{2{,}365 - 1{,}905}{275 - 225} = \dfrac{460}{50} = 9.2$

70 C

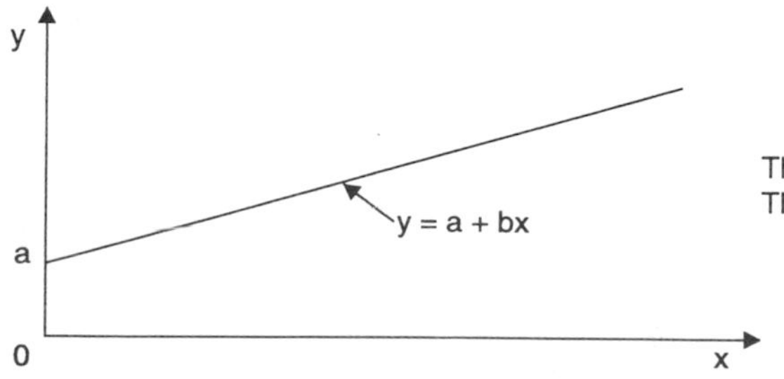

The gradient is b.
The intercept on the y axis is a.

71 D

NOTES

72 B $y = 7.112 + 3.949x$

If $x = 19$, trend in sales for month $19 = 7.112 + (3.949 \times 19) = 82.143$

Seasonally-adjusted trend value $= 82.143 \times 1.12 = 92$

73 A If $x = 16$, $y = 345.12 - 1.35 \times 16 = 323.52$

Forecast = trend + seasonal component $= 323.52 - 23.62 = 299.9 = 300$ (to nearest unit)

74 B A variation of, for example, +50% means that forecast sales are 50% above the trend value (ie trend × 150%) whereas a variation of –50% means that forecast sales are 50% below the trend value (ie trend × 50%).

∴ Trend × seasonal variation = actual

∴ Trend × 150% = 240 (for Q_2)

∴ Trend = 240 ÷ 1.5 = 160

Variation in $Q_3 = -50\%$

∴ Forecast = 160 × 50% = 80

75 C At 19X4 quarter 3, t = 15. Hence $y = 25 + 7 \times 15 = 130$

The seasonal component is –20

Forecast = y + seasonal = 130 + (–20) = 110.

76 C As a 12-month moving average is used, each observation occurs at the mid point (month 6.5 or midway between June and July). However this is a centred moving average and the first point occurs halfway between the moving average at point 6.5 and that at point 7.5. In other words at point 7. This corresponds to the seventh month, which is July.

77 C The third point is $\frac{720 + 780 + 900}{3} = \frac{2,400}{3} = 800$

78 A 800 hours

79 A $x + 2y \leq 800$

80 B $C = 3x + 4y$

81 C The two constraints are:

$x + 2y \leq 800$

$2x + y \leq 850$

The two equations formed from them are:

$x + 2y = 800$ (1)

$2x + y = 850$ (2)

Solving: (1) × 2 – (2)

$3y = 750$

or $\underline{y = 250}$

From (1) $x + 2(250) = 800$

$\underline{x = 300}$

ie (300, 250)

NOTES

82 A

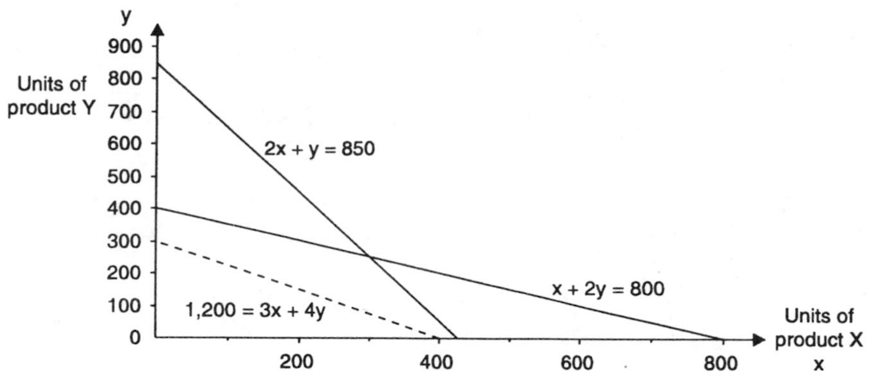

The optimal solution is seen to occur at the point of intersection of the two constraints (300,250) found in question 81 earlier.

The maximum weekly contribution is:

£(300 × 3 + 250 × 4)

= £(900 + 1,000)

= £1,900

83 D Product mix remains unchanged

The objective function line would change from connecting the two points (400,0) and (0,300) to a line connecting the two points (300, 0), (0,300). Moving the new objective function line away from the original, it is clearly seen that the last point that the line will touch is (300, 250), ie the product mix remains unchanged.

84 D Product mix remains unchanged

The new constraint should be added to the graph, drawn in question 82 (above). It can be seen that this line which cuts the axes at (600,0) and (0,600) is outside the feasible region and does not, therefore, affect the product mix.

85 A

86 A $\frac{dd}{dp} = 12 - 6p$. Demand is at a maximum when $\frac{dd}{dp} = 0$ and $\frac{d^2d}{dp^2} < 0$

$$12 - 6p = 0$$
$$-6p = -12$$
$$p = 2$$
$$\frac{d^2d}{dp^2} = -6$$

As this is less than 0, p = 2 gives a maximum.

87 A $\frac{dy}{dx} = 20x^4 - 40x^3 + 40x + 4x^{-3}$

$$\frac{d^2y}{dx^2} = 80x^3 - 120x^2 + 40 - 12x^{-4}$$

At x = 1, $\frac{d^2y}{dx^2} = 80 - 120 + 40 - 12 = -12$

88 A $\frac{dy}{dx} = 3x^2 - 20x^3 + 2$

At $x = 1$, $\frac{dy}{dx} = 3x(1^2) - 20x(1^3) + 2 = 3 - 20 + 2 = -15$

89 D $\frac{dy}{dx} = 4x - 3 = 0$ when $x = ¾ = 0.75$

90 B $\frac{dy}{dx} = 8x + 24x^7 + 4x^{-3} + 7$

$\frac{d^2y}{dx^2} = 8 + 168x^6 - 12x^{-4}$

91 A Contribution per unit = £(50 – (10 + 2.5r)) = £40 – 2.5r where r is the rate per hour paid to the workforce.

To break even, total contribution must equal fixed costs at the required sales level.

$$\begin{aligned} \therefore \quad £5{,}000 &= 1{,}000 \times £(40 - 2.5r) \\ 5{,}000 &= 40{,}000 - 2{,}500r \\ 2{,}500r &= 35{,}000 \\ r &= 14 \end{aligned}$$

∴ Milly Ltd should pay the workforce a maximum of £14 per hour.

92 C Breakeven point = $\frac{\text{Fixed costs}}{\text{Contribution per unit}} = \frac{500}{(33-8)} = \frac{500}{25} = 20$ per week

= 1,040 per year

93 C

94 C Expected duration $= \frac{\text{Optimistic duration} + 4\,(\text{likely duration}) + (\text{pessimistic duration})}{6}$

$= \frac{6 + 4 \times 9 + 18}{6}$

$= \frac{60}{6}$

$= 10$

NOTES

95 D The network is as follows.

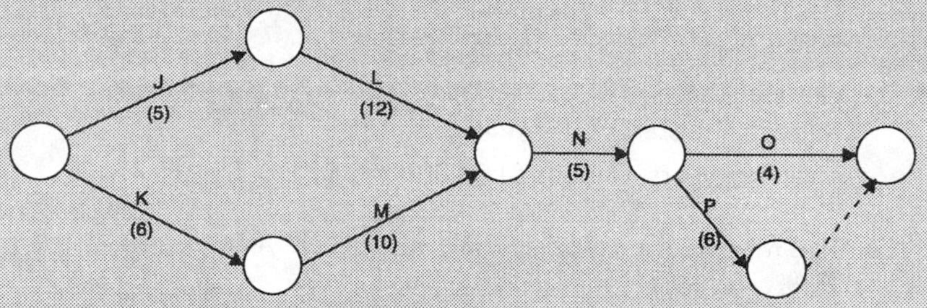

The paths are:

	Duration (days)
JLNO	26
JLNP	28
KMNO	25
KMNP	27

The path with the longest duration, the critical path, is JLNP.

96 B The new network is as follows:

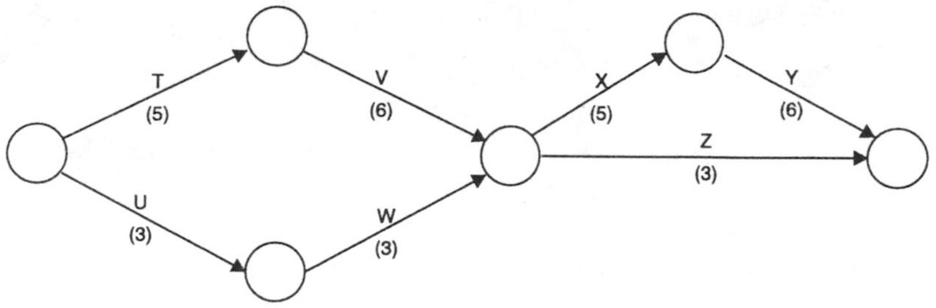

Activities U and W can both be performed at the same time as activity V, thus avoiding any overlap with activity T which uses 8 staff as against V's 6. The peak requirement in the first half of the network is then 6 + 7 =13 staff.

Activity Z should be performed concurrently with activity X rather than with activity Y, giving a peak requirement of 6 + 8 = 14 staff. The peak requirement over the whole project is therefore 14 staff.

97 D £1,200 × (1 + cumulative present value factor at 14%) = £5,319.60, where 1 in the brackets takes account of the payment now, at time 0.

∴ 1 + cumulative PV factor at 14% = £5,319.60 ÷ £1,200 = 4.43

∴ Cumulative PV factor at 14% = 4.433 – 1 = 3.43

From looking in cumulative PV tables in the 14% column we see that this PV factor corresponds to that for 5 years from now.

∴ The final payment is 5 years from now but the lease runs out 12 months after the final payment.

98 B Current rate is 6% pa payable monthly

∴ Effective rate is 6/12% = ½% compound every month

∴ In the *six* months from January to June, interest earned =

$(£1,000 \times [1.005]^6) - £1,000 = £30.38$

NOTES

99 B The interest is 15 parts of the total of £2,070, which is 115 parts.

The interest = $2{,}070 \times \frac{15}{115} = £270$

100 C Value at the end of each year is (100 – 2.5)% = 97.5% = 0.975 times the value at the start of the year.

After five years, value is £160,000 × 0.975^5 = £140,975.

101 C The ratio of the value at the end of each year to that at the beginning is 95% or 0.95.

The value at end of year 4 is therefore £10,000 × 0.95^4 = £8,145 to the nearest pound.

102 A We use the cumulative present value tables for r = 12%, but n = 9 because the first payment has to be paid immediately (not in one year's time) and hence the final payment is in nine year's time. We then add the present value of the immediate payment.

PV = (5.33 × £8,000) + £8,000 = £50,640

103 C We need to calculate the effective rate of interest.

8% per annum (nominal) is 2% per quarter. The effective annual rate of interest is $[1.02^4 - 1] = 0.08243 = 8.243\%$.

Now we can use $S_n = P(1 + r)^n$

$S_n = 12{,}000\ (1.08243)^3$

$S_n = £15{,}218.81$

∴ The principal will have grown to approximately £15,219.

104 C $S_n = P(1 + r)^n$

$S_n = £2{,}500\ (1 + 0.08)^3 = £2{,}500\ (1.08)^3 = £3{,}149.28$

S_n to nearest £ = £3,149

105 D

		£
PV of £1,200 is one year	= £1,200 × 0.93 =	1,116
PV of £1,400 in two years	= £1,400 × 0.86 =	1,204
PV of £1,600 in three years	= £1,600 × 0.79 =	1,264
PV of £1,800 in four years	= £1,800 × 0.74 =	1,332

106 C There are ten flows but one is at time 0. We therefore need to look up in tables the present value of £1 per annum received at the end of nine years at an interest rate of 8%.

NPV = £[(1,000 × 1) + (1,000 × 6.25)]

= £7,250

107 D Effective quarterly rate = 1% (4% ÷ 4)

Effective annual rate = $[(1.01)^4 - 1]$

= 0.0406 = 4.06% pa

ANSWERS TO EXAM STYLE QUESTIONS

NOTES

1 PRODUCING BATCHES

> *Tutorial note.* This question tests your understanding of non–linear cost behaviour and involves the manipulation of equations. Because there are three unknowns in the general form of a quadratic equation (a, b, c), you will need to use three simultaneous equations. Don't forget to label the axes and provide a title to the graph in (a)(ii).
>
> Profit is the difference between revenue and costs and hence, in part (b)(iii), profit = revenue – cost.

(a) (i) The general form of a quadratic equation is $ax^2 + bx + c = 0$

We are given the following information.

Let x = size of batch.

When	x = 10,	cost = £700	(1)
	x = 20,	cost = £400	(2)
	x = 40,	cost = £1,600	(3)

We can substitute these values into $ax^2 + bx + c$ = cost to determine the values of a, b and c.

Using (1)	100a + 10b + c	=	700	(i)
Using (2)	400a + 20b + c	=	400	(ii)
Using (3)	1,600a + 40b + c	=	1,600	(iii)
	400a + 40b + 4c	=	2,800	(iv)(4 × (i))
	20b + 3c	=	2,400	(v)((iv) – (ii))
	1,600 a + 160b + 16c	=	11,200	(vi)(4 × (iv))
	120b + 15c	=	9,600	(vii)((vi) – (iii))
	120b + 18c	=	14,400	(viii)(6 × (v))
	3c	=	4,800	(viii) – (vii)
	c	=	1,600	
	120b	=	14,400 – 28,800	Sub into (viii)
	b	=	–120	
	100a – 1,200 + 1,600	=	700	Sub into (i)
	100a	=	300	
	a	=	3	

The relationship is cost = $3x^2 - 120x + 1,600$

(ii) Substitute different values for x (batch size) into the equation above to determine the cost for different batch sizes.

Batch size x	*Cost* £
0	1,600
10	700
15	475
20	400
25	475
30	700
40	1,600
50	3,100

NOTES

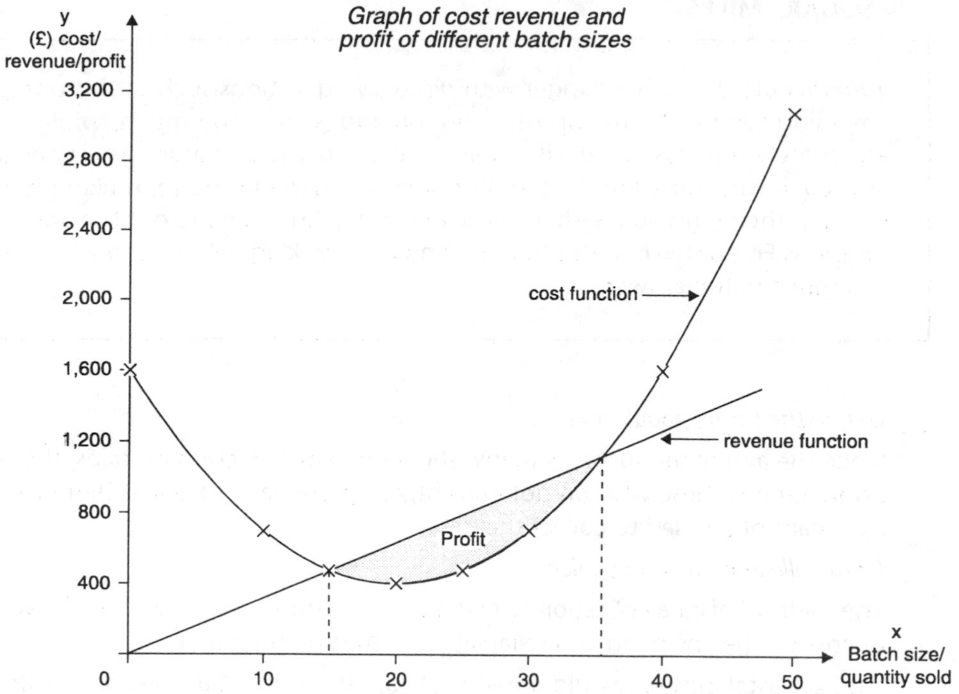

(iii) From the graph, the batch size which minimises total cost is 20 (the x coordinate of the lowest point on the cost function curve).

(b) (i) Let x = quantity sold and y = revenue

If x = 0, y = 0

If x = 10, y = 10 × 30 = £300

If x = 50, y = 50 × 30 = £1,500

We can plot the revenue function on the graph using these values.

(ii) The product makes a profit when total revenue is greater than total cost. Revenue is greater than cost in the shaded region on the graph. The product therefore makes a profit if the batch size is between approximately 15 and 35.

(iii) Profit = revenue – cost

Revenue function is y = 30x because for every increase in x (quantity sold), revenue increases by £30.

$\therefore$ Profit $= 30x - (3x^2 - 120x + 1{,}600)$

$= 30x - 3x^2 + 120x - 1{,}600$

$= -3x^2 + 150x - 1{,}600$

NOTES

2 100 SQUARE MILES

Tutorial note. There is a danger with discursive questions such as this one of spending too much time on the question and writing too much, while not adequately addressing specific points raised in the question. The way to approach such questions is to draft out your answer in rough, making brief notes of the points you wish to make before starting to write out the answer properly. Five or ten minutes thought and note making beforehand will result in a much better answer.

(a) *Define the target population*

Since the aim of the survey is to investigate means of increasing sales, the target population is those who do not currently buy the paper. Hence the newspaper itself cannot be used to collect the data.

Data collection method choices

The method of data collection selected by the company will have to take account of cost on the one hand and reliability of results on the other.

(i) A postal survey would be the cheapest option but response rates are notoriously low, even where incentives such as entry into a prize draw are given, and it is impossible to ascertain the opinions of non-respondents. The results of such surveys are therefore very unreliable.

(ii) All other methods involve the employment of staff to conduct interviews and these staff will need some training to ensure that they do not introduce interviewer bias. They are consequently more expensive.

(1) A telephone survey would avoid the costs of travel and would enable more interviews to be completed per day than face to face interviews. A slight problem is that some people do not have telephones but this is unlikely to be the case with the new readership in which the newspaper is interested. A more important problem is refusal to be interviewed, which is much greater in telephone surveys than face to face. All surveys are intrusive and it is easier to say 'no' to someone over the telephone. Additionally respondents may well be reluctant to disclose personal information such as age or income when no identification can be shown by the interviewer.

(2) From the standpoint of reliability of results, face to face interviews are the best data collection method. In this instance the area to be covered is small, so neither travel time nor cost need be a big problem. The company should be advised to use this method even if, for reasons of costs, it necessitates a somewhat smaller sample than a telephone survey.

(b) The electoral register will provide an acceptable sampling frame and the sampling scheme should begin by stratifying the population according to area. Assuming that potential new readers have the same characteristics as existing readers, 10% of respondents should be selected randomly from rural areas, 30% from suburban and 60% from town. At the same time respondents can be stratified by gender since the electoral register shows forenames and half of those selected in each case should be female and half male.

It is not possible to stratify either by age or by income using the electoral register. This need not be a problem since non-readers may not be similar to readers in that respect. If the company strongly wishes to mirror its existing readership in these respects, the questionnaire should contain quota control questions which would enable the correct proportions of people in the various age and income groups to be interviewed.

If the company does not wish to survey any existing readers, such interviews could be aborted but they would actually be well advised to include existing readers. The proposed changes might perhaps alienate existing readers and the company would benefit from this information.

The electoral register would not give access to people below the age of 18 but this seems to be a minimal problem since the existing readership contains only a small proportion in this group and the proposed changes do not seem to be aimed at a young readership.

3 TELEVISION ADVERTISING

(a) Cumulative monthly sales are the total of the sales so far, including the sales in the month in question.

The first figure in the moving annual total is calculated by taking the total sales for 19X1, adding those for January 19X2 and subtracting those for January 19X1. A similar approach is used for the rest of the year (adding on the new 19X2 month and deducting the corresponding 19X1 month).

	(i) *Cumulative monthly sales*	*(ii)* *Moving annual total*
Jan	54	490
Feb	109	515
Mar	164	540
April	219	561
May	269	574
June	315	581
July	358	584
Aug	399	585
Sept	439	585
Oct	479	580
Nov	521	573
Dec	565	565

(b) The Z chart shows monthly sales during 19X2, cumulative monthly sales and the moving annual total.

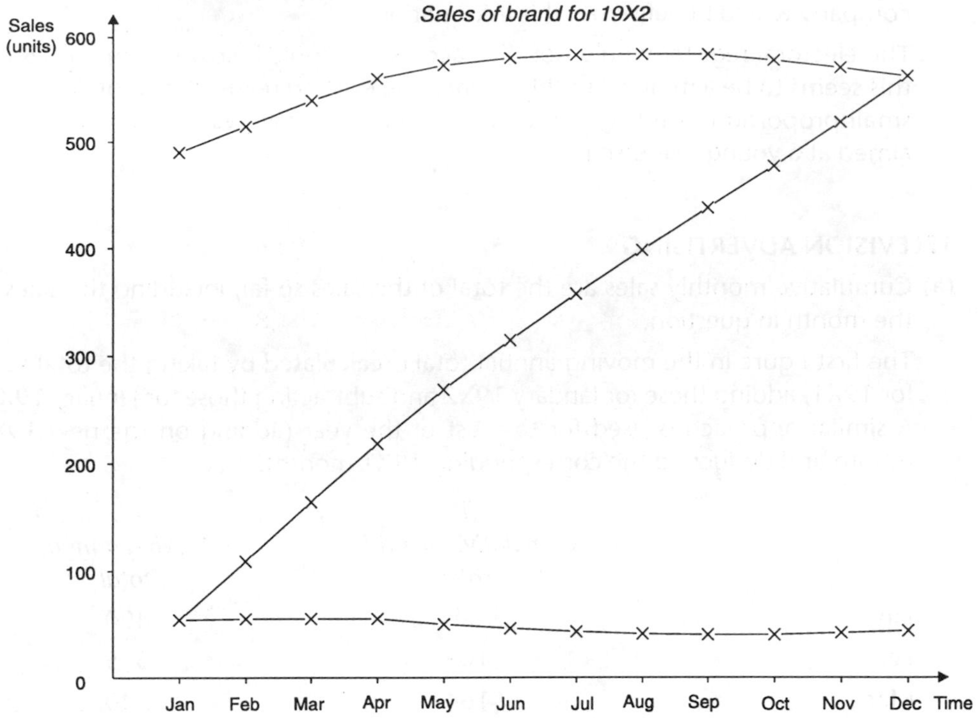

(c) The monthly sales are fairly constant, reaching a peak of 55 units in April and a trough of 40 units in September and October.

The peak in April may be due to the advertising campaign in March. Sales are growing towards the end of the year, which could be a result of the advertising campaign in September. The trough between April and the end of the year may well be due to the competition.

The cumulative monthly sales grow fairly steadily during the year.

The moving annual total (a form of trend) shows that, although sales were increasing until August, there was a slight decline towards the end of the year.

4 PRODUCTION INDUSTRIES INDEX

> *Tutorial note.* The main requirement of this question is to use the Retail Prices Index (RPI) to find real earnings. We have given the general formula for this at the beginning. In such a question you cannot be expected to show all your workings but should include examples of your workings so that the examiner can see your method.

(a) Deflated value at constant 1988 prices

$$= \text{value given} \times \frac{\text{RPI for 1988}}{\text{RPI for the time being considered}}$$

For example, February 1989, deflated value $= 104.9 \times \dfrac{107}{111.5} = 100.7$

NOTES

Production industries index at constant 1988 prices (to one decimal place)

1989	
Feb	100.7
May	100.6
Aug	100.9
Nov	101.9
1990	
Feb	101.7
May	100.2
Aug	100.0
Nov	101.8
1991	
Feb	102.3
May	103.6
Aug	103.9
Nov	104.0

Average earnings in production industries have risen by 31.8% from 1988 to the end of 1991 but when adjusted for inflation the real increase is seen to be only 4%. The increase did not occur gradually over the whole period. By August 1990 earnings were identical to their 1988 value in real terms and the real 4% increase occurred between then and November 1991.

(b) We need to do two sets of calculations: update the £5,000 using the Average Earnings Index for service industries with May 1989 as the base period and convert the £5,000 into real terms using the RPI.

Time	*Value of pension (pa)*	*Chain index* £	*Value in real terms*	*Chain index* £
May 1989	5,000.00	100	5,000.00	100
Nov 1989	$5{,}000 \times \frac{112.7}{107.2} = 5{,}256.53$	105	5,152.17*	103**
Nov 1990	$5{,}000 \times \frac{123.0}{107.2} = 5{,}736.94$	109	5,652.17	110
Nov 1991	$5{,}000 \times \frac{129.7}{107.2} = 6{,}049.44$	105	5,895.65	104

* Example of workings: $5{,}000 \times \frac{118.5}{115} = 5{,}152.17$

** $\left(1 + \left[\frac{5{,}152.17 - 5{,}000}{5{,}000}\right]\right) \times 100 = 103$

The value of the pension has increased in real terms: in the middle year its value was more or less in line with the RPI but in the other periods its value increased above the rate of the RPI.

NOTES

5 AGE STRUCTURE

(a) Our calculations must relate to the current year.

Our values for x relate to the midpoints of the age groups. The age groups cover five years and hence the midpoints are two and a half years from the lower limit.

Age group (years)	*Midpoint x*	*Frequency f*	*fx*	*x^2*	*fx^2*
25 < 30	27.5	5	137.5	756.25	3,781.25
30 < 35	32.5	10	325.0	1,056.25	10,562.50
35 < 40	37.5	13	487.5	1,406.25	18,281.25
40 < 45	42.5	28	1,190.0	1,806.25	50,575.00
45 < 50	47.5	21	997.5	2,256.25	47,381.25
50 < 55	52.5	12	630.0	2,756.25	33,075.00
55 < 60	57.5	8	460.0	3,306.25	26,450.00
60 < 65	62.5	3	187.5	3,906.25	11,718.75
		100	4,415.0		201,825.00

$$\text{Mean} = \frac{\Sigma fx}{\Sigma f} = \frac{4,415}{100} = 44.15 \text{ years}$$

$$\text{Standard deviation} = \sqrt{\frac{\Sigma fx^2}{\Sigma f} - \bar{x}^2}$$

$$= \sqrt{\frac{201,825}{100} - 44.15^2} = 8.31 \text{ years}$$

(b)

	Now	*Five years ago*	*Absolute change*	*% change*
Mean (years)	44.15	49.05	–4.90	–10%
Standard deviation (years)	8.31	8.45	–0.14	–2%

The mean age has dropped by 10%, principally because most of the workforce have shifted from being in the 50+ age groups to being in the 25 to 50 age groups. This shift downwards in the age of the workforce has had very little effect on the standard deviation, however.

(c) A multiple or compound bar chart will best illustrate changes in the age structure of the workforce over the five–year period.

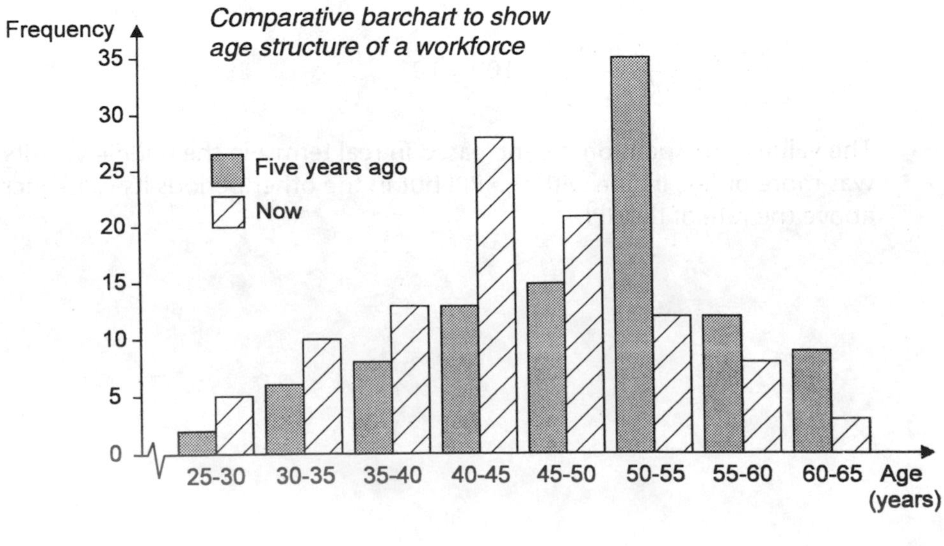

NOTES

6 PHARMACEUTICAL COMPANY

> *Tutorial note.* Many students have difficulties with conditional probabilities. When the question says 'given that he or she has received the treatment' in part (b), you should restrict your attention to the 750 people for whom this is true. Of the 750, 600 people showed some improvement and this enables us to calculate the probability.

Begin this question by reproducing the table but add row and column totals. This will make the calculations far more straightforward.

	Treatment	*Placebo*	*Total*
Some improvement	600	125	725
No improvement	150	125	275
	750	250	1,000

(a) Probability of some improvement = $\frac{725}{1{,}000}$ = 0.725.

(b) Probability of some improvement given treatment received = $\frac{600}{750}$ = 0.8.

(c) Probability that treatment received given that no improvement observed = $\frac{150}{275}$ = 0.545

(d) Probability that placebo received given that some improvement observed = $\frac{125}{725}$ = 0.172

(e) The table suggests that the treatment was more effective than the placebo, with 80% of those treated showing an improvement compared to only 50% of those obtaining the placebo.

Given the large numbers of people in the survey it seems unlikely that these differences result from the randomness of the sampling process.

7 NORMAL DISTRIBUTION

(a) Let X = invoice value

$P(40 \leq X \leq 50)$

$= P\left(\frac{40-48}{5} \leq z \leq \frac{50-48}{5}\right)$

$= P(-1.6 \leq z \leq 0.4)$

$= P(z \leq 0.4) - P(z \leq -1.6)$

$= [0.5 + 0.1554] - [0.5 - 0.4452] = 0.6554 - 0.0548 = 0.6006$

(b) $P(X > 60) = P(z > \frac{60-48}{5})$

$= P(z > 2.4)$

$= 0.5 - P(0 \leq z \leq 2.4)$

$= 0.5 - 0.4918$

$= 0.0082$

NOTES

(c) Let X_1 represent the highest value of the lowest 10% of invoices.

We can now say:

$P(X < X_1) = 0.1$ (ie 10%)

or

$$P(z < \frac{X_1 - 48}{5}) = 0.1$$

Since X_1 represents the highest point of the lowest 10%, X_1 must be less in value than 48.

This implies $X_1 - 48$ is negative. The above equation can be rearranged:

$$P(z < -\left[\frac{48 - X_1}{5}\right]) = 0.1$$

Therefore $\quad P(z > \frac{48 - X_1}{5}) = 0.1$

or $\quad 0.5 - P(0 \leq z \leq \frac{48 - X_1}{5}) = 0.1$

or $\quad P(0 \leq z \leq \frac{48 - X_1}{5}) = 0.4$

We now obtain from tables:

$P(0 \leq z \leq 1.28) = 0.4$

and so we can equate

$\frac{48 - X_1}{5}$ with 1.28

Hence

$$\frac{48 - X_1}{5} = 1.28$$

$$\begin{aligned} 48 - X_1 &= 6.40 \\ X_1 &= 48 - 6.40 \\ &= 41.60 \end{aligned}$$

ie the highest value of the invoices in the lowest 10% is £41.60.

(d) $P(45 \leq X \leq 55)$

$$\begin{aligned} &= P\left(\frac{45 - 48}{5} \leq z \leq \frac{55 - 48}{5}\right) \\ &= P(-0.6 \leq z \leq 1.4) \\ &= P(0 \leq z \leq 1.4) + P(0 \leq z \leq 0.6) \\ &= 0.4192 + 0.2257 \\ &= 0.6449 \end{aligned}$$

The expected number is $1,000 \times 0.6449$

= 644.9

= 644 (rounding down)

8 NORMAL DISTRIBUTION AND SAMPLING

(a)

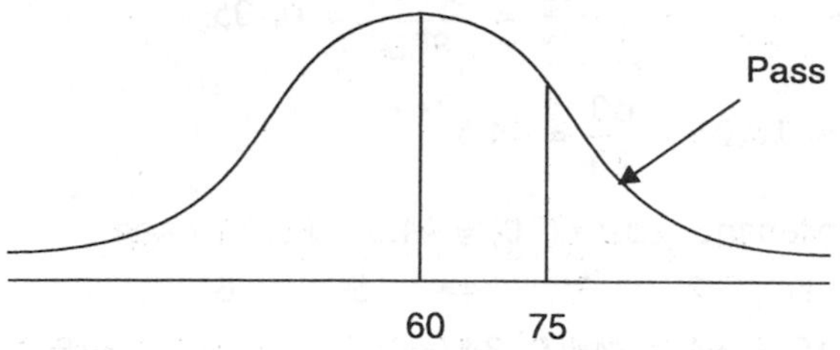

75 points represents $\frac{15}{12}$ = 1.25 standard deviations above the mean. From normal distribution tables, the probability of a value between the mean and 1.25 standard deviations above the mean is 0.3944, so the probability of exceeding 1.25 standard deviations is 0.5 – 0.3944 = 0.1056. The percentage of candidates expected to pass the test is therefore 10.56%.

(b) n = 100, $\bar{x}$ = 1.75m and s = 10cm = 0.1m

∴ Standard error (se) = $0.1/\sqrt{100}$ = 0.01

95% confidence limits = $\bar{x} \pm 1.96$se

= $1.75 \pm (1.96 \times 0.01)$

= 1.75 ± 0.0196

= 1.7304m to 1.7696m

9 FLEET OF VEHICLES

Tutorial note. The only problem you may have had with this question was failing to spot that the units for maintenance were £10s, not £s.

(a) $b = \frac{n\sum xy - \sum x \sum y}{n\sum x^2 - (\sum x)^2}$, $a = \frac{\sum y}{n} - \frac{b\sum x}{n}$

x	*y*	*xy*	x^2
2	60	120	4
8	132	1,056	64
6	100	600	36
8	120	960	64
10	150	1,500	100
4	84	336	16
4	90	360	16
2	68	136	4
6	104	624	36
10	140	1,400	100
60	1,048	7,092	440

NOTES

$$b = \frac{10 \times 7{,}092 - 60 \times 1{,}048}{10 \times 440 - 60^2} = \frac{8{,}040}{800} = 10.05$$

$$a = \frac{1{,}048}{10} - 10.05 \times \frac{60}{10} = 44.5$$

Hence maintenance cost £(10) = 44.5 + 10.05 × age

(b)

Age	1	2	3	4	5	6	7	8	9	10
Cost (£)	545.5	646	746.5	847	947.5	1,048	1,148.5	1,249	1,349.5	1,450

The cost is given by substituting the age into the above equation and multiplying the result by 10.

(c) Estimated cost for 12-year-old vehicle is 10 × (44.5 + 10.05 × 12) = £1,651

The validity of making such an estimate depends on whether or not the cost behaviour is linear. It is unlikely that maintenance cost varies in direct proportion to the age of a vehicle since a vehicle tends to cost increasingly more to maintain the older it gets. An exponential growth model may therefore be more appropriate.

Twelve years is outside the range of the data, albeit not far outside, which reduces the reliability of the estimate. Other factors such as mileage, type of journey and driver and so on may also affect the maintenance cost. The estimate is therefore nothing more than a rough approximation.

10 YELESOL ICE CREAM

(a)

Year	*Quarter*	*Sales (thousands of units)*	*Moving annual total (thousands of units)*	*Moving average of annual total (thousands of units)*	*Centred moving average (trend) (thousands of units)*	*Seasonal variation (thousands of units)*
19X1	Q4	14				
19X2	Q1	16				
			100	25		
	Q2	30			25.5	4.5
			104	26		
	Q3	40			26.0	14.0
			104	26		
	Q4	18			26.5	–8.5
			108	27		
19X3	Q1	16			27.5	–11.5
			112	28		
	Q2	34			27.5	6.5
			108	27		
	Q3	44			27.0	17.0
			108	27		
	Q4	14			27.5	–13.5
			112	28		
19X4	Q1	16			29.0	–13.0
			120	30		
	Q2	38				
	Q3	52				

NOTES

(b)

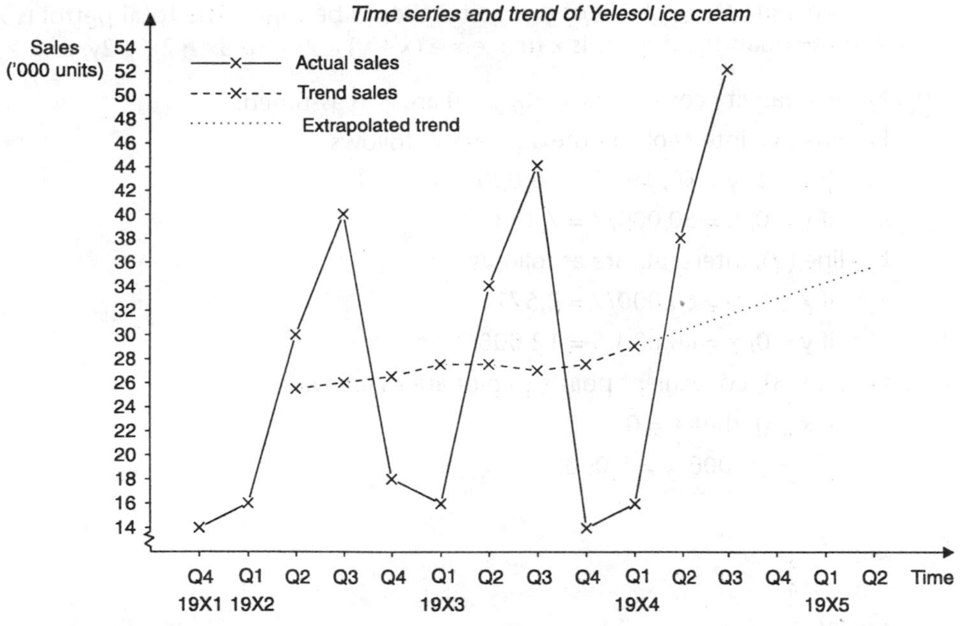

(c)

	Q_1	Q_2	Q_3	Q_4
19X2		4.50	14.00	-8.50
19X3	-11.50	6.50	17.00	-13.50
19X4	-13.00			
Total	-24.50	11.00	31.00	-22.00
Average	-12.25	5.50	15.50	-11.00

(d) The extrapolated trend line would seem to indicate the following forecast trend values.

19X4	Q_4	33.0
19X5	Q_1	34.5

Adjusting by the seasonal variations gives the following forecast.

19X4	Q_4	33 – 11	= 22	ie 22,000 units
19X5	Q_1	34.5 – 12.25	= 22.25	ie 22,250 units

11 CRUDE OIL

Tutorial note. This was a straightforward maximisation problem, but you may have found the formulation of the market conditions constraint a little tricky. Note how it appears on the graph.

(a) Let the quantities produced in gallons be x of super and y of regular.

The objective is to maximise profit given by 0.25x + 0.10y, subject to the following constraints.

Heavy crude: $\frac{7}{10}x + \frac{1}{2}y \leq 5,000$, or $7x + 5y \leq 50,000$ (1)

Light crude: $\frac{1}{2}x + \frac{7}{10}y \leq 6,000$, or $5x + 7y \leq 60,000$ (2)

Market conditions: $x \geq 2y$ (3)

NOTES

Tutorial note. At least 2/3 of the petrol should be super. The total petrol is x + y and the quantity of super is x hence $x \geq (x + y) \times 2/3$, or $3x \geq 2x + 2y$, or $x \geq 2y$.

(b) Non negativity constraints $x \geq 0$, $y \geq 0$ are also assumed.

For line (1), intercepts on the axes are as follows.

If x = 0, y = 50,000/5 = 10,000

If y = 0, x = 50,000/7 = 7,143

For line (2), intercepts are as follows.

If x = 0, y = 60,000/7 = 8,571

If y = 0, x = 60,000/5 = 12,000

For line (3), convenient points to plot are as follows.

If x = 0, then y = 0

If x = 10,000, y = 5,000

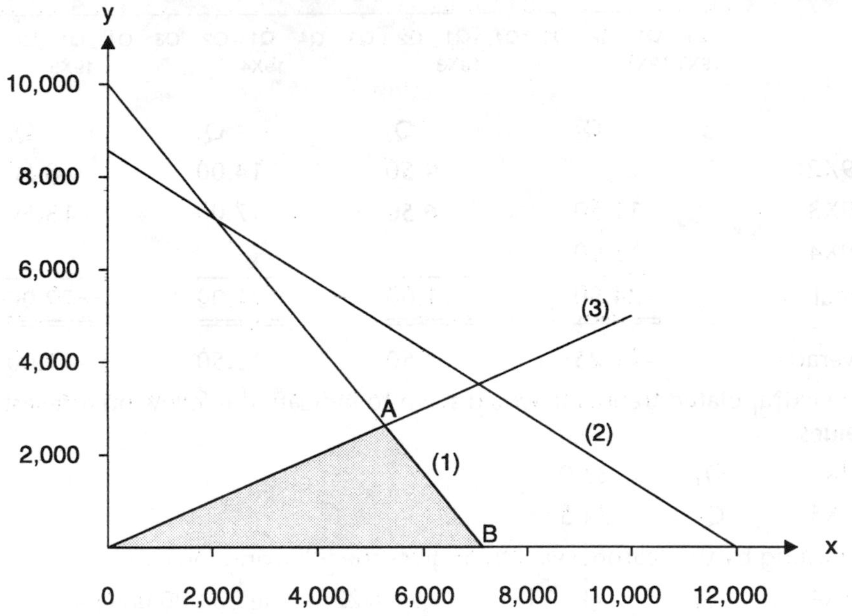

(c)

Vertex	*x*	*y*	*Profit = 0.25x + 0.1y*
			£
A	5,263	2,632	1,579
B	7,143	0	1,786

The optimal policy is to produce no regular petrol and 7,143 gallons of super petrol. The profit generated will be £1,786.

This policy will use all supplies of heavy crude but will leave a surplus of light crude. If this policy were followed throughout the industry it seems likely that the cost of light crude would fall, which would disproportionately reduce the cost of regular petrol. Assuming also that there is a market for regular petrol, this policy would make a higher price for it possible. Both would tend to increase the unit contribution of regular petrol. The above policy would therefore be likely to need modifying in the light of market changes, and should be seen by the company as a fairly short-term policy.

(d) The graphical method of solving resource allocation problems cannot be used when there are more than two decision variables. There are a number of mathematical techniques that can be used in these circumstances, for example the *Simplex method* which involves introducing slack variables into the equations to represent unused resources, shortfall in demand and so on and step–by–step trial calculations until the optimum solution is found.

In practice, faced with these sort of difficulties the business will construct a mathematical model of the scenarios on a computer and use software tools specially designed to solve such problems.

12 TOTAL REVENUE AND TOTAL COST

> *Tutorial note.* When plotting a straight line you can just use two points but it is often safer to use more in case you have made a mistake when calculating one or both of the first two. In part (c), you could have calculated marginal cost as marginal profit minus marginal revenue or, as we have done, found the first differential of the total cost function.

(a) Total profit (TP) = total revenue (TR) – total cost (TC)

$= (-x^2/2 + 1{,}500x) - (330x + 415{,}000)$

$= -x^2/2 + 1{,}170x - 415{,}000$

(b) (i) Marginal revenue (MR) = d(TR)/dx

$= -x + 1{,}500$

Marginal profit (MP) = d(TP)/dx

$= -x + 1{,}170$

(ii) The profit-maximising output occurs at a turning point of the profit function (when d(TP)/dx = 0, ie when marginal profit (MP) = 0).

MP = 0 when $-x + 1{,}170 = 0$

ie when $x = 1{,}170$

We can confirm that this is the profit-maximising (as opposed to the profit-minimising) output by taking the second differential of the profit function.

$d(TP)/dx = -x + 1{,}170$

$d^2(TP)/dx^2 = -1$

As the second differential of the profit function is <0, we have found the profit-*maximising* point.

(c) Marginal revenue (MR) = $-x + 1{,}500$ (from (b)(i)).

Marginal cost (MC) = d(TC)/dx = 330

x	*MR*
1,000	500
1,100	400
1,200	300
1,300	200

We can now plot these values for MR against x and a straight line for MC on a graph.

NOTES

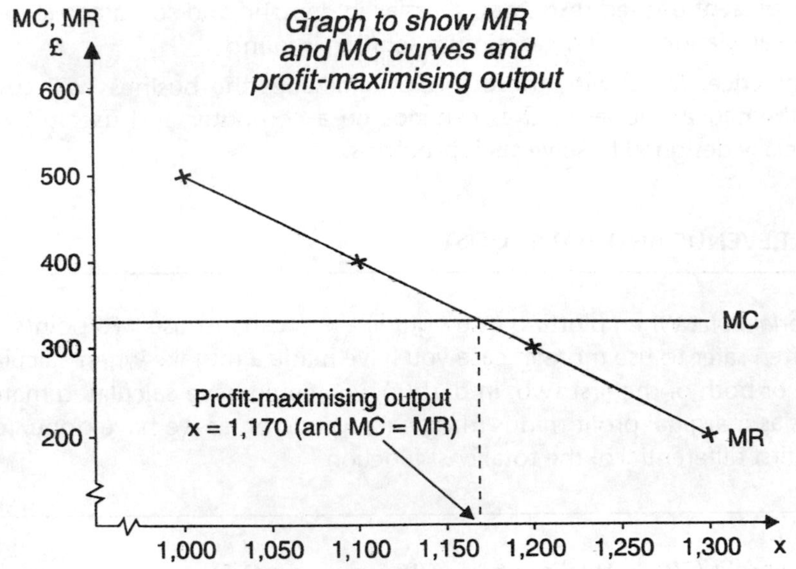

The profit-maximising output occurs (from (b)(ii)) when x = 1,170

It also occurs at the point where MC = MR.

(d) Revised TP function = TR – revised TC

$= (-x^2/2 + 1{,}500x) - (330x - 1{,}779{,}750)$

$= -x^2/2 + 1{,}170x + 1{,}779{,}750$

The business breaks even (ie makes no profit) when TP = 0

ie when $0 = -x^2/2 + 1{,}170x + 1{,}779{,}750$

We can find the x value(s) to satisfy this equation using the formula

$$x = \frac{-b \pm \sqrt{b^2 - 4ac}}{2a}$$

$$x = \frac{-1{,}170 \pm \sqrt{(1{,}170^2) - (4 \times -\tfrac{1}{2} \times 1{,}779{,}750)}}{-1}$$

$$= \frac{-1{,}170 \pm \sqrt{4{,}928{,}400}}{-1}$$

$$= \frac{-1{,}170 \pm 2{,}220}{-1}$$

$= 3{,}390$ and $-1{,}050$

As output cannot be a negative number, the business now breaks even when output is 3,390 units per period.

NOTES

13 BUILDING COMPANY

First we need to calculate the fixed costs for the period using the high-low method.

	Units	*Profit*
		£'000
High - March	30	250
Low - June	16	40
	14	210

Variable cost per unit (£210,000/14)	£15,000

Taking March as an example	£'000
Sales (30 × £30,000)	900
Profit	250
Total costs	650
Variable costs (30 × £15,000)	450
Fixed costs	200

Fixed costs for the six months = 6 × £200,000 = £1,200,000.

We now need to calculate the breakeven point as follows.

Per unit	£'000
Selling price	30
Variable cost	15
Contribution	15

Breakeven point is where total contribution = fixed costs. Breakeven point is therefore where £15,000N = £1,200,000, where N is the breakeven quantity of units.

N = £(1,200,000/15,000) = 80 units

Breakeven sales revenue = 80 × £30,000 = £2,400,000

Breakeven chart

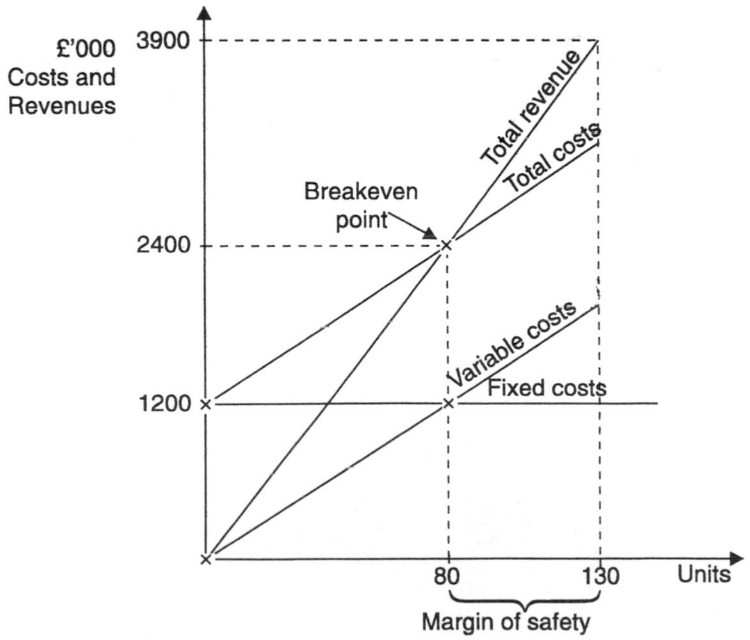

Note that at 80 units, the variable cost is 80 × £15,000 = £1,200,000.

NOTES

14 EIGHT ACTIVITIES

(a)

Path	*Time required*	
1, 2, 5, 6	10 + 6 + 13	= 29 days
1, 3, 5, 6	11 + 9 + 13	= 33 days
1, 3, 4, 6	11 + 4 + 12	= 27 days
1, 3, 4, 5, 6	11 + 4 + 3 + 13	= 31 days

(b) The critical path is therefore 1, 3, 5, 6. Its duration of 33 days is the minimum duration of the entire project. The importance of this critical path derives from the fact that, if the project is to be completed in the minimum time, the three activities on the critical path must each start on time and may not have their durations extended.

(c) *Tutorial note.* The question did not ask for a network to be drawn showing earliest and latest event times but it is easier to complete the table with the aid of such a diagram.

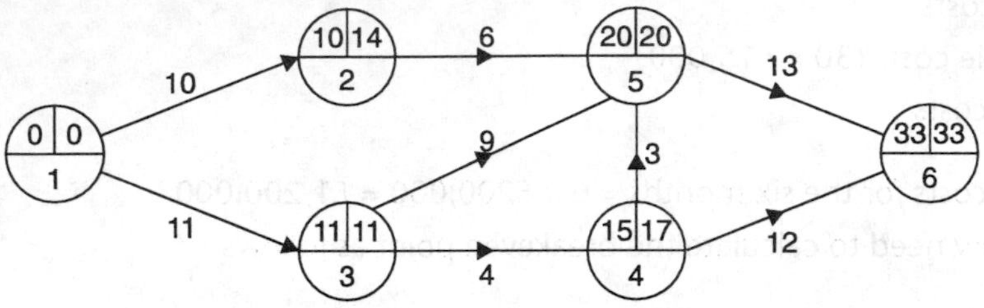

Activity	*Time*	*Earliest start*	*Earliest finish*	*Latest start*	*Latest finish*	*Total float*
1 - 2	10	0	10	4	14	4
1 - 3	11	0	11	0	11	0
2 - 5	6	10	16	14	20	4
3 - 5	9	11	20	11	20	0
3 - 4	4	11	15	13	17	2
4 - 5	3	15	18	17	20	2
4 - 6	12	15	27	21	33	6
5 - 6	13	20	33	20	33	0

(d) The total float tells us the absolute maximum number of days by which an activity's duration may be extended without increasing the duration of the entire project.

It is important to note that the total float does not tell us whether use of the float on one activity will reduce the float available on other activities. For example, activities 3 - 4 and 4 - 5 both have total floats of two days but if 3 - 4 is extended by two days then 4 - 5 will become critical and will have zero total float.

NOTES

15 DAISY HOOF LTD

(a)

Year	Cash flow £	Discount factor 16%	Present value £
0	(50,000)	1.00	(50,000)
1	18,000	0.86	15,480
2	25,000	0.74	18,500
3	15,000	0.64	9,600
4	12,000	0.55	6,600
		NPV	180

(b) The IRR is a little above 16%. Try 18%.

Year	Cash flow £	Discount factor 18%	Present value £
0	(50,000)	1.00	(50,000)
1	18,000	0.85	15,300
2	25,000	0.72	18,000
3	15,000	0.61	9,150
4	12,000	0.52	6,240
		NPV	(1,310)

Using interpolation, the IRR approximately equals

$$16\% + \left[\frac{180}{(180 + 1{,}310)} \times (18 - 16)\right]\%$$

= 16.24%.

INDEX

D

E

F

G

H

I

Q

R

S

T

U

V

W

Y

ORDER FORM

To order your BUSINESS BASICS books, ring our credit card hotline on 0181-740 2211. Alternatively, send this page to our Freepost address or fax it to us on 0181-740 1184.

To: BPP Publishing Ltd, FREEPOST, London W12 8BR **Tel: 0181-740 2211**
Fax: 0181-740 1184

Forenames (Mr / Ms): ____________________

Surname: ____________________

Address: ____________________

Post code: __________ Date of exam (month/year): __________

Please send me the following books:

	Price	*Quantity*	*Total*
Accounting	£13.95	....	....
Human Resource Management	£13.95	....	....
Law	£13.95	....	....
Organisational Behaviour	£13.95	....	....
Economics	£13.95	....	....
Information Technology	£13.95	....	....
Marketing	£13.95	....	....
Quantitative Methods	£13.95	....	....

Please include postage:

UK: £3.00 for first plus £2.00 for each extra	....	....
Europe (inc ROI): £5.00 for first plus £4.00 for each extra	....	....
Rest of the World: £8.00 for first plus £6.00 for each extra	....	....
	Total	

I enclose a cheque for £ ______ or charge to Access/Visa/Switch

Card number

Start date (Switch only) __________ Expiry date __________

Issue number (Switch only) __________

Signature ____________________

REVIEW FORM

Name:

College:

We would be grateful to receive any comments you may have on this book. You may like to use the headings below as guidelines. Tear out this page and send it to our Freepost address: **BPP Publishing Ltd, FREEPOST, London W12 8BR.**

Topic coverage

Objectives, activities with solutions, chapter roundups and quizzes

Glossary

Multiple choice and exam style questions

Student-friendliness

Errors (please specify and refer to a page number)

Other